Mad Med

Myths, Maxims and Mayhem in the National Health Service

"I'm sorry, we're all administrators, but I'm sure there'll be a doctor along in a minute!"

Andrew Bamji

ISBN: 9781688011892

To Liz:

Colleague, then friend, then wife

First published in the United Kingdom in 2019
© Andrew Bamji
All rights reserved

Typeset in Times New Roman

Cover picture: The Scream (Edvard Munch, 1893)

Title page cartoon by "Jak" (Raymond Jackson) from the "Evening Standard, 1991, courtesy of Solo Syndication/British Cartoon Archive

Mad Medicine: Contents

Acknowledgements

I owe most to my wife Liz, who has put up with my irregular disappearances to the study to write, often at short notice when I thought of something. She has also patiently accepted finding my letters in "The Times". She is my foremost critic, followed closely by my daughter Alex. Son Nick is less critical (Yeah, whatever!") but we two share a sense of humour and of the ridiculous.

My late parents, Nariman and Elizabeth, turned me to medicine and pushed a rather lazy teenager hard.

Peter Savage, erstwhile surgeon at Queen Mary's Hospital, Sidcup has done me the substantial service and honour of reading my manuscript and acting as my editor. His input has been most valuable and is greatly appreciated, but I have learned he does not like Oxford commas.

Some of my medical student friends fuelled my debating nature, in particular James Dooley, Paul Hutchins, John Kirwan, Liz McHenry and Richard Tedder. I met Rod Bateman and Anna Beales at the Brompton, and one of my bosses there, Peter Cole, merits specific mention as a wise counsellor. Richard Salisbury, whom we first met in Bath, has been a steadfast friend.

My other work colleagues have brought me much workplace contentment. I would single out my secretary of many years, Karen Brickenden, who kept my show on the road. Then there are my clinic nurses, in particular Jean Adams, Christine Day, Margaret Fewell, Eileen Lott, the late JoAnn McIntosh and Eileen Wheatley who shared my sense of humour. Jean Hines, one of my receptionists at the Brook Hospital, Woolwich later became a patient. Sheila Woodcock, pharmacist at Erith Hospital, Dorothy Marshall, Senior Sister on the Elmstead Rehabilitation Unit, physiotherapist Elaine Willett, consultants Bill Alexander, David Black, Mary Gibbens, Kevin Kelleher, Richard Mainwaring-Burton, David Oliver, Chris Pinder, Charles Shee, Jeremy Wilson, Julian Woolfson and Gloria Yu were Sidcup colleagues with whom I bounced things around. Praful Sutaria, Gopi Menon and Tom Stokes at the Brook Hospital and Alf Franklin and Michael Sharr at Chelsfield Park Hospital also chewed the fat. General practice colleagues include Caroline Fraser, Mohan Ghosh, Steve Gregson, James Heathcote, Ian Jessiman, Nick Joyner, Britta Knigge, Tony McCullagh and Bill Pomeroy. And, of course, Liz Millard, who sensibly chose to practise under her maiden name, as described above.

Stephen Collinson was the best NHS manager I ever encountered, Colin Campbell the best Chairman.

Tony Bradlow, Robin Butler, Dame Jane Dacre, Jane Griffin, John Halsey, Ian Hartley, Andrew Keat, Clive Kelly, Chris Kelsey, Alison Leak, Ken Morley, Gabriel Panayi, Tom Price, two Scotts (DGI and DL), Nick Sheehan, Mike Shipley, Peter Williams, Azad Zoma, and the late Peter Blower and Gabrielle Kingsley stand out in the wider world of Rheumatology.

I owe a particular debt to two consultants at the Middlesex Hospital. Ken Saunders gave me my first career advice when finishing my first house job, and Bill Boyle who gave me a second tranche almost ten years later, suggesting I would fare better as a large fish in a small pond than a small fish in a big one. I learned much from Chris Pallis at the Hammersmith and from Maurice Pappworth's Membership course. Elsewhere plastic surgeons Brian Morgan and Roger Green have been happy collaborators in my medical history work and John Hayes Fisher helped smooth my media appearances.

Local friends Barry Nealon. John Gurney and Kyriacos Hajikakou have listened to, and often agreed with my moans.

And then there are the patients; Alan Archer, Helen Claxton, Chris Dyos, Gillian Eames, Siddiqua Habib, Janet Kent ARPS, Ken Murphy, Shantaben Patel and her family, Kasimierz Sroka, and others who became friends as well as clients. To them all, many thanks.

Illustrations

Over the years I amassed a large collection of medical cartoons which I used to illustrate talks and some seemed suitable for this book..

My grateful thanks are due to:

Andrews McMeel Syndication (Raegan Carmona) for the Lola strip (p.141)

Jeremy Banks (Banx) for the final instruction (p.278)

Peter Brookes and Chris Beetles for Peter's cartoon of Gordon Brown (p. 8)

Mike Flanagan (Hambone, p.158). See more of Hambone at http://www.flantoons.co.uk/main/medical.html

Karen Glasbergen for permission to use three of Randy's splendid cartoons (pp28, 155 and 205); for more see http://www.glasbergen.com.

Flora Smith of TopFoto (Punch Cartoon Library) for David Haldane's lions (p. 55) and Birkett's flying faith healer (p. 63)

Solo Syndication / British Cartoon Archive, University of Kent for the frontispiece by Raymond Jackson ("Jak")

Robert Thompson for Tarzan's meeting (p.51).

Malcolm Willett for his fruit machine cartoon (p.100)

Paul Wood for NHS waiting (p.114)

Every effort has been made to trace copyright holders and to obtain their permission for the use of other cartoons which may be copyright material. I apologise for any omissions in the above list and would be grateful if I might be notified of any corrections that should be incorporated in future reprints or editions of this book.

The photographs are my own with the exception of the flag-raising, which was taken by the hospital photographer at Queen Mary's, Bill David.

Introduction: The Wry Observer

This series of essays and anecdotes is based on my experience at an English District General Hospital as a National Health Service (NHS) consultant. I am no great researcher, but I have written a lot; review articles; around 500 letters to "The Times" (78 published); letters, Rapid Responses and Personal Views to the British Medical Journal; two memoranda to the House of Commons Select Committee on Health and a monthly comment column for five years in the British Society for Rheumatology's journal under a pen name amongst others. I have now clocked all the broadsheets, "Country Life" and "The Spectator". My thinking is that if you have a point of view you should express it. If others find something in it then it may be aired widely. If not, it is only you who will care.

If you are a doctor, some of the lessons may help you to be a better doctor. If you are not they may provide some unexpected insights into the NHS. Not much of it relates to medicine as it is taught. Some lessons are clinical. Most are common sense. However, as time has gone by I have become increasingly aware that the majority of doctors think in a medical way. That needs to be adapted so that one can deal with non-doctors (other, that is, than patients, although there may be some branches of the profession, and some individuals, that need lessons in that too).

There are some simple principles and parables. If you don't understand, then go to some of the recommended background reading. I write as someone who retired from clinical practice in 2011, so some of the jargon, and reference to organisations and structures that no longer exist, may seem out-dated to the current generation of doctors. But that doesn't make the principles less valid. I did at least manage to hang on in the NHS until I was 60, and can provide a consultant perspective, albeit in a low-risk and clinically relatively low-stress specialty. Thus my 40 years or thereabouts experience is different from that of Adam Kay, whose suffering as a trainee in a high-pressure environment was awful.[1] But some of his tales do bring a sense of *déjà vu*. As do the stories I have heard from friends in the teaching profession, where many of the same institutional stupidities occur; substitute "hospital" for "school", and "doctor" for "teacher" (or vice-versa) and the sense of organisational dysfunction is shared. Further add the law profession

---

[1] Adam Kay, *This is going to hurt. Secret Diaries of a Junior Doctor.* Pan Macmillan, 2017

and one is minded to believe that it is not organisations that are dysfunctional but society as a whole.[2]

Working in a small place can lead to professional isolation. In my case the closure of my hospital's Accident and Emergency (A&E) department, and the relocation of most of my acute side colleagues to other hospitals for much of the time, worsened this markedly. However one can still learn what's going on around the country by talking to friends at meetings, and one learns about the systems in other countries from passing colleagues from abroad. Thus it remains a sad and salutary fact that many of the "reforms" proposed for the NHS over the last 30 years have come from the United States – about 10 years later, and all too often introduced just as the USA is learning that theirs have failed. Confronted with arguments for change one must never stop asking "Why?" It will irritate people but is the only way to learn – and may be the only way to stop the introduction of useless or poorly researched ideas – or indeed ideas that have been tried already.

That said, some of the advances in medicine (and in my own specialty the transformation of the management of inflammatory arthritis in the last 15 years is an example) has been magical. So is the dedication and stoicism of workers in the National Health Service in the face of all the odds and wherever they are from.

Why the Wry Observer? I have found that cynicism and pragmatism are sometimes lacking in decision making and strategic planning. Some of my prophecies have come true, and I cannot therefore resist a dig at those who pooh-poohed my projections; and it is a rather feeble pun on the name of our local paper. You may disagree with my arguments, but |I hope they will make you think.

Andrew Bamji
Rye, East Sussex

****

---

[2] See Anon, *The Secret Barrister. Stories of the Law and How It's Broken*. London. Macmillan, 2018

Looking back at 70 years of the National Health Service: which R-word?

The NHS was 70 in 2018. Like some people of that age it is respected, on the whole, but getting a bit frail. It has had health crises of its own. Some of the applied remedies have been experimental and not all have worked very well. So the old lady limps on, rather like someone with chronic anaemia, pale, dizzy and breathless. But she is still with us.

There are many myths in healthcare. The first is that the Labour government of 1948 invented the NHS. It didn't. The basic principles were put together by the Socialist Medical Association some 15 years previously. The first official stab at an NHS was laid down by Sir William Beveridge in 1942, and the definitive report by Henry Willink followed two years later.[3] Thus, had there not been a Labour landslide in the General Election of 1945 it would have been a Conservative government that introduced the NHS. Aneurin Bevan's difficulty in getting it through (exemplified by his oft-quoted statement that he had had to stuff consultants' mouths with gold) was not really a problem of principle, but of detail. That everyone still gives him credit for it is fake news, not least because Lloyd George introduced a National Insurance scheme, on which the NHS was based, back in 1911. If credit should be given to a single individual it should be to Dr Charles Brook of the SMA, who set out the broad principles. He was a general practitioner in Mottingham, South-east London and happened also to be first Chairman of the Sidcup and Swanley Hospital Management Committee, thus in charge of Queen Mary's Hospital in Sidcup, where I worked and largely responsible for its updating and redevelopment from a First World War hutted hospital.. Therefore I have a soft spot for him.

Analysis of healthcare in the era between 1930 and 1945 reveals a split hospital service that was largely bankrupt. Large teaching hospitals were cushioned by their endowments. The local authority hospitals were run on a shoestring, while the voluntary hospitals were under severe financial pressure and, if they had not been subsumed by the NHS, many would have had to close – witness the frantic fundraising of the 1920s and 1930s. Bevan fondly believed that the NHS would so improve public health that the cost of

---

[3] W. Beveridge, *Social insurance and Allied services*. HMSO 1942 Cmd 6404. For a brief summary, with references, see J. Tudor Hart, *Our feet set on a new path entirely. To the transformation of primary care and partnership with patients*. BMJ 1998; 317:1. Also see Brian Abel-Smith, *The Beveridge report: Its origins and outcomes*. International Social Security Review 1992: 45 (1–2): 5–16

provision would fall, failing to see that the eradication of some diseases such as TB and diphtheria would prolong lives and that perinatal and maternal mortality would drop. These latter, and immigration, would increase the population more than was expected; previously untreatable conditions would become treatable (heart disease, stroke, venous thrombosis, cancer, diabetes); but the expense of these treatments, - drugs, scans, surgery – would negate any saving, and so it proved – and proves today. Life expectancy is much longer, and all the souls who would have been snatched away by infections, heart disease, bleeding stomach ulcers and cancer now survive into their dotage, suffering from multiple medical problems including dementia. The elderly fall, get infections, cannot cope and end up in hospital to an unprecedented extent. Technology has advanced to a stage where we can cure far more than ever.

It is perhaps strange to reflect that in 201 teaching hospitals remain cushioned by their endowments but many of the general hospitals are once again bankrupt.

I have little doubt that despite all the inefficiencies of a state monopoly the NHS is a fundamentally sound idea. Indeed it is, in many respects, a communist system, where all parts of the country have by virtue of provision (and salaries) been rendered similar. However, successive governments, in seeing the problems and costs, have chosen to think that these can be swept away by reform. I have lived through too many, going back to Minister of Health Kenneth Robinson in the 1960s; I remember several meetings of north London family doctors at my parents' flat, which he attended (not a likely scenario today) and I still possess an extensive handwritten correspondence, which shows, at least to my eyes, that he had a better strategic grasp of the system than my father and his GP colleagues. Then we had the abolition of health boards, the establishment of district and area health authorities, the purchaser-provider split, fundholding, the development of Trusts and then Foundation Trusts, the introduction of the Private Finance Initiative and then the idea that GP consortia should and could run the NHS by forming Clinical Commissioning Groups. Meanwhile the topmost structure of the NHS was revised, and proposals for further devolution of services to the private sector encouraged. In fact all the changes happen so often that however many times I revise this section (seven so far) it will be out of date by publication. Furthermore, just as in the great communist societies of the 20th Century, the NHS has been plagued by bureaucracy that has eventually stifled it, not least because it has become preoccupied with saving itself, and money, and the jobs and reputations of its managers, many of whom have risen beyond their competence level and job-hopped when the going got tough, often to a post with a higher salary and with some gigantic payoff. This movement remains a way of disposing of the incompetent. Overlying the NHS is a Stalinist doctrine of Five Year Plans, Maoist principles of Great Leaps Forward, Stasi-like suppression of dissent, the punishment of "whistleblowers" by exile and a North Korean publicity machine fuelled by Directors of Information who begin to believe their own propaganda. So it's really very communist indeed.

Undoubtedly there have been changes in what we can do for people (much of it good), but not one of the reorganisations or reforms has solved the underlying problems. I do not believe they ever will.[4] Is this an implementation failure, or is it an indication that it's the wrong thing to do?

One thing that I have learned from experience is that the NHS is not good at reflection. The plans for reform have come up at fairly regular intervals and are introduced with great fanfare. Some were carefully thought through; others (notably the Thatcher reforms of the 1980s) were sketched on the back of an envelope (literally) and then worked up on the hoof. However, analysis of the benefits of each reform is superficial – except that it is deep enough to force realisation that the last one did not work. So another reform is dreamed up. It seems odd to me that, as each reform fails in its turn, politicians, managers and doctors spend all their time on yet more reform, as if we seek ceaselessly for the Holy Grail. There is an old saying that a surgeon is a blind man looking for something, a physician is a blind man in a dark room looking for something, and a metaphysician is a blind man in a dark room looking for something that isn't there.

As far as NHS planning is concerned we are all metaphysicians. Doctors must remain physicians and surgeons. Medicine is science, not metaphysics. There are various reasons for reform failure. Sometimes it is because the change is impractical. On occasion it is too expensive, and distracts effort, and money, from the real business of patient care (the Private Finance Initiative, or PFI for short, is a good example, as I will argue). Sometimes it is because science moves on and the world has evolved; the classic example is Bevan's firm belief, in 1948, as I noted above, that providing a national service would reduce costs as the people's health improved, not understanding that the costs of medical advances would more than wipe out such savings.

Reform, from long experience, merely shuffles the pieces on the board. It is rare for any to be added or removed. Reform is destabilising and demoralising. As it doesn't work we should understand that the only way to

---

[4] See my letter in "The Times", *We need a proper discussion about the NHS*, 30th June 2018; in 70 years the best brains in the country have not solved the problem by "reform".

6

save costs is to ration care, and plan sensibly how we do this. It is a pity that politicians fail to understand that much of the resistance to reform by the medical profession is not stick-in-the-mud stuff but is based on experience. We are here today and tomorrow; they are gone tomorrow.

It is also a pity that modern politicians, managers and to some extent the public have developed their ideas for the NHS from the wrong starting point. If you look carefully at the proposals of the last ten years you will find that they have a common theme – that care in the NHS consists of discrete packages. People become patients; they consult their GP; they may be referred to a specialist; they have an operation; they are discharged. Alternatively, they get suddenly sick and are admitted to hospital through the emergency department; they get better; they are discharged. And they stop being patients, becoming ordinary people again. Some, of course, die, but if you predicate the whole of healthcare on such a simplistic pathway you omit great swathes of the medical spectrum that do not fit into it. It is bad enough doing rheumatology, as I did, where a proportion of patients do not "get better" in the way those outside medicine perceive "getting better" (in other words, they revert to normal); it is worse being a rehabilitation specialist, as I also was, where a large proportion of patients inevitably and inexorably get worse.

A further concern is that of "patronisation". The police, criminal lawyers, teachers, social workers, doctors and health professionals may come from the middle classes but all have wide experience of the underclasses – the poor, those from broken homes and sink estates, gang members, drug addicts and the abused. Most lawmakers and health service planners have no experience of these. They may encounter them in their constituency surgeries, washed and brushed, but they have never seen them on their home turf or in an A&E department, filthy, damaged physically and mentally, with no apparent way out. Thus, to be frank, they have little idea of a large tranche of human existence although some reality TV programmes have redressed this. Many is the time I have bleated to a politician that they should accompany me or one of my nurses or occupational therapists on a ward round or on a home visit. Not one has done so (a manager did once and was jolted out of his bubble by what he saw).[5]

There is a nice set of posters reproduced from the Second World War by the London Transport Museum. These show a series of reconstructive processes required after damage from enemy action. There's a picture of it later. The

---

[5] I formulated this concern back in the 1980s. In 2019 Matthew Syed published a book which expressed the same concern (*Real Ideas: The Power of Diverse Thinking,* John Murray). Only 30 years later.

strapline reads "Rehabilitation Takes Time". So does good clinical care. Time and again my clinics overran because I talked to my (chronic) patients. Time and again they told me that they did not get such time with their general practitioner – that is, if they could actually see their own GP and were not allocated whoever was free that day. I had patients who told me that if they tried to introduce a second problem they were told to go away and book another appointment. So much for holistic care, not least if each system problem (and with rheumatoid arthritis patients develop all sorts of other problems ranging from heart disease to skin ulcers) then gets managed by a different doctor. But such stories stem both from growing pressures on time and from a spreading trait in doctors – that they must do as politicians and managers ask. Do these folk really know what is best for patients? If so, how? What qualifications have they got to make decisions on *medical* management? It is a sad day when medicine is planned by focus groups of the middle-class well who do not understand some of the consequences of their aspirations.[6] It is sadder when clinicians order clinicians of other disciplines to do as they are told when they have no concept of inter-specialty differences.

I fear that many doctors have lost the skill (or will, perhaps) to ask "Why?" I asked why I had to discharge follow-up patients to meet a ratio target (see "Data, data, don't compare a rosy apple with a pear" below), among many other things, and I was not popular for doing so. In fact I suspect many managers adopted the Henry the Second's approach to Thomas à Becket: "Who will rid me of this turbulent priest?". I know of others who have suffered likewise.

The concept of institutional memory is also important to understand, and respect. It derives from those who have been around a long time. It is useful (like that infallible medical instrument, the retrospectoscope) and should rarely be ignored.[7] Often the guardians of institutional memory could point out that a "reform" had been tried before. Beethoven tried, in one famous example, to reform a sonata by pasting pieces of paper over lines in the manuscript score that he didn't like. When musicologists unstuck the amendments, they found the first draft was identical to the last. A "modern" colour scheme for Paddington Station turned out, after dozens of layers of old paint had been burnt off, to be almost identical to the original. So it would be helpful to stop talking about reform as if it will improve things.

---

[6] I exclude a few from this blanket condemnation, in particular Kenneth Robinson and my erstwhile Chief Executive at Queen Mary's Hospital, Sidcup, Stephen Collinson.
[7] We have microscopes, sigmoidoscopes and other scopes; the retrospectoscope is the imaginary instrument we use for examining the past.

That said we doctors must be honest in setting our relative priorities and accept that the common good may downgrade us. Richard Smith expressed this beautifully in an editorial in the British Medical Journal, writing about the lobbying he got from frustrated doctors who thought not enough attention was being paid to their particular branch of medicine:

> "The BMJ never publishes anything useful to leechologists. You haven't got a single leechologist on your editorial board. Once in a blue moon you publish a leechology paper, and it's always bloody awful. I don't know who you get to review them. What you don't seem to understand is that leechology is one of the most important specialties in medicine. There aren't enough of us, we're overworked, and general practitioners don't seem to know even the basics. Everyday we're dealing with dreadful cock ups. It's time your journal taught ordinary doctors the rudiments of leechology."[8]

He reminded me of this when I asked for space for a special plea for rheumatology nearly 10 years later. Fair comment.

Management-speak is a joke in the NHS. New phrases assail us every month as the change-drivers hear what we say. Doctors have a number of defence mechanisms, ranging from passive acceptance to cynical subversion – into which latter category fall the players of "Bullshit Bingo" (take your grid of management words and phrases, tick them off as they are used and shout "Bullshit!" when you complete a line in any direction. There is also a perverse reverse variant, in which participants have to use words in the grid appropriately. Polite people know it as Baloney Bingo.)

"Reform" is on the grid. "Modernisation" is another. In the NHS context they set the background for politically driven change and, if ministers are correct, the NHS cannot move forward (and that's on the grid) until it has reformed and modernised.

Modernisation likewise is a synonym for doings things differently, but with an outcome that may be better, the same or worse. A modern hospital may perform better in some functions because it has smooth surfaces and piped oxygen, for instance, but if it starts to fall down after twenty years, or the flat roof develops a terminal leak, then it may, overall, be no better than a soundly built Edwardian voluntary hospital.[9] If I am tied to paperless

[8] Richard Smith, *The BMJ and the 77 specialties of medicine*. BMJ 1997; 315: 1680
[9] As an example consider the Royal Liverpool Hospital, completed in 1978, which is falling down but still operating because the PFI builders of its replacement went bust

records, a server failure, generator test, power cut or hack makes them inaccessible. I've seen them all. My analogy is of a clock. Why should I "modernise" my timekeeping by replacing a serviceable and decorative 17th Century grandfather clock with a digital version that automatically updates itself via a satellite link to an atomic clock? Assuming I remember to wind it up it tells the same time to an acceptable precision, and a satellite clock won't run without a battery. Our church clock, the oldest working tower clock in the world, was first modernised in the 1740s, two centuries after its installation, and now has a set of electric motors to rewind the driving weights automatically. But when there's a power cut the weights don't rewind, hit the floor and cause the motor cables to unravel. It's a devil of a job to put straight.[10] Technical advances may have their problems.

So "modernisation" is a smokescreen. Keep people modernising and it distracts them from their real jobs. Remember that famous quotation which appears in many offices:

> "We trained hard, but it seemed that every time we were beginning to form up into teams, we would be reorganized. I was to learn later in life that we tend to meet any new situation by reorganizing; and a wonderful method it can be for creating the illusion of progress while producing confusion, inefficiency, and demoralization."[11]

That's not to say we must set things in aspic; lateral thinking may achieve huge benefits. Managers call that "thinking outside the box", or "blue-sky thinking" and, of course, moves to take down local Chinese walls between health and social services will promote joined-up thinking and we can move forward. (My God, I've got a line! Bullshit!)

We have all become preoccupied with getting what is *best*. We cannot afford perfection and so must look at planning what is *least bad*. They are not the same. I believe we should consider changing the R-word from Reform (including Reconfiguration) to Rationing.

---

in the middle. See https://en.wikipedia.org/wiki/Royal_Liverpool_University_Hospital for a summary of the whole sorry tale (accessed 8th August 2019).
[10] Climb the tower of St Mary the Virgin, Rye to see our clock (and help raise funds for upkeep – it's our biggest earner). Should you visit after a power failure you may find two old men balancing on buttresses or lying on the floor fiddling with wires. Say hello to John Gurney and me and I'll know you've read this book.
[11] Petronius? Erroneous. First coined by Charlton Ogburn in Harper's Magazine, January 1957

There is another important word that sounds as if it starts with an 'R' –
Wrong. This should be a key word for planners. When devising a project you
should apply the finishing touches and then ask someone, anyone, to go
through it and see if there's anything that could go wrong. One major
problem and the whole thing will fall flat on its face, and you will find
several examples of this in my essays. These contain elements of "Just a
Minute"; deviation, repetition and hesitation, though the last of these is the
least.[12] I do not apologise for any of them.

Experience is one of the benefits of getting older. Then you learn from
experience that once you have learned from experience, no-one listens to
you. I wrote a short verse about this once. There is a longer one saying much
the same thing in more words (Blaise Pascal: I would have written a shorter
letter, but I did not have the time) which appears at the end.

> When appointed consultants, we all seemed quite young –
> Looked up to our elders and betters;
> But time passes by, and we cease to give tongue
> Or write all those Young Turk-like letters.
> And then we all find that the new ones around
> Are the ones now creating the fuss –
> For *they* carry the torch of the bright and the bold
> And the elders and betters are us.

****

---

[12] For those who don't know, "Just a Minute" is a BBC Radio 4 show in which the
contestants have to try and speak for one minute on a subject given to them by the
host, the nonagenarian Nicholas Parsons. Any of the three above will prompt an
intervention by one of the other panellists who, if their intervention is correct, will
continue until the time runs down or they in their turn are interrupted.

Oxymoronic medicine

Oxymoron: a figure of speech in which apparently contradictory terms
appear in conjunction. Many of my essays contain an oxymoronic element,
but here are a few specific ones.

The dichotomy between holistic practice and reality

We are supposed to treat patients as people and practise patient-centred care
(as if what we do is somehow not focussed on the patient, but the concept is,
I think, supposed to prod us to treat patients holistically – whatever that
means). How this is possible in a general practice session I am unsure.
Pressure on appointment slots is intense, and I have heard of practices who
insist that consultations can only cover one problem. Not holistic at all. I
have many a time spent 20 minutes with a patient whose arthritis was not the
problem, but the fact that their spouse, who cared for them, has suddenly
died; or there was the lady trying to look after her granddaughter (her own
daughter was an alcoholic, also living at home, and disruptive) as well as her
own elderly and demented mother. Real patients cannot be shoehorned into
set slots.

The prescription saga

A circular appeared in the hospital email inbox, indicating that in future
consultants would not issue prescriptions but would fill in a recommendation
form for the patient to take back to their GP. There was no clear indication
of what this new process was supposed to achieve except to transfer the cost
of drugs from the hospital to the community budget. It certainly was not
going to cost less overall.

I have some understanding of how this would work.

The patient would not be able to go straight to the chemist and start the
medication the same day. Instead they would have to book an appointment
with their GP, which might take 5 days or more. Their GP might then decide
that the prescribed drugs were not right. Or they would refuse to prescribe
because they "didn't know enough about the drug". (What's wrong with
you? Can't you read your National Formulary?) So the patient would either
be delayed, or would have to come back to the specialist, or both. And
inevitably they would be subjected to a grumbling tirade from the
overworked GP who could see no reason why he was being imposed upon to

do the consultants' work for them. So the whole experience would be extremely negative. For everyone. Or, put another way, it doesn't work.

From my own point of view I was incensed that my ability to practise was being interfered with and wrote to the General Medical Council seeking an opinion. It replied that the new procedure seemed to be driven by cost alone and was unacceptable in principle. I relayed this to the Trust management, who took no notice.

The way to a cheaper NHS is not to practise futility medicine

No doubt this essay will raise hackles but I have often said that I am prepared to say things that other folk do not dare to think. I have been appalled at how the hospital side of the NHS (I cannot speak for the primary care side of the fence except in generalities) has become obsessed with money. In financial terms money is supposed to follow the patient, but in reality the patients will get whatever the money can buy (or, in hard times, won't get). A large number of my colleagues have become infected with the virulent plague that turns them from caring for people into ruthless money-saving machines, and so interfere with all sorts of clinical necessities, like seeing follow-up patients, prescribing drugs and treating patients as people and not as diseases. I understand the temptation; I have nearly fallen for it myself, when trying to wear a management hat. But let us then pursue this approach in a logical and complete way and see where we end up.

Much money is expended on very old, very sick and very demented people who get acute illnesses and end up in hospital beds being made "better". If one asks "For what purpose?" there is no good answer. Often these poor husks of people will be sent back to the care home from which they were admitted (or transferred to one because the home situation is unsupportable). There has developed what perhaps is an unhealthy obsession with making sure that anything treatable is treated. Thus an 89-year old with a urinary tract infection who does not really want to go on living, confused and in renal failure, is given large doses of gentamicin as the infecting organism is only sensitive to that, and ends up with worse renal failure and possibly deafness to boot. Even if the doctors have agreed that all is hopeless the patient is then left to die by natural decay, which may take days or longer. Pain relief is kept to a minimum because great care is taken not to do anything that might actually cause death. So patient, relatives and staff all hover, waiting. It is a most unpleasant business. Inevitable unconsciousness develops and still they linger on.

I term such things "futility medicine".

How much kinder it would be in this situation to do something positive to advance the inevitable outcome. And this is what we should do to save bed days, care costs and so on. It is actually the best answer to saving money in the NHS (except, perhaps, for giving chemotherapy at £60,000 a pop to prolong life by two or three months). But we cannot; Harold Shipman perhaps must carry some of the blame and events at Gosport War Memorial Hospital, on which a critical review was published in June 2018, have not helped. My mother's death was slower than I would have liked; it took 11 days. Her actual death was in the middle of the night, so we were not there, and I would have preferred it if we had been. Planning the time of death would have saved much distress and sadness. But at least it was quiet and painfree, unlike that of the mother of one of my colleagues left screaming in pain during her last days (I might add in her own hospital) for whom the excuse was that the syringe driver medication had not been written up – except that it had not actually been given. But we concentrate on the patient, and we forget the relatives. They are the ones who have to live with the bad memories. We should not prolong the horrible existence of many folk, in my view, but certainly once death is clearly inevitable then we should certainly not prolong the process of dying.

In March 2013 an article in "The Times" suggested that 30,000 lives a year might be saved by screening the middle-aged for killer conditions (heart disease, obesity etc). My reply was published.

> The prevention of 30,000 deaths a year will not be achieved by screening the middle-aged; that is far too late. The problems of obesity and smoking (and their attendant diseases – in particular heart problems and diabetes – are set in childhood behaviours and lifestyles, and the way forward is to screen, and educate, young people.

> Anyway we wouldn't be saving lives, but postponing deaths. "Saving" lives is of no benefit if they are sick lives; people with major health needs, in surviving longer, will cost the NHS more.[13]

There are, of course, other ways of saving money, including the re-financing of Private Finance Initiative hospitals and the abandonment of statins (which cause an effect on cholesterol, but what that means is uncertain – more of that elsewhere). But we should sometimes think the unthinkable as well as challenge established "facts". As Malcolm Kendrick elegantly dissects in his book "Doctoring Data", some so-called facts are actually based on nothing

---

[13] *Time to look abroad and reconstruct the NHS,* 6th March 2013

more than a guess, which becomes "fact" by repetition.[14] I won't re-write his book; read it and be alarmed. But think, do not close your mind and learn how to sort the wheat from the chaff.

[14] Malcolm McKendrick, *Doctoring data. How to sort out medical advice from medical nonsense.* Columbus Publishing, 2014

Commissioning new services in the NHS: a game without rules[15]

> "In that direction," the Cat said, waving its right paw around, "lives
> a Hatter: and in that direction," waving the other paw, "lives a
> March Hare. Visit either if you like: they're both mad."
> "But I don't want to go around among mad people," Alice remarked.
> "Oh, you can't help that," said the Cat: "we're all mad here. I'm
> mad. You're mad."
> "How do you know I'm mad?" said Alice.
> "You must be," said the Cat, "or you wouldn't have come here."[16]

The National Health Service is Wonderland. Whether it is run by the Hatter
on the right or the March Hare on the left it has always been underfunded.
The Fourth Annual Report of the Sidcup and Swanley Hospital Management
committee in 1952 stated:

> The year under review was again difficult, owing to the ceiling
> placed on expenditure... and it was apparent from the outset that it
> would not be possible to provide adequate services within the sum
> allotted... In response to the appeal of the Minister of Health for
> economy, all demands for expenditure have been strictly scrutinised
> and many economies have been effected.

If every demand is met, the pit of resources needs to be bottomless, so it
comes as something of an irritation to be told by outsiders that more and
more can be done without more and more cash – and in hospitals with fewer
and fewer beds. There is much pontification by them that don't know and
won't listen. When things do go wrong (and the lack of neurosurgical
intensive care beds in London so that a Sidcup patient was once flown to
Leeds is an example) politicians move with unbelievable speed to blame the
doctors.

---

[15] I include this essay as an example of several phenomena – the enduring nature of
politicians' desires to fiddle with the NHS, their deceit (by making statements they
abandon), the innate immovability of an over-bureaucratised system, and censorship.
I was asked to write the piece by a magazine for MPs called "The Parliamentarian",
which offered me a fee, accepted the article and then not only refused to publish it,
without giving any reasons, but didn't pay either. It may seem a little dated now, but
it was written in 1994. I reworked it for a Personal View which did appear in the
British Medical Journal (A N Bamji, *Brain injury rehabilitation: jaw-jaw not war-
war*, BMJ 1996; 312: 916-7)
[16] Lewis Carroll, *Alice in Wonderland*. The Cheshire Cat's analysis predates Joseph
Heller's "Catch-22" by 96 years

Doctors are expected to be perfect but are not given the wherewithal so to be. The new NHS has failed to free hospitals from any of the old constraints on development. Indeed in many respects it has made things worse. The rise of a new management bureaucracy has failed to streamline or speed up decision making, and decisions are still made (or as is more often the case not made) as a result of political expediency. All planning is based on yearly contracts and the NHS is supposed to run as a business. It cannot. The catchphrase is "money follows the patient"; so no patient, no money. But if there is no money, there can be no patient. Someone somewhere has forgotten that new businesses need money up front.

Suppose then that I, as a clinician, wish to develop a new service. I start by defining the clinical need— in my case the absence of facilities for brain injury rehabilitation in South East London and Kent. The service is specialised, and no single small district could justify a single unit for itself, so a unit to serve a wider area is planned. The combination of physical and psychological disturbance in patients with head injuries requires a labour-intensive approach, so staff costs are very high for small numbers of patients. In other words, this is a high-cost, low-volume service.

Models of care at home and abroad are examined. The unit can serve also as a base for research and education of NHS staff; these costs are included. Direct estimates of need are prepared by consulting clinicians who receive such patients— neurosurgeons, orthopaedic surgeons and rehabilitation specialists. The final capital and revenue costs are identified and the business case finalised.

But there it stops. The proposal is aired before the several Commissioning Agencies. They accept the projections of the numbers of patients likely to need the service. "But" they say, "we cannot commit ourselves to buying this service, because we can't see what you are offering. And of course we would only meet the service costs, not the costs of education and research."

"But," I say, "money *follows* the patient. So without the money I can't offer the service in the first place. And proper education and research will help us all to develop."

"Well, we're very sorry" they say, "but we won't buy a service sight unseen."

"But there isn't any service at all anywhere *and if you don't commit the money there never will be a service.*"

Gallic shrugs. And you can hear them counting the number of hip replacements they won't have to leave unfunded. "That's your problem, not ours."

Which it is, of course.[17] I would be mad to set up a costly service without a commitment to use it. Managers are of course immune from this Cheshire Cat Catch-22; several dozen millions of pounds followed Wessex Regional Health Authority's computers down the plughole.[18]

The government has made an effort to bring in pump-priming money to solve this
sort of problem with an exercise called the Private Finance Initiative. Its first impact was to blight several projects already in the pipeline, as they had to be held up while they went through the new procedure. I had high hopes of priming the brain injury rehabilitation project this way, until Mrs Margaret Beckett announced in the House of Commons that companies committing their assets to this kind of scheme might, under a Labour government, have them confiscated.[19] Hands up those who think the next government won't be a Labour government. So private investors run a mile, given such a friendly guarantee, and the system is itself Catch-22— damned if you don't use private funds, and potentially damned if you do.

A further perturbation was introduced by the rise and rise of General Practitioner fundholding.[20] The commissioning of specialist low-volume services on behalf of small populations results in wild and unpredictable fluctuations in contract demand. Add to that the possibility that contracts may be moved between providers on a yearly basis and any possibility of strategic planning vanishes. The uncertainty of the contracting process makes it difficult to reassure staff that their future is secure; a workforce that is constantly on the hop is a deeply unhappy workforce, and becomes

---

[17] And remains so; 17 years later there is still no specialised brain injury unit provided by the NHS in South London
[18] Several billions followed when the NHS tried to implement its new IT strategy at the turn of the century
[19] Two points here; I didn't at this time realise how PFIs would be set up, so thought they would be like decent house mortgages; and Mrs Beckett's threat was not only not carried out but positively reversed, as the incoming Labour government saw a great opportunity to expand the NHS on the never-never, in a completely unaffordable way as we shall see, and yet keep the expenditure off the government balance sheet.
[20] Later abolished, but resurrected in a slightly different form by the Coalition government of 2010

uncommitted and unproductive.[21] Certainly, much of the unrest in the NHS today is engendered by the fickle, almost ephemeral nature of the purchaser-provider system with contracts that may be here today and gone tomorrow. Patients with chronic diseases do not have sell-by dates and to encourage a system that jumps their care from place to place is as unkind as it is absurd.

The commissioning of new services is caught by Catch-22, but even the development of existing services is constrained. My department received more outpatient referrals weekly than there were clinic slots. I did more clinics than the national average already, so to meet the demand extra staff were needed. The situation was exacerbated temporarily by the closure of the Queen Elizabeth Military Hospital, which had been providing a rheumatology service to the locality for years at no cost to the NHS; all the patients under regular review with chronic arthritis were being discharged to have follow-up elsewhere, and we expected about a hundred complex patients all at once. No money came with them, let alone followed them. To accommodate them, other referrals had to be put off. The waiting time for a new appointment lengthened and Patients' Charter went through the window. A business case for a new consultant was put, but the Commissioning Agency had no money to fund the extra work, unless it takes it from another area. So, on the one hand we are faced with a demand for appointments that we cannot meet, while on the other we are denied the funds to meet them.[22]

What then is the answer? Overt or covert rationing will not go away. Neither will gratuitous waste. Wessex's computers apart, I am told that £6 million would have been saved if the Department of Health had spoken to the Department of the Environment before forging ahead with plans for a new hospital for Bromley on a Green Belt site— which the DoE turned down; half a million was blown at the Brook Hospital in Greenwich on a magnetic resonance imaging scanner that never worked.[23] A failed attempt to rationalise and update the NHS's IT systems cost nearly £20 *billion*. It's well to remember that these expenditures were never sanctioned by doctors.

---

[21] This is exactly what happened – again – in 2010 as the result of financial cuts, outsourcing and tendering. Plus ça change…

[22] The sorry saga of the QEMH closure is detailed below in the essay entitled "Dumping Syndrome"

[23] It was designed to go into a temporary building, which was not solid enough to damp out the vibrations generated during the scanning process as the magnet switched on and off. Furthermore it was purchased from the USA second-hand; it was assumed that its previous usage pattern was what it would have been in the UK (about 6 hours per day) but it had in fact been used regularly for over 20 hours a day, so was pretty clapped out.

Firstly it is up to government to concede that its financial commitment to the NHS never has met and never will meet the demand, and stop playing the game of the Emperor's clothes.[24] Secondly the contracting system must be stabilised so that long-term strategic planning is not blighted; and the wasteful duplication of the contracting bureaucracy, with negotiators in every hospital and General Practice, must be abolished. Thirdly a sensible pump-priming system for new developments must be introduced— one which is not prey to political dogma. Fourthly, it's time to stop knocking doctors, and time to listen to what they say. I believe that the patience of the medical profession, and its steadfast attempt to continue to be positive in the face of constant sniping and senseless change, caught between the rock of patient demand and the hard place of underfunding, is little short of miraculous. But then, like the Cheshire Cat, we are all mad here.

A&E and whiplash

Two things appeared simultaneously in the news in 2013. The first was a backlash against whiplash. Whiplash injuries, it is said, are costing motorists hundreds of pounds per year in insurance premiums that have to cover the growing cost of whiplash injury claims. Many of these are fraudulent. Cue media hysteria and demands that all such patients be assessed by neurologists.[25]

Now neck injuries as the result of a sudden acceleration/deceleration, such as when a car comes to a dead stop in a hurry, the occupants are thrown forwards and then jolted back by the airbag going off, are not infrequent. But if such a movement results in ligament or muscle tears, or even strains, then nothing will show up, except for a bit of stiffness. Nothing will appear on an MRI scan or X-ray. Nor do you need a neurologist to diagnose a nerve root injury; pins and needles, numbness and weakness, or even muscle wasting, are very easy even for a lay person to fathom. And if an X-ray shows a neck fracture (and I saw one of these which had been missed in A&E) then QED. I wrote a letter to "The Times":

> Just because a test doesn't show anything does not prove that nothing is wrong. The majority of "whiplash" injuries are due to tears of muscles or ligaments and these may be very painful – for a

---

[24] An analogy I repeated in an article in 2007 (Bamji AN, *The Emperor's new business clothes*. British Journal of Healthcare Management 2007; 13: 294-297)
[25] Another backlash and attendant hysteria occurred at the beginning of 2018. Flag, say you have to do something, send it to a committee, forget it. Repeat every five years.

while. But they won't show on X-rays or scans, and clinical examination will show no evidence of nerve damage. However well over 90% will settle down and the best treatment is early mobilisation, which significantly reduces the risk of chronic symptoms.

Whether such injuries should be compensated is doubtful. In countries where compensation is not available people just get on with life, and that is what should happen here. Physiotherapists and rheumatologists will be far more use in achieving this. Neurologists tell patients nothing is wrong and the patients get upset because they know something is wrong. They need to be told they are right, but that it will get better.[26]

It was printed (I think my 65th, but I have lost count now). Things went quiet.

The second thing that pitched up was related to the financial problems of hospitals, as it was a stark warning that accident departments were now so overstretched that they could not cope now, let alone during a winter epidemic, of which one is overdue. So cue more hysteria about increasing staffing levels urgently.

There is an oxymoron in this alone, as increasing staff numbers mean more costs, which hospitals cannot afford. The solution – to merge departments so that the staff can be redistributed through a smaller number of departments – is sensible, but a second oxymoron looms. If you have fewer hospitals then you have fewer beds to admit the patients who are ill enough, so the A&E departments clog up with sick folk waiting to be admitted. Send them home! But there is no evidence either that doing that is safe, or that it is cheaper. Even if you can get them home, which with the shortages in social work and social care is proving difficult. As sometimes do the relatives who won't agree the care plan. So there's oxymoron No 3.
But what of whiplash, you ask. I was coming to that. Suddenly the press was alive with the whiplash thing once more following a report suggesting that all such victims should be refused any form of compensation – unless they have been assessed in an A&E department! What good will that do? There are no tests to prove injury (though don't forget that X-ray – abnormal but missed) – and anyway the onset of symptoms may be delayed by a day or two. Think about your sprained ankle. The day you injured it you limped around uncomfortably, didn't you, only to find that the next morning it had swollen horribly and you couldn't walk on it at all.

---

[26] The Times, *Whiplash* injuries, June 22nd, 2013

So. The UK's emergency services are stretched to breaking point, rationalising them makes them less accessible and reduces the ability to admit patients and suddenly it is suggested that you flood them all with whiplash patients who will demand useless and expensive investigations for no purpose whatsoever.

In early 2017 the crisis facing A&E departments was once again acute. Masses of patients were flooding in; delayed discharges meant that there were no beds to which to admit them, the departments filled up, patients were left waiting in ambulances, so these could not go and collect any new emergencies. Routine operations were cancelled by the score. In an apparent attempt to relieve the pressure, NHS England put out a series of advertisements in the media suggesting that anyone with a cold should immediately consult their pharmacist because it could turn into something worse. Such a move will, of course, do nothing to stem the flow of acutely and seriously ill patients, but will have the effect of flooding pharmacies with infectious people. Colds get better on their own, mostly; it's when they go to the chest and your spit goes green that you may need more than lemon and honey. You will not be better for a bus ride in the freezing cold to the chemist, and neither will your fellow passengers once you have coughed and sneezed all over them. *Und so weiter*, in German.

Oxymoronic? I think we can leave out the oxy- bit.

To be fair, hospitals have, with the blessing of the high and mighty, been able to post notices asking patients with diarrhoea and vomiting not to come in. This may at least stop norovirus from infiltrating, and then closing wards. How that happens is insidious. Patients come in, are identified, the ward is closed, staff are redeployed to other wards to fill shortages, and take the norovirus with them.

New buildings, old problems

Talk to many doctors and you will hear them say that their crumbling Victorian buildings had a charm and ambience (feng shui if you will) that is unmatched by a modern glass tower. But is the new building actually better? It may be filled with labour-saving and energy efficient devices but if the glass windows face into the midday sun it will get unbearably hot. And as it is air-conditioned you cannot open the windows. And maybe the air-conditioning cannot be used because the water cooling tanks harbour legionella. So the wards are sealed, and all the miasma of stale breath, infected wounds and sweat is unable to dissipate. This may be why so many modern hospital wards stink – made worse because there are not enough nurses to wash the decrepit patients.

On a personal note I will exempt Torbay Hospital from this diatribe, because the personal care my mother received during her terminal illness was exemplary and gave me hope that if the NHS can return to standards like theirs, all could be well.

The Victorians knew a lot about cross-infection, which is why they built serried ranks of wards separated by open corridors to prevent transport of infectious agents across the whole hospital. Lots of nurses kept the patients clean. Any floating microbes would drift through the ward to the centre, where a coal fire burned constantly, so that air was sucked into the tall chimney and the bugs were incinerated as they followed the air flow. Of course there were side-wards for highly infectious folk and the windows were often left open (or more recently extractor fans maintained flow; one has of course to remember that if the sideroom contains the infection and the main ward holds the immunocompromised then the fan must suck out, not in, while if the patient with no white cells is in the sideroom for their own safety…).[27]

I like the idea of burning bugs. So let's redesign all hospitals to include a gas or coal heating system, complete with tall chimneys, so the methicillin-resistant Staphylococcus Aureus (MRSA), Clostridium Difficile (*C. Diff*) and other such can be massacred.

Except we can't, because with all the hysteria over climate change we won't be allowed to burn fossil fuel, and electric fires won't work. Let's hope for a supervolcano eruption, releasing so much dust that we will have a mini Ice Age and can stop worrying. Or stop third world countries from cutting down their rainforests. Or stop cotton production in Russia so the Aral Sea can re-fill. Sorry. Got distracted.

That's not to say that old hospitals are perfect. At the Brook Hospital in Woolwich the doctors' dining room was in a converted ward. A couple of consultants thought the water tasted odd and complained. On the third complaint an investigation began, and the work department were puzzled to

---

[27] This was brought home to me as an SHO at the Hammersmith Hospital, when the team visited a sick and septic patient in a sideroom on the haematology ward, which was full of aplastic and neutropenic patients. My boss, neurologist Nigel Legg, spotted the fan was going the wrong way so the bugs, instead of being sucked out of the window, were blowing under the door into the ward. As we shut the door to leave he looked down, stamped his foot carefully and grinned at us "Got one!" he said.

find that the water pressure to the drinking water tap seemed rather low. They had a thought, and went up into the roof space, to find the tap was fed from an uncovered cold water tank which contained several dead pigeons.

Ward infections: acquired or identified?

My musings on the value of old-fashioned techniques for sterilisation reminded me that there is another myth, sadly believed by politicians, that there is an important problem called hospital-acquired infection. There is a problem with hospital infections, but is it rightly named and if we changed a word might it take some of the hysteria out of MRSA?

Let me make it clear that I have no doubt that patients may acquire MRSA or *C. Diff* during a hospital admission. That's why we had a policy on my rehabilitation unit that no patient could be admitted without being screened first – not that our bed managers cared, and we had frequent occasion to complain when unscreened patients were dumped on the unit so that A&E patients could be decanted within the four hour target time[28]. Indeed I got into trouble when our experience was reported in "BMA News Review" in 2004[29] and I was threatened with disciplinary action for breaching the hospital's whistleblowing policy, which I hadn't (and it was unedifying to see managers lying about the issue). But MRSA doesn't spontaneously appear like magic on a hospital ward, does it? I was seized with schadenfreude when, in a letter of response to my resignation, our Chief Executive told me how wonderful the Trust's success has been in reducing hospital infection – when all he had done was to introduce my seven-year-old plan which he had never read!

One of the good things to come from targets (and the target was to reduce MRSA septicaemia, not actual surface infection) was that our microbiologist had to develop a good data set both to look at numbers of MRSA infections on wards and where in each case it had come from. Analysis over several months in 2009 revealed an interesting but perhaps unsurprising conclusion; the vast majority of MRSA came in from the community. Patients did not acquire it after hospital admission. They came in with it. Of course we all know that out there in the community the district nurses carry it about and the care homes let it spread among their inmates – or that's how it seemed to me when I compared the lazy, laissez-faire attitude to MRSA colonisation with the stringent curative and preventative measures on my rehab unit. But it underlined the truth – that most MRSA is not hospital-*acquired*, it is

---

[28] Andrew Bamji, *Tackling MRSA*. Hospital Doctor, 22nd April 2004
[29] Alex Wafer, *A&E Targets damage MRSA safeguards*. November 13th 2004

hospital *identified*. How then it is government writ that a hospital can be penalised for high MRSA rates is beyond me, when its only "fault" is in admitting unscreened patients who are ill, and then testing them! So let's have a campaign to distinguish acquired from identified, realise the scale of the problem is not that great, and concentrate on dealing with the source – the place where everything is better – the community!

Politicians like to pretend that they have fixed things, and I was particularly amused by a report in the "Sunday Times" in mid-April 2010 in which the then Health Secretary, Andy Burnham, trumpeted the news that good ideas from the NHS were to be exported worldwide – including how to manage MRSA! I found this rich coming from a government that, when my experience on how to manage MRSA was reported, threatened my managers; it was this that resulted in the attempt to silence me with disciplinary threats when all I had done was describe my unit's good practice.

We went to Venice for a long weekend. I was tempted to visit one of the many shops catering for Carnival and purchase a Venetian cloak and hat together with a plague doctor's mask, and wear this into the hospital during the next norovirus outbreak…

Paul Fürst, engraving, c. 1721, of a plague doctor of Marseilles (introduced as 'Dr Beaky of Rome'). From Wikipedia:
(https://en.wikipedia.org/wiki/Plague_doctor_costume)
- accessed 4th September 2019)

Bare below the elbows: safe, or silly?

This is an example of a failure to examine the evidence base.

Many hospitals imposed a bare below the elbows policy as a result of research showing that cuffs, jewellery, watches and neckties can carry bugs. Bugs can infect patients. Ergo, all of the above, which could cause patients to become infected, must be banned.

When the Department of Health appeared to endorse such a policy (and some Trusts were quite hysterical in imposing it, with ward sisters screaming at offending staff like little Hitlers), the Royal College of Surgeons of England tried to commission a "for and against" pair of articles. It printed a pair – but both were against, as the journal's editor was unable to find anyone who would write in favour. The reason was simple. While there is good evidence that ties etc can harbour bugs *there is no evidence at all that anyone has been infected thereby*.[30] Now I am no Luddite and am the first to remind students about Semmelweis (who? they say) but I cannot endorse a policy for which there is no evidence of benefit and which is founded on myth, supposition and unreasonable extrapolation.[31] I would have conformed when there was some evidence (the Black Swan principle does not pass me by). I used my common sense – something that seem to have been bred out of many in authority – and stripped down appropriately on the ITU and ensured my tie never dangled in an infected bedsore.[32] [33]

The corollary of this is that if managers insist you conform to a stupid policy then you cannot trust their judgement. People do not have isolated blind

---

[30] This has actually been properly researched. See CA Willis-Owen, P Subramanian, P Kumari, D Houlihan-Burne. *Effects of 'bare below the elbows' policy on hand contamination of 92 hospital doctors in a district general hospital*. Journal of Hospital Infection; 75: 116-119. Result? BBTE is a waste of time

[31] Ignaz Semmelweis was a Hungarian physician who first recommended washing hands with disinfectant solution between operations to reduce the incidence of childbed (puerperal) fever on labour wards. This was in 1847 but his views, though supported by his results, were not supported by his peers. Ostracised, he went mad.

[32] The Black Swan principle was developed by Nicholas Nassim Taleb in a financial setting. A black swan in markets is an event that has not occurred in the past, thus rendering useless risk management models based on historic data. Such a risk model would assume that all swans were white. See NN Taleb, *The Black Swan. The Impact of the Highly Improbable*. Allen Lane, 2007

[33] Even bow ties were not exempted from the "no tie" edict. Paediatricians often wore them; perhaps the sanitisers thought that some kid would cough on it, and the next might lick it.

spots, and if they cannot take in and understand a scientific analysis of one thing it is almost certain that they will display the same failing in others.

Another infection issue raises the risk versus benefit question. For decades we used skin prep swabs which came in little paper packets and were very cheap. Suddenly I found that they had disappeared, to be replaced with some fancy ampoules (of three different sizes) which took up cubic feet of storage space and were very fiddly to use (indeed I found it impossible to break the smallest ones without the tube splitting at the back and spreading a slightly tacky antiseptic over my fingers, not to mention driving sharp plastic splinters into them). On enquiry I was told that the evidence base for their clinical superiority was unquestionable. However where the old swabs cost about £2.50 per 100 the new ones cost upwards of £30 per 100.

In fact the risk of infection from a no-touch technique joint injection is almost zero, but one feels obliged to spread some sort of bug killing substance on the patient just in case, so you can say you have done it. If this new delivery system was to be used in phlebotomy services the NHS would be bust in months.

Actually… in "The Times (9th June 2015) it was reported that some of the damp wipes not only failed to kill the bugs, but spread them about… so maybe my cynical colleague who used to wave a dry cotton wool swab over the injection site and chant "Just a little bit of magic" was not so far off the mark.

While the MRSA hysteria was at its height Gordon Brown was Chancellor of the Exchequer, being mean with NHS funding despite the wiles and wails of the Health Secretary, Alan Milburn. The cartoon on the next page appeared in "The Times" and as it was irresistible I bought Peter Brookes' original. Randy Glasbergen has another take on this. Both appear overleaf.

28

© Peter Brookes and The Times; courtesy Chris Beetles Gallery, St James's, London".

The rise, fall, rise and fall of the community hospital; or, small is not always beautiful

Once upon a time every small town supported a cottage hospital. Usually they were funded by subscription or by company and charitable donations and bequests (it's interesting how many War Memorial hospitals there are) and when subsumed into the NHS in 1948 they became satellite outpatient services, sometimes with inpatient beds for surgery or convalescence and often with a physiotherapy service and diagnostic facilities such as X-ray. When I worked in Bath I did satellite clinics for my various bosses in Bradford-on-Avon (excellent toys in the OT department), Frome (good cakes), Warminster, Trowbridge (sandwiches), Chippenham, Calne, Radstock and Devizes – and there were others). My own cottage hospital in the grimy South-East corner of London, near the Thames, was another such. Postcards were made of it; orthopaedic surgeons did hip replacements there; the X-ray department was in a WW2 underground hospital (the subject of another essay); the outpatients department was a typical 1960s cottage hospital design with rabbit warrens of consulting suites and a Women's Royal Voluntary service (WRVS) canteen down the end. The hospital opened on its present site in 1928 by the Prince of Wales; a photograph includes the surgeon grandfather of one of my retired orthopaedic colleagues. Its activities were regularly and fully reported in the local paper (making a mockery of the partly closed modern hospital Trust Board public meetings). It raised money by raffles and fetes, where a tug-of-war competition between the local large armaments companies (and the police) was rewarded with a 16oz silver cup (Mappin & Webb) presented by the local armaments firm Vickers in 1898, which still exists. Our outpatient sister found it in a cupboard.

In the 1980s cost-cutting by rationalisation began. Small units such as ours became expensive, and just as the rise of Tesco killed the corner shop and high street by undercutting, so the cottage hospitals became uneconomic to maintain as standalone units, especially when new health and safety regulations effectively condemned the operating theatres (never mind that the infection rate was almost zero). Lengths of stay also diminished and the need for convalescence did likewise as it became apparent that rapid post-op mobilisation reduced complication rates. So Erith lost its inpatient wing to the mental health service (which later showed its ignorance by re-signing the site with large direction arrows in NHS blue and white).

Here is one of the new signs. It was repainted fairly quickly but not before I had sent the photo to "Private Eye" and got £10 for my trouble. I was initially puzzled as to why the entire outpatient staff had lined up to greet me in the car park, hoping I had brought my camera.

We watched as around the country numbers of similar units, including many I worked in around Bath, closed their doors and left their communities reliant on the big DGH miles away, thankful that at least a lack of outpatient capacity at the main hospital made our cottage hospital's closure almost impossible. It was sad but an inevitable consequence of trying to save money.

In the late 1990s and Noughties the new New Labour government decided it would bring care closer to home. Part of this was stimulated by Fabian Society policy driven by a local MP (and GP) who wrote a pamphlet with the provocative title "Challenging the Citadel: Breaking the hospitals' grip on the NHS".[34] This was to involve the diversion of hospital outpatients "into the community". Among other things it would require the building of a network of community hospitals where patients could be seen as outpatients, have tests done and receive things like physiotherapy. This new philosophy really took off, and when the government decided it was to launch an NHS "Constitution" the head of the NHS, David Nicholson, announced at the inaugural meeting, in 2008, how pleased he was that in his own little town (one of the Chippings, but whether it was Camden, Norton or Sodbury I cannot recall and don't care anyway) had a brand new community hospital, and it was wonderful and the way forward.

---

[34] H Stoate, B Jones, *Challenging the Citadel: Breaking the hospitals' grip on the NHS*. Fabian Ideas 620, 2006

It was all I could do not to stand up and say "HANG ON! We have spent the last 10 years closing cottage hospitals because they are uneconomic, and now you are talking about opening them all again! WHERE IS THE MONEY COMING FROM?" Actually I knew the answer to the last bit. More on that elsewhere. But the moral of this tale is that things may be nice and patient-friendly and touchy-feely, but in times of trouble methinks that financial prudence might be a Good Thing. Tesco knows best. Small may be beautiful, but not if it's unaffordable (and it's interesting to note that Tesco's local "One-stop" shops charge 18% more than the supermarket price).

Our cottage hospital suddenly became the focus for a re-profiling exercise of the "move care into the community" type. Two meetings were held to brainstorm plans. These were organised by the local Primary Care Trust (PCT). It was only after the second meeting that I discovered all of this. Perhaps it was unreasonable to expect the PCT to be interested in the views of the (many) consultants who provided an outpatient service there. After all I only worked there for 27 years. But even this initiative came to nought, as we got a new government and PCTs were abolished. This raises another issue – or system fault. You can negotiate all you like but if someone changes the system, or the finance, then you have to start all over again. Old lags like me who have been around a bit have spent a lot of time trying to plan the same services with literally dozens of different people, which become tedious. If you compare some of my discussion papers from 1985 with those twenty years later it is disconcerting to realise how similar they are (except that the early ones are printed with a dot-matrix printer and the stored version is on an unreadable floppy disc, unless you happen to have an old BBC B computer knocking about…)

As a corollary, one should bear in mind that the affordability issue is stealthily rearing its head again. The Labour government of Gordon Brown created some new peers so it could boast it was a government of the talents. None of them lasted very long, but Ara Darzi, a teaching hospital surgeon, took on the total reorganisation of the NHS, general practice included, and reinvented the polyclinic concept. I remember seeing the video trailer to this where he was meandering down a hospital ward and stopped to talk to a lady who had rheumatoid arthritis; he asked her how long she had been in, and hearing it had been for some weeks expounded at length on how such hospital stays were avoidable. Had he talked to me he would have found that such admissions are so rare that they are remembered for years; we rheumatologists hardly admit a soul these days, so it was a very bad example. I also recall that he brought over some enthusiast from Berlin to support the polyclinic cause, and remember thinking, as this chap was wheeled out all over the place, that one could not build a nationwide system based on a single example. Where were other successful models? Why were people from these not speaking also? Perhaps there weren't any.

I was particularly upset when an extremely senior physician (indeed a College President) addressed my specialist society – of which they were also a member – and stated that Care in the Community was where we were going, and if we didn't tag along then we would get no money, so we better had. I restated my usual arguments about dilution, dispersal and the lack of evidence of cost-effectiveness, and suggested we should not pursue a political agenda if it was wrong.[35] If scornful looks could kill I would not be writing this now.

I do have some sympathy (or synergy?) with the polyclinic concept. A couple were built in London and opened to the blast of many trumpets. Two years on, and they were closing – because they were too expensive to run.[36]

Told you.

As a PS to this, in May 2014 the new head of the NHS, Simon Stevens, was reported as suggesting the resurrection of "cottage hospitals". Shortly after it was denied that the report (in the "Daily Telegraph") was correct, but I got a letter off making the above points yet again (DT, 2nd June 2014). It was suggested that, rather than write letters, I should take to Twitter, but thanks, David O'Reilly, I cannot think of anything worse...

Oxymorons and unintended consequences

For a while I received a daily digest of articles from the HSJ, or Health Service Journal in full. In January 2017 there were two headlines:

- More trusts considered for 'financial special measures'

- All trusts given new targets to achieve provider sector surplus

Now Trusts considered for special measures are, basically, in financial trouble, in other words in deficit. Many such Trusts have been unable to solve their deficit problem and have had a succession of managers who have come and gone as the impossibility of balancing the books and maintaining

---

[35] Margaret McCarthy has made many of the same comments about telemedicine (*Show us the evidence for telehealth,* BMJ 2012;344: e469)

[36] In October 2011 the GP magazine "Pulse" listed 9 centres that were either closing or being considered for closure, on the grounds of cost or service duplication

safe clinical services becomes apparent. Reducing deficits means cutting services, while maintaining these with adequate staff means increasing the deficits; there is a limit to how long the pips can squeak for. The disastrous failure of clinical safety in Stafford will almost certainly be accepted to have been due to the cutting of corners, but the Care Quality Commission can put a Trust into special measures if its finances are wrong (even if its clinical services are fine) or if its clinical services are wrong (but its finances are fine). Heads I win, tails you lose.[37]

To achieve a provider sector surplus requires Trusts to save more money still. If they cannot do it now, how will they possible do it tomorrow? And what will be the effect on their clinical services if they succeed?

So these two juxtaposed headlines are, effectively, mutually exclusive. The irony of the juxtaposition appeared to have escaped the HSJ. However there is another ingredient to this toxic mix. Jeremy Hunt, the Rachman landlord of the NHS, spoke at the Conservative party conference to announce that he intended to force trainees to stay in the country after qualification for four years, because too many were leaving and abandoning patients to foreign doctors who can't speak good English.[38] He also intended to increase medical school entry to make it less necessary to recruit NHS medics from abroad, but also fill the unfilled posts currently washing around the system.

But herein lies a problem. If Trusts are bust then how will they be able to employ more doctors? It won't help the provider sector surplus, will it? Cutting deficits means shedding staff, not employing more.

Of course what Mr head-in-the-sand Secretary of State (at the time I wrote this, Jeremy Hunt, but it could be anyone and indeed the Brexit crisis in July 2018 resulted in his move to the Foreign Office, and by July 2019 he was out altogether, having lost to Boris Johnson in the Conservative Party's leadership election – which underlines my "Here today, gone tomorrow" concern) failed to realise, or chose to ignore if he had realised, was that doctors were voting with their feet because life as an NHS doctor employee was becoming intolerable. Why are GPs all retiring early? Medical school places will not be filled when all the prospective students are being put off by their medical friends, parents and relatives. So before trying to induct

---

[37] See: Report of the Mid Staffordshire NHS Foundation Trust Public Inquiry at https://www.gov.uk/government/publications/report-of-the-mid-staffordshire-nhs-foundation-trust-public-inquiry (accessed 8th August 2019)

[38] In 2018, of course, foreign doctors are finding it increasingly difficult to get visas due to a crackdown on immigration, so there will be no doctors. Peter Rachman was a notorious slum landlord in London in the 1950s

more people into this uncomfortable and failing system any S of S should first address the concerns of doctors over workloads, continuing education, regulation and bullying (viz the attempt to enforce a new contract). Then we might get somewhere. But no-one will produce results from a sullen and rebellious workforce.

The way the NHS is financed is anyway mad. Consider this; the purchasers have a budget from government that is supposed to cover GP services and all hospital referrals. If it isn't enough to do everything they want, they will have to effect economies. If they do this by restricting hospital referrals, as many have tried to do, then the hospitals (or provider sector) having planned for a certain capacity and worked out their book-balancing on that basis, will find their income has dropped. So far from making any surplus they will be making a loss. There is only one way that both purchasers and providers can both be in surplus, and that is if the total money coming in (from government) is in excess of both what purchasers need to meet their plans, and if what they then pay to providers is in excess of what the providers require to meet theirs. Which, as we all know, it isn't. Throw in the money that goes straight in and straight out again (eg Private Finance Initiative recharge payments, employers' National Insurance contributions and pay) and it is obvious there is a problem. People have suggested that a hypothecated NHS tax will solve the problem, but only if that tax covers all the demands. Which, I would guess, it won't. It might make the shortfall more transparent but it will not make it go away.

I will put this another way and suggest a solution rather than continue to be negative.

WHAT PART OF "NO" DO YOU NOT UNDERSTAND?

My son taught me this response and very useful it has been in defusing my internal tensions. However they built up again as I read that the acute sector of the NHS is to undergo a "reset". A reset would be fine if it delivered. It won't.

The acute sector is in crisis. Two-thirds of acute Trusts are in serious deficit.[39] A "reset" would work if (1) it wrote all the deficits off and (2) it ensured that they would not come back. This requires a lot of money which isn't there.

---

[39] When I first wrote this in 2012 it was bad; in May 2018 the acute sector deficit was, at £946m, twice what was "planned" – and getting worse.

Large numbers of Trusts scattered across England (all of them, in my area, without exception, in 2017) were in "special measures". This means they were not performing to the required standard, whether in financial or clinical terms. If it's the financial state that is the problem, see the above paragraph. If it's a clinical problem it is almost certainly due to a lack of staff. Fixing this requires a lot of money which isn't there, not least if a Trust needs to cover gaps with agency locums, which cost even more lots of money.

Bust Trusts are often burdened with serious debt from Private Finance Initiative (PFI) funding, as many projects are based on long repayment terms at crippling rate of interest, which sucks a lot of money out of real healthcare.

Many Accident and Emergency departments are working at full capacity despite being short of staff, burdened further by bed shortages (or blocking because patients well enough to leave hospital but with no system to get them out, or both). To fix this problem requires lots of money – either to increase acute beds, or to upgrade social services support, or both – which isn't there.

Many Commissioning Groups, or CCGs, which replaced PCTs and buy acute services, are facing severe financial difficulties and are trying to reduce costs, in one instance by the quite extraordinary suggestion that GPs stop referring any non-urgent patients to hospital.

So (I put that in because it now appears essential to preface a response from anyone in research). Acute services, which are commissioned by CCGs, are bust and/or judged to be failing clinically. To be less bust they need to cut staff, and to stop failing clinically they need to employ more staff. This is another oxymoron. Of course, failing units could be shut. After all that's what failed businesses do. However that then reduces the already perilously low bed numbers and shifts the problem elsewhere – and given that every hospital is in the same boat will cause chaos. Naturally the hospitals that remain open, requiring vastly more beds to cope with the displaced patients, could always expand, but would have to do so by adding to their PFI burden with a rebuild.

Meanwhile the government merrily and on the basis of misinterpretation of data pushed the concept of a seven-day service, which requires even more lots of money to cover rotas, overtime etc. It also appears to be indifferent to the scandal of generic drugs manufacturers escalating their prices without any apparent justification. And the public still expects, in this Kafkaesque situation, everything to be completely free. This is not a case of trying to fit a quart into a pint pot but trying to fit Kielder Water reservoir into a test tube.

The purchasers cannot purchase, the providers cannot provide and yet everyone sits round thinking up yet another reorganisation or "reset" to add to the list of failed solutions since the 1950s.

These have never worked. Some were devised by highly sensible and intelligent people. If they haven't fixed it after all this time, what makes anyone think that it can actually be fixed at all? I feel a sense of *déjà vu* creeping up. I have said all this before, and while it gets steadily worse, and deficits pile up in yet more places, "Nero" Hunt fiddled as Rome burnt. And, of course, made things even worse by slagging off the doctors.

All right, you say, you have identified problems, and irreconcilable ones at that, but what are your solutions? I suggest some or all of the following.

- Abandon PFI or refinance every PFI project to reduce historic and ridiculous interest rates to today's levels.
- Stop talking about the scandal of drug overcharging and sort it out.
- Stop some free prescriptions. If someone needs thyroid replacement let it be free, but not the multitude of other drugs that are also prescribed but have nothing to do with replacement.
- Stop doing some expensive and marginal things. For example, is there any reasonable point in administering anti-cancer drugs at £30,000 per course to gain six weeks of life? And likewise is there any justification for resuscitating, or indeed treating, elderly mentally frail people in intensive care units when their quality of life when they leave the unit is awful? This is of course contentious, but we must face the reality that the NHS as currently working is unaffordable.
- Stop statins (bee in bonnet here, but the costs are astronomical)
- Abandon any idea of seven day working until finances are demonstrably stable. Which may be forever.
- Run the NHS either as a fully subsidised state monopoly enterprise, or as a business, but don't pretend that it's possible for it to be both. And if it's a business, then close bits when they go bust. A true market will soon work out what works and what cannot. That will focus the mind wonderfully!

The cost of capacity: MRI

If doctors are to be credible they must not only say what they want to do for patients and why, but they must employ economic arguments as well as medical ones to make their case.

Take MRI, short for Magnetic Resonance Imaging. It's an amazing modality of investigation, not least to those of us old enough to remember neurology and oncology pre-MRI, when one relied on careful physical examination, intuition and guesswork, with a bit of diagnostic surgery thrown in. No longer the risky and inexact myelogram for diagnosing disc prolapses, just a quick if claustrophobic run through a magnet.[40] It works because all molecules get pulled into line like minute compass needles when the magnetic field is switched on, and when the magnet goes off they spin back to their original position, but water and fat molecules spin at different speeds, releasing tiny quantities of energy which can be measured and plotted.

So our dear government decided to get in on the act. If MRI is good then everyone should have one whenever they want. For anything. Bit of backache, neck pain, knee pain, whatever. But the hospital waits are too long! So let's provide scanners all over the place – in large general practices, polyclinics, allow access to private scans...

Wait a mo. Let's look briefly at the medical issues and principles. We should do a scan if it's likely to change our management. If a patient has back pain then (a) it is likely to get better within 6 weeks (b) a scan in a patient without root compression signs is unlikely to be helpful in planning treatment (c) a minor abnormality (eg a disc bulge) may be quite immaterial but may alarm the patient and (d) if the patient then goes to a specialist who cannot see the scan itself it wastes time. Indeed what is the process of radiological investigation? It is as follows:

- Patient develops symptoms
- Patient goes to GP
- GP fixes X-ray or scan, writing brief and often unhelpful clinical details on the request form (occasionally without taking a full history or examining the patient)
- Radiologist looks at film (or rather, now it's all digitised, image) with only half a sentence to go on and reports film accordingly (Question - ?fracture; answer: no fracture seen – never mind the other maybe important things such as arthritis, deformity, secondary malignant deposit).
- GP tells patient investigation is normal
- Patient still has symptoms

---

[40] A myelogram involved a lumbar puncture and the injection of a dye opaque to X-rays. One could be allergic to this and the side-effects of the lumbar puncture alone can be most unpleasant.

It's actually a game of Chinese Whispers unless the clinician can see the film and interpret it (which many non-radiologists cannot anyway) in the light of the considerable clinical background.

But I ramble. Let's suppose an NHS hospital MRI unit is open 9am to 5pm and has a waiting time of 12 weeks. The cost of reducing that waiting list to zero is the cost of staffing the scanner from 7am to 9pm – six hours of radiographer cover as overtime daily, which equates to perhaps £90,000 per annum. Now consider the cost of providing a new scanner "in the community" – capital cost £1.5-2m, revenue consequence 10% annual capital writedown, staff costs (at least 4 radiographers to cover, plus cost of radiologists' time). At an annual cost of £200,000+ we now have two MRI scanners, neither of which will have enough business to work at full capacity. Or the Primary Care Trust contracts with a private scanner on a fixed contract basis and pays for more scans than it needs (many of which are not necessary) but is happy because it is doing the contracting rather than leaving scan decisions to expensive specialists. This is not cost-effective. Specialists don't do scans because patients want them, and do do them because the result may alter management. So the NHS unit is cheaper. Why is this not obvious?

Ward nursing standards; the decline of patient-centred care

There have been numerous scare stories about the poor standards in hospital. Maidstone lost its Chief Executive; Basildon has been pilloried; Stafford has been taken apart (see above) and a government report has castigated the care of the elderly[41]. In December 2012 the newspapers were full of tales exemplifying the "culture of cruelty" in the NHS. Are these unique cases? I fear not. For decades my consultant colleagues in my hospital have criticised the nursing numbers on wards. For decades we have been told that the numbers meet the norms (well, almost). That does not mean the norms are right. However the constant ignoring of doctors' concerns – made all the worse by professional divisions that have seemed to allow nurses organisational autonomy that cannot be criticised – means that they have largely given up reporting them. When a report like that on Stafford comes out the politicians bleat "If you knew what was going on, why didn't you say something". When people do, they are accused of whistleblowing and

---

[41] *Care and compassion? Report of the Health Service Ombudsman on ten investigations into NHS care of older people.* http://www.ombudsman.org.uk/care-and-compassion/home

threatened with disciplinary action. So they're damned if they do and damned if they don't.

I would not wish to be racist, but it is an open secret that some nurses from overseas have a different attitude to sick people from me – and from many others. There is an authoritarian streak in nurses from some parts of the world that appears to be cultural and requires patients to do as they are told. One of my patients told me a story about her mother. She (the mother, that is) had been admitted with something or other and had been written up for her usual raft of medication. On the 6am drug round she was presented with her morning pills. She remonstrated mildly that at home she took them at 8. The nurse grabbed her hair with one hand and forced the tablets into her mouth with the other.

You may wonder why no complaint was made. So did I. My patient told me that she was too frightened to say anything in case the nurses took it out on her mother later. Perhaps this is an argument to close hospitals, but people in medical difficulty must be looked after somewhere and the scenario could occur in a nursing home just as in an acute ward.

The most appalling example of bad care happened with one of my long-term rehabilitation patients. Let us call him James. He had had multiple sclerosis for many years and had slowly become quadriplegic. However, he could drive his electric wheelchair with a chin control and led an active life, going out for meals (he could swallow normally, so only had to have food put to his mouth) and to the theatre and cinema. Indeed he led the life of a normal retired man.

James came into my unit for one week in eight to give his wife a rest. Both of them were into their seventies, so she found it difficult to manage 24/7 and our care gave her a much-needed rest and enabled us to sort out any medical issues.

One Friday evening James was admitted through A&E. There were problems with his indwelling catheter and he had become unwell. Considering what happened, maybe it was no accident he was admitted on April 1st.

Patients with MS who suddenly deteriorate, or "go off" as we say, should be presumed to have an infection until proved otherwise. They go off fast and bounce back just as quickly. If treated properly. But James was admitted to an acute ward, although his relatives asked if he could be transferred to the rehab unit where he was well known. They also asked that he be put on a low air loss mattress; he had one at home, and with careful turning he had been kept free of pressure sores.

A mattress went up to the ward under the trolley. James was put into a bed in the acute bay (nearest the nursing station) without it. After a bit he became quite uncomfortable, so asked for help. Nothing happened so he began to shout. The response of the nursing staff was to put him in a side-room as he was disturbing the other patients. He was at least given a buzzer to communicate. Being tetraplegic, he was unable to use it. Perhaps he would have been less uncomfortable if he had had some analgesia. Although he was on quite a lot at home, no-one had written up his drug chart.

The blood results from A&E suggested that James' blood sodium level was low, so he was placed on a restricted fluid regime. Possibly no-one had considered the possibility of failure of his adrenals to respond to stress, or some weird effect on antidiuretic hormone (we see this low sodium problem quite often in MS patients). However, the regime was very restricted indeed; he was given a jug of water. His intake was recorded (it was actually short of what was suggested), but the level of water in the jug did not alter. Perhaps this was unsurprising, as he was tetraplegic. He passed enough urine either through or round the catheter for the sheets to get wet, but they were not changed.

Two days passed and James had developed pneumonia. He was, at least, on an appropriate mattress by now and he was given antibiotics but it was probably too late by then; the doctors had not appreciated the need for speed, indeed pre-emptive action, needed for MS patients. So he was now quite ill, probably septicaemic.

At this point one might ask why the medical team decided, without knowing any of his previous background, that he should not be resuscitated. They sprang their recommendation on the relatives who, taken by surprise and realising that he was very ill, thought that the doctors must know best. On the evening of the third day they asked if they could stay but were told they had to leave at 11pm. On the fourth day when James' son rang at 9am to ask how his father was he was told that he was unchanged. At 1pm a message came through that James was very sick and just as his son and wife arrived James took a deep gasp, and then stopped breathing.

James' wife asked their son to fetch a nurse. He shot from the room and found one at the nursing station, telling her, very agitated, that his father had stopped breathing. She told him he would have to wait as they were about to do their shift handover. Perhaps unsurprisingly he lost his temper and became "abusive".

As if all this was not bad enough, at 6.30 the grieving relatives were astonished by a knock on the door from the ward hostess, who asked "Would James like his dinner now?"

When James' son came to see me two days later to report all of the above he was angrier than anyone I have seen. Indeed he said he could not trust himself to draft a complaint as he might do something silly.

I was pretty angry, too. So I wrote it.

Quite a cover-up ensued, but an independent review found that what is recorded above was essentially the truth. As it happened James' district nurse had, unknown to me, written an equally damning report of his care. No-one lost their job, or was even subjected to a warning.

I was at a meeting with the Chief Executive a while later and the case came up in conversation. I commented on its dreadful nature and my concern about what followed. "Hmm" was the reply "There was rather a lot of Dr Bamji said this and Dr Bamji said that".

Not many consultants have written formal complaints about their own hospitals. Perhaps, given my brush-off, not many will. But if a hospital's response to the raising of serious concerns is this negative (or more so – one consultant was suspended for doing this recently and took the Trust to court – and won) then it is hardly surprising that we have problems in the NHS. I do not know for sure, but suspect, that the consultants at Stafford knew exactly what was going wrong in their place but had either been cowed into silence or not bothered because they knew it would make no difference.

The day after I wrote about this case the "Daily Mail" printed another ghastly story, which I reproduce verbatim below.

Dying hospital patient phoned switchboard begging for a drink after nurses said 'No'

A patient desperate for a drink of water had to telephone the switchboard of the hospital he was being treated in to beg to see a doctor.

Derek Sauter, 60, used his mobile phone to request medical attention after his pleas for help were ignored. But when the doctor arrived he was turned away by ward nurse Caroline Lowe, who said Mr Sauter was 'over-reacting' and threatened to confiscate his phone. Eight hours later the grandfather-of-three, who was suffering with a chest infection, was dead.

Rather than offering sympathy to Susan, Mr Sauter's wife of 41 years, Miss Lowe later told her that he could have been prosecuted for harassing the doctor on call.

Yesterday his daughter, Ruth Sauter, 42, said she was appalled at the way her father, a former administrator for the Healthcare Commission, the former NHS watchdog, had been let down by the NHS. 'My father went into hospital for a routine chest infection, but never came out,' said Miss Sauter, of Thurrock, Essex. 'His condition was not life threatening and the nurses had specific instructions to keep close tabs on him. 'But their appalling lack of care, and cruel behaviour killed my father. He should not have died that weekend; it was not his time. 'It's so much worse knowing that he died alone, thirsty and scared on that ward.'

Mr Sauter was admitted to Queen Mary's Hospital, Sidcup, in Kent, at 9am on June 27 2008. He was admitted to a ward and given intravenous antibiotics and oxygen, but at 8.30pm he telephoned Mrs Sauter, a midwife, in distress claiming nurses were refusing to give him any water because he had accidentally knocked over the first cup he had been given. A note scrawled by Mr Sauter and discovered by his family after his death said: 'Asked for a jug of water at 6pm and again at 8.30, told to wait for handover. Said I knocked cup of water on floor.' In another note Mr Sauter said he was 'getting depressed'.

Some time between 9.30pm and 11.30pm Mr Sauter was moved to a side room where there was no monitoring equipment and, although he was supposed to be checked every four hours, no observations on his condition were made. At 11.35pm Mr Sauter, who had still not had any fluids, made his desperate call to the switchboard. The following morning, at 6.51am, a distressed Mr Sauter telephoned his wife to ask her to come back to the hospital. But he died of pneumonia brought on by the chest infection less than half an hour later - before Mrs Sauter, 60, arrived. She had not been able to see him before because the events had happened outside of visiting hours.

An investigation by the hospital revealed Mr Sauter's oxygen levels, which should have been routinely monitored, were not checked for 11 hours and had dropped 35 per cent below the recommended level.

The report concluded that were it not for the failings of Miss Lowe Mr Sauter would have survived. She has since been sacked by the hospital but has not been suspended by the Nursing and Midwifery Council, who are investigating. 'It's absolutely appalling that they haven't struck the nurse off their register,' Miss Sauter added.

Miss Lowe, who lives in Essex, said: 'I am so sorry about what has gone on, but there are key facts the family haven't picked up on. 'He didn't press the buzzer. We got him water, but then he spilled it, so we got him another glass. We got him a jug and everything. 'I have been through such trauma with this. I am still traumatised by it.'

A spokesman for Queen Mary's Hospital said: 'The Trust would like to convey their sincerest apologies for the failings in care which have been revealed.'[42]

I should hope so.

The Francis Report on Stafford broadly confirms the problems that will arise when targets come before patients. I was surprised and horrifed to read that a number of individuals had made contact to report that their institution faced many similar problems (as shown above, mine did, though I was not one of the correspondents). However such reports were deemed to be outside the scope of the Stafford enquiry. Oh dear. So what enquiry will follow these up? I am quite sure that many doctors are aware of major problems in their hospitals but have dared not speak for fear of victimisation or intimidation.

Duh-duh-duh-duh Duh-duh-duh-duh – VAT man!

In July 2013 it became apparent that there was a problem with the transfer of NHS property (transferred from parts of the organisation that "disappeared" under the Health and Social Care Act 2012) to a company called – unsurprisingly – NHS Property Services. It is in fact a state-owned company.

---

[42] Daily Mail, 29th March 2010 (http://www.dailymail.co.uk/news/article-1261457/Dying-hospital-patient-phoned-switchboard-begging-drink-nurses-said-No.html)

This company is supposed to collect rents from the various users, but because of the way it has been set up it will have to charge VAT on the rents.

So the NHS, which is state funded, pays an extra 20% back to the government! Those who have to pay will have to trim expenditure elsewhere (ie make cuts).

I suppose you could adjust all the rents downwards so that the overall bill remains the same. But wouldn't it be easier not to pay the tax? After all it requires an army to collect it.

I expect the government will simply increase allocation to compensate. Then of course it will say that it is pouring even more money into the NHS but will forget to add that it is all pouring straight back out without any benefit to patients whatever.

Holiday or not?

It has become a fact of medical life that leave can no longer be taken when you want it but must fit into the rigid rota systems now commonplace. There is no longer the flexibility in staffing numbers to accommodate more than a couple of people in a team being away at once, partly because the European Working Time Directive means that working longer hours is now illegal. What it does in terms of patient care continuity and safety is something for another day…

I recently learned a new management trick played on unsuspecting trainees. Their posts rotate and are of short duration at the start of their training. To fit all the holidays in it's necessary for some of them to be allocated slots right at the start of a new rotation. However – it is also necessary for them to undergo hospital induction (to learn about form-filling, health and safety and the vagaries of senior colleagues to name but three).

So – you have a compulsory three day induction but discover that your compulsory leave slot is in the first week of the job. It appears that induction is more compulsory than leave. If that's not an oxymoron then I don't know what is.

Death of a Hospital (or two): a fable for our time

Change the names and dates and this essay with its stuffing of oxymorons is as true now (2019) as when I wrote it in 2006, about Tony Blair, Gordon Brown and Patricia Hewitt.

Dear old Labour Party! In and out of government it has bristled with resentment over 1948, when hospital consultants had, in the words of Aneurin Bevan, to have their mouths stuffed with gold. Never mind that the basis of the NHS was a plan hatched by the British Medical Association almost a decade earlier, delayed because of the Second World War. No opportunity was spared to lambast the consultants, who strutted arrogantly in their patronising way and maintained their private practice by rationing appointments and operations within the NHS. Oh, sighed the Labour Party collectively, how wonderful it would be if we could only control these independent and anti-socialist folks!

So, Uncle Tony and Uncle Gordon hatched – the target. Targets for waiting times for outpatients; targets for waiting lists for operations; targets for waits in A&E; targets for new services, networks, frameworks, you name it. And the new consultant contract would mean that at last managers would have CONTROL! And the consultants would have to work like slaves and would not have time for private practice or the golf course and anyway private practice would shrink away because the NHS had suddenly got so much better.

So the consultants, being of a kindly and accommodating nature, and hating to see people suffer, worked harder and harder to see every patient referred within thirteen weeks, and operate on them all within six months And they succeeded. Never mind that to avoid "breaches" the hospitals found it cheaper to pay the consultants at private rates to do extra clinics because it was cheaper than being fined – nor that referrals between consultants didn't count and were stuffed in drawers and forgotten.

But sadly no-one, except the consultants, that is, had sussed that doing operations twice as fast, and operating on twice as many people as a consequence, and paying hospitals for each case done, would cost twice as much money. And although the two Uncles had piled money into the NHS as if there was no tomorrow, it wasn't the twice as much as was being spent. There were other things, too, like forcing all the hospitals to employ more trainee doctors because none of them were allowed to work as hard, and a thing called Agenda for Change, which sent all the other staff salaries up, and inventing things like Private Finance Initiatives, or PUFFYs, as a way of giving money to banks and puffing up expenditure by ten per cent, and allowing one and a half per cent for inflation when six would do. So the Uncles and Nanny Patricia said "Hang on a mo, all the hospitals are going bust. This will not do. Balance is essential. OK, hospitals, no deficits are allowed from now. If you have one, we want it back and to encourage you to obey we will take away the deficit from next year's allocation. As well. You must start sacking all the staff that you have just taken on to meet our targets". And Nanny Patsy said, in that nanny voice that only she can do "And anyway if you keep patients in for half the time, it will save simply oodles of dosh." But Nanny Patsy had never been that good at sums because she hadn't worked out that beds were there, empty or not, which costs, and staff needed whether they were empty or not, which costs as well, so to actually save the money you would have to close lots of beds which would reduce capacity and so the targets would be buggered up.

So the hospitals started to sack staff, but because they were in such a rush to make ends meet yesterday they too forgot that some staff were needed to meet the targets, and the targets were still there because Uncle Tony and Nanny Patsy hadn't taken them away. So the hospitals thought that instead of cutting costs they could see even more patients and bring in extra money that way, especially if they could see the patients twice and get as third as much again, and then the books would balance.

But then the Primary Care Trusts said "Hang on a mo, we are going bust, what with all these new health and prevention targets, and GPs getting huge pay rises for meeting their targets, so there's no way you hospitals can go on at this rate, mate, seeing all these patients that get referred to you, or we'll be even more bust that you are."

But the hospitals said "If we can't get all this income then we can't do the work to meet our targets" and the PCTs said "That's your problem, sunshine, not ours, we haven't got time for all this whining when we are so nearly bust, so please go away, and anyway we've thought up this wizard set of wheezes to put everything right, like we just slow things down a bit. So don't see anyone until the last day of the thirteen week outpatient target is up, and certainly don't operate until five months and thirty days are up, or twenty-eight if it's February and we'll forget the leap years. Oh, and by the way we will reduce the pressure of patients banging at your doors by vetting all the referrals. That'll keep down the numbers so there won't be such big queues so you won't go on about demand exceeding supply, because we can't afford your supply, especially if we send it all to Independent Treatment Centres which we then pay even if they don't do the work. So basically if the GP is crap and sends you crap we'll send it back and if the patient needed a neurologist and not a urologist we'll redirect it and maybe we'll get some of the patients sorted by a bunch of half-trained nurses because they're cheap, or by specially trained gypsy GPs, who aren't cheap, but we can pretend then we're keeping it all in primary care and meeting the new target of Care in the Community!"

Then the consultants said "Hang on a mo. We've been working all the hours God gave us to meet these targets and now you are saying that you are going to filter the referrals so there won't be so many, so what happened to Choose and Book which we never wanted anyway and you said would give every patient the right choice? Never mind the sick and needy, never mind the quality, you are going to get one hell of an angry load of patients asking what jumped-up prat is denying them their right for a second opinion from a specialist, an opinion that their GP asked for, now you are saying all that's out the window, and who is going to pay when someone dies because we have years of training and some half-baked feldsher that's been on a two week course is going to mess up big time." And the PCTs said "Now look here, we are broke and prevention is better than cure, don't you forget it."

And a few wise and weary consultants said, "Funny thing, that – it's just what that Bevan chap said when the NHS started but 50 years on it hasn't worked out like that, so what makes you think something's going to change?" And then they said "Hang on a mo. All those years you have accused us of rationing care to improve our private practices, which was a bloody lie, and we have worked our balls off here to meet your bloody targets and we have and suddenly you are saying we can't afford it so we must ration again and it will make the targets easier if YOU do the rationing? By Jove, we've got it! We are back to square one, but this time none of you bastards can point the finger at us, at least. But wait a minute, what are we going to do, if our workload is cut in half because sitting twiddling our thumbs waiting for tomorrow is not something we are good at – action men, us. And women, of course, ethnic origin not a problem."

And the PCTs and Nanny Patsy, using her nanny voice again, said "Look. If we haven't got the money, you can't do the work. Like, this is very simple. If you were a plumber you wouldn't do a job if you knew you weren't going to get paid, innit? And we actually would really like to rub your noses in it because our new systems, targets and whatever are designed to turn you consultants into the medical equivalent of Dyno-Rod operators, tradesmen even, take the calls, do the jobs, wherever, whatever, no job too small and so on, sorry if one takes a bit long and you've waited in all day but next Friday week looks clear. That's business!"

And the consultants said "But patient care will…" which was as far as they got because the PCTs and Uncle Tony and all shouted "LOOK! Shut up the lot of you. We never listen to consultants anyway. If you want to be busy go

48

and... do something. Do private practice. Play golf. Just shut up and bugger off, will you?"

So the consultants, who anyway earned three times as much in the private sector as they did in the NHS but mostly chose not to, shut up and buggered off.

Which couldn't possibly happen. Could it?

There's a space here, so just to prove that not everyone downed tools I include a photograph taken in 1996 of the Clinical Tutor (me) on a stepladder dealing with a wasps' nest in the wall of the Postgraduate Centre. You can see one just above my head.

****

Who is in charge – Doctor or Manager?

Once was the case that clinicians decided how to run their service and managers facilitated; now doctors find ways to meet management targets set by the managers (or politicians). What surprises me is how the new generation of doctors do not seem to have a problem with this; they obey like sheep. My failure to persuade colleagues that they must stand up was one of the reasons I left the NHS early.

Ponder for a moment and recall what I said in an earlier essay. How long is the average senior doctor in a single place? And how long a manager? (And to that add – how long a politician?) So where resides the institutional memory?

No doubt it will be said that as a geriatric with a bus pass I am the last person to be pontificating, as times have changed, I am an old stick-in-the-mud, poor old chap can't keep up with the times etc. And it is true that consultants are no longer as blindly loyal to their hospital as they once were and look for the greener grass on the other side of the hill quite often. But you should remember – I was young once and I don't think I have changed greatly, except that when I pontificate I do so from a position of experience, both of life and of pontification.

How many times have the keen and thrusting new generation come up to me and my fellow old farts with a new plan to save the NHS? Reform, modernisation, I have seen it all before. I am likely to say gently that we tried that 25 years ago, and it didn't work then, and I am not clear what has changed that will make it work now.[43]

It's not always the managers' fault. Sometimes they are driven by political pressures. I can think of two of our managers who went over to the doctors and suffered for it. But doctors must be prepared to embrace change if it's good and be equally prepared to resist it if it isn't. As I have said before, that requires doctors to step outside the evidence-based culture of clinical practice and consider finances, common sense and history.

---

[43] It still happens. I tried to persuade one of my friends and neighbours that taking on a non-executive director role in the local Trust would be a can of worms. I think it was after his second board meeting that he told me all the problems they had. The sense of *déjà vu* that hit me was almost fatal. And he keeps telling me tales to which I respond either "Seen it all before, Barry" or "I told you that would happen".

Consider the plan. Be prepared to raise Cain if you have not been consulted at the right time. Do a proper SWOT analysis on it if you must.[44] Look for unforeseen consequences. Think of the cost of doing it compared to the cost of not doing it. Check it hasn't been tried before somewhere, and failed. Have your arguments ready marshalled for the showdown. Be prepared to concede if you have missed a trick but be prepared to enlist support from without if you cannot find any flaws in your own argument.

Let's look at some global and parochial examples.

Crossing the line: can clinicians ever become managers?

The argument rages on over whether doctors can become managers without losing their principles. I tried my hand at management a couple of times. On the whole the arguments were not about improving services but saving money and I used to lose sleep over how to contain overspends. I was not a good manager because I put the patients first; while I was a clinical director the management board decided to move its main meeting from 8-9am to 10.30 to 12 – to allow more time for discussion, forgetting perhaps that the doctors would have to cancel clinical commitments to go. I made a fuss and the move was abandoned. When I stepped down the change was made within a month.

I was also not a good manager because I was always looking for the consequences of decisions and raising the possibility of trouble before the decision was made.[45] This usually delayed things, so I was sometimes unpopular. I also upset one senior manager when we considered a staff survey that suggested 40% had been subjected to some form of abuse by patients; I proposed the development of a red card system for abusers, to be told that we must consider why people abuse, and what has led them to do it, and try and understand how we might be making things worse. Talk about turning the other cheek! You will never get it to stop like that, but my accusation that this view was wishy-washy liberal nonsense raised a few eyebrows and made me one enemy for life.

Just before I left the NHS we were debating the future of my rehabilitation unit. It provided an important service to the long-term neurologically disabled, who get a bad deal generally from the NHS (as with James above) and whose "care in the community" often amounts to almost no care at all (which is why it can be so cheap). I found myself arguing that we must

---

[44] Strengths, Weaknesses, Opportunities, Threats
[45] See the essay below entitled "One fault will do"

concentrate on selling the business to the Primary Care Trusts and thus concentrate on the bits that could make money. Afterwards I realised that I could be ditching all my low-key patients whose ongoing care was not very hip, or interesting, and felt ashamed of myself. But that's what happens when you start on management agendas and forget the patients. However you could argue that some service is better than none. And, as you have read above, now there is none.

I went on a management course once (and still have the group photo to prove it). One thing that stuck out was the likening of medicine to chess rather than space exploration. With the latter each step leads logically and inexorably to the next. With the former, each move completely changes the possibilities. The NHS is like chess, not building space rockets. People need to realise this and alter their way of thinking to fit the pattern.

The cartoon below has a lot of truth in it.

'To be honest, Tarzan, we all feel we'd get much more done if you stopped calling us for these bloody meetings'

The Lancashire/Cumbria ISTC debacle

While I was President of the British Society for Rheumatology (2006-8) a grand design was developed in the north-west of England to construct a series of independent sector treatment centres for musculoskeletal services (ie orthopaedics, rheumatology, physiotherapy etc). A detailed proposal was drawn up showing where these new centres would be and indicating how much more convenient they would be to a large part of the population.

There had been no consultation with any of the people providing the existing services in District General Hospitals. Cain was therefore raised. It became apparent on careful review of the plan that it would be funded by a transfer of work from existing centres to the new ones – there was no new money that would allow both to co-exist. So the SWOT revealed an unforeseen consequence. A quick calculation indicated that the existing centres would lose so much elective work that one-third to one-half would have to close as they would be uneconomic. This had a further knock-on effect as emergency services would immediately be threatened. On this basis, although the new centres would provide better elective access to some of the population, the loss of existing centres would mean that other parts would have worse access.

The local consultants enlisted the support of colleagues nationwide, and of their local MPs. Backed up by a firm medical opinion, the trade unions started to kick up. The plan was abandoned. As the government had paid a private company on the basis that it would be the preferred bidder a considerable sum of money was irretrievably lost.

If only they had consulted with the locals, and worked with them instead of behind their backs…

Choose & Book

Choose and Book appeared in a previous essay. It was the catchy name given to a new system for arranging hospital outpatient appointments by computer. The rheumatologists in SE London were approached by the clinical lead for the Choose and Book project to be briefed on its introduction. We looked at the system and realised that, while it had been extensively consulted on at the consumer end (ie with GPs) it had not been consulted on at all with the providers of outpatient services (ie the consultants). So we wrote our own analysis pointing out all the likely difficulties and flaws, and duly turned up for the meeting. The team were quite taken aback by our negativity. When challenged on why they had not sought specialists' advice they retorted that there were too many specialist organisations to consult. The meeting ended with dissatisfaction on both sides.

A month or so later the Royal Colleges and specialist societies were circulated with a request for their input to the provider side of the scheme. Funny, that. Wonder why…

In fact there has been widespread dissatisfaction with the system on all levels. Getting the first available appointment via computer matching may be good in some ways, but may lead to the division of care between hospitals and there is risk in that. Anyway, the waiting time for an appointment may be an inadequate indicator of quality. Consider the following fable.

Pestonjee Bomonjee sat under a palm tree, wearing his hat, from which the rays of the sun were reflected in more-than-oriental splendour. Beside him was the cooking stove but, O Best-Beloved, I wouldn't ask about that if I were you. Word of the cake-crumbs had got about, and them that could sort out thieving rhinoceroses were in demand. So it was no surprise when a little old man appeared from the Almost Undoctored Exterior (which abuts on the islands of Tobacco, Sago and Tapioca, and the promontories of Salmonella), and stood before him, and bowed 'scrutiatingly deep.

"Oh Sage," quoth he, and pitiful it was to hear the tremble in his voice, "Oh Sage, I am needful of your superior advice on a matter of the Utmost Importance. My water is stopped up, and something must be done."

"Might I assume that this is not a problem of the mains supply to your accommodation that has been obstructed on account of an overloaded articulated lorry squashing the main, or more likely of you not paying your water rate?" said P.B., "but that of which you complain is a personal affliction caused by the benign enlargement of the prostate gland and resulting in Hesitance, Penitence and Dribbling?" And, on a sign of assent, he continued: "Why, then, you must find a urologist (or a general surgeon if you are less particular) to whom you may submit yourself for surgery."

The old man nodded gravely. "I have myself reached the same conclusion," he said, and added rapidly, "That itself is not the problem. But I have been told that there are many who will perform the operation, yet I may wait for years before it can be done. I have consulted the Great Wise Minister, K. Neth Clariq, second only in the land to Queen Tat Cha, and he said (or at least he has written on a White Paper that this is what will come to pass) that I must travel to the Uttermost Ends of the Earth to find him that has the Shortest Waiting List. He has told me that my personal physician, Dr Geepi, will herself conduct the search using a Fabulous Machine, which some call a Computer."

Pestonjee Bomonjee, whose face had darkened at the mention of K. Neth Clariq, was silent for a moment. Then he smiled, kindly.

"Pay no attention to the words of Clariq." he said. "I advise you to seek out the surgeon with the longest waiting list, and apply to him (or her) for attention."

But why should this be?" exclaimed the Pensioner. "Your advice makes no sense! If the operation is required, it must be done with all haste!"

"That is but one of the factors involved in your case;" said P.B., "there are others. In the Old Days your Doctor Geepi would have sent you to the surgeon whose bedside manner was politest, whose scar was neatest, whose postoperative complication rate was lowest, and whose hospital was cleanest. Naturally, then, the waiting list will be long. The surgeon that might hack you about, let you bleed pints postoperatively, and discharge you with a hideous scar and a wound abscess will no doubt be well known as a butcher, and no-one will send him patients. Naturally, then his waiting list will be short. If you are that desperate then take Slasher Harry with alacrity but blame not me if you end up in trouble."

The old man nodded. "I understand and can see what you say is true. But why should Clariq not see this?"

"He might," said P.B., "when he needs what you need. But he is ignorant of the First Law of Audit. Facts may be Facts, but there is always more than one explanation for why the facts are Just-So."

"Clariq that dictates and cuts the docs' rates makes dreadful mistakes."

And there was a great deal more in that than you might think.[46]

---

[46] AN Bamji, *How the NHS waiting list got its length*. Hospital Doctor, 6/4/89. Read this 30 years on and you will wonder at its acute relevance. You are correct to identify the tale derives from "How the Rhinoceros got his Skin" by Kipling. I have a soft spot for it, not least as my great-grandfather was hakim to the Maharajah of Baroda, whom Kipling would have encountered. That his name was Pestonji Bamji (of which Bomonjee is an alternative spelling) may thus be more than coincidence.

"'Ere, Brian! Isn't that the bastard who botched your operation?"

Data, data, don't compare a rosy apple with a pear; the new and follow-up game

The funding system of Payment by Results (PbR – perhaps more aptly termed payment by activity) was responsible for the development of a new game. My local Primary Care Trust sent down an instruction (not a request, mind) that my department reduced its follow-up appointments because the ratio of new to follow-ups was too high (we averaged 1:4.2 and they wanted 1:2.1). We refused and they sought a meeting to discuss the issue. We were informed that we "had to" reduce our follow-ups because our ratio was much higher than the comparator hospital – which was not in fact far away. We had done some homework and identified that our casemix was substantially different from theirs, largely because we had a back pain triage service that creamed off a large percentage of patients who would by the nature of things be seen only once and then in the main sent on to physiotherapy. The other hospital counted all such patients under rheumatology. Inflammatory joint disease required ongoing specialist review (as it turned out, later guidelines from the National Institute for Health and care Excellence (NICE) underpinned this). We pointed out that if we discharged the numbers needed we would have to discharge over two-thirds of our rheumatoid arthritis patients. Would the GPs be happy to monitor their disease-modifying therapy? What about review of biologics patients?[47] What would happen to

---

[47] The biologic drugs are antibody-derived preparations requiring injections. Very expensive (a review of drug costs in late 2016 revealed that of the top ten drugs by cost in the UK, five were used wholly or partly for inflammatory joint disease) there are strict guidelines for both use and monitoring

emergency flare-ups? Our own Trust managers were quite happy that we should discharge patients, on the basis that they would have to be re-referred and then attract a new patient rather than a follow-up tariff. We thought that was, simply, stupid. We also thought our GP colleagues would agree, not least because of all the time they would waste making the re-referrals (of course, under the horrible Choose and Book appointment system there was no guarantee the patient would see the same consultant or even that they would be able to get the patients back to the same hospital).

We had not at this stage raised the casemix issue; its time had come. I suggested that we did not need to discharge our follow-up rheumatoid arthritis patients at all; there was another way of reducing our new:follow-up ratio which would actually make it better than the comparator hospital. Interest was immediate. I explained the casemix difference and said that if we included under rheumatology all the back pain patients going through our (physiotherapy led) triage service we would add another 1500 new appointments to the caseload – but of course these would all be charged under Payment by Results and add an overall cost to the PCT budget of nearly £250,000.

No further interest was taken in trying to reduce our follow-ups. At least at first. Then another attempt was made and there was an intention to reduce new patients also, which would of course have required an even larger reduction in follow-ups to achieve the magic ratio – there was a new manager on the Primary Care Trust (PCT) block (and all ours changed after major reorganisation), so the institutional memory on both sides had been lost. The second time round the required ratio was 1:1.88. This was, it transpires, signed up to by our Trust! Indeed the Chief Executive indicated to me that he would look unfavourably on me if I did not obey. I must not do work for which the Trust would not be paid. I was told that the responsibility for my patients lay with the GP, not me. I might add that he promulgated quality as the first priority of our service. Here we go again!

I actually tried to find out where this new to follow-up nonsense had come from. Rather like Athene springing fully armed from the breast of Zeus it appears to have been a thought process with the Department of Health (based, of course, on surgery, which is what so many department-wallahs seem to think hospitals are exclusively for) and then sent out as a policy document. It was predicated on the assumption that once any patient is discharged from follow-up they will never need to be seen again. It also suggested that all hospitals should aspire to achieving the 25th centile. So – if we all do, then the mean moves, so we all have to reduce further, *ad infinitum et ad absurdum*. I think it was Estelle Morris who famously said, while Education Secretary, that it was a disgrace that half the population were below average intelligence but this has been variously attributed to Lyndon B Johnson and George W Bush among others. It would help if the top team understood statistics (in case you don't, just recall that the mean is the midpoint of a population so by definition half are above and half below). But then, as my good friend Wolfgang Gaissmeyer points out, even medics don't understand statistics. A test for you, medics and non-medics. What percentage is one in a thousand? Most people come up with 0.01%. Wrong.[48]

Perhaps common sense will prevail, but why does it take such effort? Following on from my 2008 audit a large chunk of the Midlands decided to do something similar, and over a dozen units repeated our work. They found an average ration of 1:4.9 (mine had been 1:4.3) and, like us, found that casemix differences were the main determinant of whether a unit was above or below the mean. However when one hears of managers suggesting that improvements must be made so that less than 30% will be below the mean you do wonder whether any of them have even a GCSE in elementary maths (just in case you have already forgotten what I wrote in the last paragraph, the mean is halfway so 50% will be below and 50% above – always! And so, moving everyone closer to the end centiles alters the mean, and thus the centile points, and off we go again).

What might be sensible (and interesting) is if the managers made an investigation into both ends of the normal distribution to discover why some ratios were as low as they are as well as why some are so high. With all the pressure there has been, and still is, to stop GP referrals, and threats of extreme sanction if GPs over-refer, I think an investigation should be made into why some *under*-refer. Patients are more at risk from that than from being sent to hospital too quickly.

There is of course a serious side to this farce. On the one hand we had PCTs suborned into taking out block contracts with private suppliers that are then underused (like the MRI scanning contract referred to earlier). On the other they refused to pay for NHS provision that is not only necessary but is best practice according to national guidelines. If consultants had heavily overbooked clinics as I did, would we really have an interest in seeing people unnecessarily? But cutting hospital outpatients would effectively have lost us large chunks of profitable business (unless, of course, we were

[48] It's 0.1%. See also J Multmeier, W Gaissmaier, O Wegwarth, (2014). Collective statistical illiteracy in health. In B. L. Anderson & J. Schukin (Eds.), *Numerical Reasoning in Judgments and Decision Making About Health* (pp. 39–58). Cambridge, UK: Cambridge University Press. If you can read German see also G Gigerenzer, G et al, *Glaub keiner Statistik, die du nicht verstanden hast* (Do not believe statistics that you do not understand). Gehirn & Geist 2009 (10), 34–39

not paid for it). Thus it is not only in the patients' worst interests to be discharged but it is actually in the hospital's worst financial interests not to challenge the figures! Unless, of course, they return as new patients and are charged as such – wondrous effect on the ratio but increasing the cost to the PCT by at least 40%!

What amazed me was that some consultants were actually putting down on their CVs how they had succeeded in these aims and had appeared proud of it.

There was yet another twist to this. Although we were "ordered" to see less new patients our clinics were full (through Choose & Book referrals from out-of-area) and even over-full because a large number of local GPs were not using C&B on the basis that (1) they wanted their patient to see a particular consultant and (2) the patient actually agreed that their GP's advice was reasonable and was prepared to wait. I had one such in which every page contained a header in capitals saying "Dr Bamji only". But there was a "breach" target for new referrals. It didn't matter how many thousands came through the letterbox but we had to see them in 6 weeks or the hospital was fined. So we ran extra clinics (for which we might personally get paid extra – cheaper than the fine) to see the patients that the GPs wanted us to see. But the PCT then said we were seeing too many and refused to pay the hospital.

Of course the PCT got partly wise to this, and so forced GPs to submit to a vetting system for referrals – a system introduced quite widely, and called referral management. It's as if they are not trusted. What happens if they are browbeaten into not making a referral and something goes wrong may be a matter for the courts.

But where is patient choice in all this? I had lots who, when I suggested discharge, expressed both horror and fear – horror that there will be no-one who has time to listen to them and fear that their GP will be unable to look after them properly.

Managers lose their heads when targets, however mad, are threatened with breaches. One of our neurologists, a long-term locum, left the hospital. The secretary, who happened also to be mine, was ordered to cancel all the follow-up appointments – but continue with the new ones. She very reasonably pointed out that many of the follow-ups were awaiting the results of tests done after the initial consultation, and they would get very agitated if they were suddenly told that no-one was going to let them know if they had a brain tumour, MS, motor neurone disease or whatever else they feared. This cut no ice. Is this mad, or what? It's time to abandon the "target" of new to follow-up ratios for the lunacy that it is.[49]

"Internal referrals"

It amazes me that, if a specialist sees a patient and decides they need to see another specialist in a different discipline, they are inhibited or even prevented from making a direct referral but are ordered to send the patient back to their GP for them to make the second referral. This demeans the specialist, wastes everybody's time and is I think an arrogant and conceited view. The specialist may be far better placed to refer on appropriately (especially as they know who they would be happy to be referred to, or more importantly whom they would not wish to see, which is expressed in the fable above). Forbidding the practice is childish, petty power-play and completely contrary to patients' interests. It also adds to GP workload, quite unnecessarily. However, as the irritation was minor, I played along. When it was least inappropriate. Which was not often.

Contracts and PAs

Our managers decided to make everybody's contracts the same. PAs are Professional Activities, in case you didn't know, and were calculated on a sessional basis.

Pity this did not take into account the fact that some of us saw twice as many patients as others (so earning the Trust twice as much income, assuming the PCT actually paid). We had a splendid calculating program which worked out our sessional time to the second decimal place. In fact it made even more explicit that most consultants actually put in more time than they are paid for. So cutting sessions (which could mean a pay cut of 20% for some) should produce an immediate response of "Which clinical commitment shall we drop?" This will not increase productivity, the increase of which is another aim of government.

Of course, in 2019 some halfwit changed the pension rules for high earners, the result of which was that some doctors, obliged to contribute 14.5% of

---

[49] A much-condensed version of this (I think it was Mark Twain who apologised for the length of a letter on the basis that he had not had time to write a shorter one) is A Bamji, *We should scrap targets for outpatient follow-up ratios*. BMJ 2011; 342: c7450. Actually I learned, just after I retired, that the target had been abandoned "because it didn't make any sense". Fancy that.

their income to fund their pension, would find this exceeded the new annual limit for contributions and so would be taxed on it. Thus some threatened to reduce their sessions or retire.

Mad medicine indeed.

Bed-stealing

My rehabilitation unit was built for a three-district population of some 750,000 with 20 beds, but with the perennial shortfalls only 14 could be staffed. Periodically there were pressures from the acute hospital to use our six empty beds as an overflow. To avoid major problems for our own patients we set strict criteria for use – no significant infection (*C.Diff* or MRSA), no dementia (the unit had automatic doors which led to the hospital back road, which is a bus route, so wanderers might get run over, or disappear into the undergrowth not to be seen again for days) and no incontinence (disabled folk who cannot see very well will either trip on the wet patch or scoot gaily through on their wheelchairs and spread it about a bit).[50]

You can guess what came next. As pressures grew, protocols went out of the window, so we ended up on one occasion with 12 medical patients of whom all were in one or more ways in breach of our rules.

When this happened I made a fuss. It often seemed to occur when my unit manager was off duty, or at weekends. On one occasion I forbad the bed manager to admit a medical patient, not least as one of my seriously disturbed and depressed patients, who we had only just got settled in a side-room, was going to be moved out of it. The following morning I arrived to find the medical patient ensconced and my disturbed patient causing havoc in a four-bedded bay.

Now much of the time we could cope – except that it was rare for all the extra staff needed for the 6 beds to turn up, so the permanent staff ran around at double speed (if bank and agency staff did appear, we were subsequently accused of overspending). But ignoring the clinical rules had itself become a rule.

As a result we had to cancel some of our booked admissions. One such was Mrs Smith, an MS patient who was already in a state because she had just

---

[50] We actually had a few patients who managed to reach the undergrowth on the Sidcup site from the main hospital block, not to be discovered for a couple of days...

buried her best friend. The dog had been boarded out (cost £140) with a couple who had changed their holiday dates to oblige. Mrs Smith sat on the unit all day hoping one of the medical patients who was supposed to go home actually did, but they didn't. She was offered a night on an acute ward, but previous experience of care led her to turn this down, (and she knew James, whose story was well-known to the unit patients as well as the staff) so at 8pm she went home. The ambulance crew kindly drew her curtains. The next day she was stuck. She couldn't open the curtains, her telephone was not within reach and so she couldn't contact her family who, thinking she was on the Unit, had gone away.

Need I say more?

Actually, I need. A year and a month after I retired my erstwhile Unit Manager informed me that the Unit – a purpose-built unit, designed for (and partly by) heavily disabled patients – was to be moved to an ordinary, unconverted ward so the space could be used for something else. I suppose you could argue that in the last 25 years all the other units that worked like ours had gradually been closed down, and that ours was an anachronism. However, it had provided substantial care and support, on both an in- and outpatient basis, to well over 300 patients. Which kept them, on the whole, out of acute beds where they would be improperly looked after and die. Like James. Of course it was expensive; looking after severely dependent people is staff-intensive, but to run "standard" ward levels of staffing was impossible. If a heavy quadriplegic patient requires three people to move them you cannot have just two nurses, and if all your patients are in wheelchairs then they need lots of room to move about. When I started, the Unit was in an unconverted ward and we got moved out to our new premises precisely because the old ones were inadequate.

The wheel turns. Once again pennies came before patients. The large numbers of severely disabled folk we looked after included patients with multiple sclerosis, spinal cord injuries (who had often been discharged from the big centres with no backup, so couldn't cope) and young patients with muscular dystrophy. It was thus ironic that a report appeared the same week of the closure decrying the lack of support for disabled children entering adulthood. That was one of the things we did, and now it has gone.[51]

---

[51] Following reorganisation of the reorganisation that created the South London Healthcare Trust (and failed), my unit was closed altogether. The senior staff were relocated to a major teaching centre which took over one of the constituent hospitals – not mine – and intended to open a similar unit in it. So a purpose-built unit was be replaced, four miles down the road, by another, although I suspect it will be less *purpose*-built. Such is NHS progress.

If you see someone in the corridor with a clipboard it must be a manager

It is sad how I recycle all these tired clichés – but even sadder that I have to.

Our hospital was broke and cuts were raging everywhere. I was walking up the main corridor and saw in the distance two managers deep in serious conversation. There was no clipboard. As I came closer I realised that a third manager was bringing up the rear; he looked young enough to be on work experience.

He was carrying the clipboard.

For some reason this reminds me of lightbulbs.

How many lawyers does it take to change a lightbulb?

How many can you afford?

And as for lawyers…

Managers can sometimes be persuaded – by putting them in danger

Our old rehabilitation unit was a converted ward with an extension (built with charitable money from the Unit's own fund) that opened onto the lawn. It had a gently sloping path up to the service road which was negotiable by a wheelchair.

The hospital decided to extend the pathology laboratory (some 15 years later, ironically, pathology was withdrawn from the site) and to do this the service road had to be moved some 3 metres nearer to the rehab unit – at the same ground level. It was immediately apparent to us that the gradient of our access path was now unmanageably steep.[52] I tested it myself; as an able-bodied person I struggled to get up the slope in a wheelchair and when I reached the top the extra effort needed to negotiate the angle between slope and flat footpath caused the chair to tip backwards. Going down was fine until you lost your grip on the wheels and the chair then careered down the slope. Just enough speed was picked up to ensure that the automatic doors to the unit would open just as you got there, neatly sliding in between the

---

[52] I wondered about doing a drawing, but reckoned readers were bright enough to work out the geometry themselves. If not, get a pencil and paper.

footrests and smacking you in the face as you came to a sudden halt and then tipped forwards out of the chair with a head injury.

We asked for a new path, to run at an angle towards part of the road which was at a lower level. We were refused. I then persuaded one of the Works Department staff to come and actually look, and before he could comment we sat him in a wheelchair and asked him to go up the slope. Being a big chap he managed this with ease, and as he turned to grin at me as if to ask what the fuss was all about the wheelchair tipped over backwards. I then asked him to go back down. He refused, and we got our path.

Managerial threats and how to deal with them

I was threatened with disciplinary action twice. If you are sure of your ground then stand up and be counted, but be aware that you may end up, like Stephen Bolsin, as the locally unacceptable face of whistleblowing even if you are right[53]. However bullies will go on bullying unless they are resisted.

Thus what you do may be determined by your seniority and subsequent risk (if junior) of isolation, if the herd decides to lie low and not back you up. Your career might be jeopardised, as an excellent storyline in the BBC series "Casualty" made clear in 2010 when Lennie, the dysfunctional trainee, backed down from exposing a drug trial scandal.[54]

There are risks from confronting entrenched positions. A friend of mine (I won't name him) told me that he was verbally abused and had his Wikipedia entry vandalised by a pressure group who considered his views (evidence-based though they were) undermined their own self-centred prejudices. The parents who think that MMR vaccine caused their children's autism are another dangerous lot, as are those who don't believe in so-called Munchausen by proxy;[55] there are even some people still around who think that silicone implants caused their connective tissue disease. One of my patients was convinced of this, one day triumphantly bringing in a carrier

---

[53] Bolsin blew the whistle on the goings-on in the Cardiac Surgery department in Bristol, and found himself unable to get another job in the UK

[54] *Casualty* (BBC1); series 24, episode 46, 2010

[55] Munchausen's syndrome, named after the fictional Baron whose tall stories were told by Rudolph Raspe in the eighteenth century, was named by Richard Asher to describe peripatetic patients who had multiple hospital admissions all over the place for faked symptoms suggesting serious disease. Munchausen by proxy is when a parent, usually a mother, touts her child around, often having administered harmful substances (and on occasion continuing to do so while the child is in hospital)

bag from which she flourished a vile pot containing the remnants of her removed breast prostheses (one of which had leaked and was all distorted and gunky, and it was just after lunch so I was nearly sick). The problem was that although she was convinced it had caused her scleroderma, there was no evidence whatsoever that she had ever had scleroderma.

When I was a trainee I worked in a famous London specialist hospital, where for the second half of my six months I served a tyrannical professor for whom everything had to be just so. Not only did I have to clerk admissions for them, but I also had to admit another consultant's patients, all of whom came in on a Sunday afternoon and required extensive prick and delayed hypersensitivity tests. My own boss's patients were frequently on trials, so the protocol forms had to be written up, together with large numbers of pathology forms, often in triplicate. These patients came in on a Tuesday. Clerking them was difficult as the ward round was on Tuesday afternoon, and went on forever – and resumed on Wednesday morning at 8.30am. Woe betide you if by then the patients were not completely dealt with; you would be humiliated in front of an audience of worldwide visitors. Either you coped by living your entire life in the hospital, and ignored the world, or you unwound with much alcohol (or a girl, or both) or you had a nervous breakdown. I tried all except the last.

I was hauled in for a dressing-down and told I wasn't doing my job well enough. I tried harder (often finishing around 11.30pm). I then realised that my immediate senior was coming into the hospital after I had left the wards and was running round the patients doing everything all over again. So I eased off, and perhaps unsurprisingly I was called in once more.

I lost my temper and said that there was not much point in my doing things if someone else came along later and did something different; so, if he was stopped from interfering, I would continue to do my best but otherwise would not bother. Finding someone standing up to them seemed to calm things down. However, when I asked for my additional hours form to be signed, I was told that I either got the money or a reference, but not both. I said in that case I would have neither.

Later I did a merciless counter-humiliation of said boss in the hospital Christmas show, and felt I had gained sufficient revenge. However I applied for a locum post to fill in before my next substantive post, for which there was a six week gap. I got it, only to have it suddenly snatched away a few days before I was due to start because "they had got someone else". I am sure it was because my boss had put in a word. So I did not have the last laugh and that's why I am neither a chest physician, nor a cardiologist. I re-visit this time later in the book.

Another example of this serves. Chris Pallis, neurologist at the Hammersmith, was an erudite man renowned for his very left-wing leanings and was also one of those spontaneous people who disrupted the social schedule (and no doubt was a great nuisance to his long-suffering wife Jeanne) by suddenly announcing that the entire team must collect for dinner at his place – tomorrow night. They were great evenings. Chris fancied himself as an expert on comparative religion and one night I came back from a quick trip to the facilities to find him expounding on Zoroastrianism with great intensity. I suspect his interest in this minority religion had been stoked by an earlier Parsi colleague.

The only trouble was that he was getting it wrong (I should know – my father was a Parsi)) and in front of the assembled multitude I put him right. That led directly to the other trouble – for the next three weeks he relentlessly found fault with everything I did – clerkings, examinations, letters, the lot.

The moral is simple. If you are going to put down a senior colleague choose your time and place most carefully. As far as Chris Pallis was concerned he held no grudge; we wrote a much-quoted paper together, and I was the only non-neurologist invited to his 70th birthday party at the Athenaeum. Indeed for many other reasons he was, perhaps, the person who had the most influence on my medical career. It was a tragedy that someone with such a brilliant brain, and a fierce interest in Parkinson's disease, should be struck down and immobilised by the very disease he researched.

Political threats and how to deal with them

There have been several attempts by politicians in the last ten years to bully, harass and intimidate doctors. Some have been extremely unpleasant.

One was the Alder Hey incident. Some people may recall the furore over the collection of body parts at this well-known children's hospital in Liverpool, and possibly remember that the then Secretary of State for Health, Alan Milburn, stated that the doctors at Alder Hey Hospital should be immediately referred to the GMC.

At the time I was Clinical Director for Pathology in my hospital and was therefore sent the report so I could assess our potential problems with my manager. There had already been a few hysterical people ringing up to recover any material to reunite with their dead loved ones, even if it was only a microscope slide of a bit of tumour. Most people in my experience never want to see their relative's tumour ever and nor do most patients.

"I don't trust these surgeons -
So I make them keep everything they take out."

I did say most. Bizarre really – but it was not long before I realised that the whole incident had been completely distorted. No-one had actually read the whole report before sounding off.

The report was written like a racy novel.[56] The problem was, in fact, that a rather strange man had been appointed to a professorial post based at Alder Hey. It was an academic post. Thus the job description had been constructed by the university, not the hospital clinicians. The clinicians at Alder Hey and some outside advisors had expressed serious reservations about the job description itself and indicated it would be almost impossible to do. The university disagreed and went ahead with interviews. The clinicians on the panel expressed serious reservations about the appointed candidate but were overruled. So, far from the clinicians being to blame for the appointment, they had actually tried at two points in the process to stop it. If anyone should have been held to account it was the university. So much for fairness!

---

[56] You can find it at https://assets.publishing.service.gov.uk/government/uploads/system/uploads/attachment_data/file/250934/0012_ii.pdf. It is interesting how many such reports are so readable. Try the Denning Report on the Profumo affair, which was one of the first such to make sure that the facts did not get in the way of a good story.

The clinicians were pilloried in the press, harassed and vilified but it was nothing to do with them. Even now the Alder Hey affair is written about in horrified hyperbole. However it doesn't matter what systems you put in place; it won't stop the determined mad or bad; revalidation may weed out the under-competent but will not stop another Shipman.[57] And all of this regulation costs money. Is the cost worth the benefit?[58]

Revalidation was the final nail in my professional coffin. Having left the NHS I was doing private work only and the cost of the process was pretty well two months' earnings. Worse, the process required "360°" feedback from more patients than I was seeing, and the required reflection on problems simply could not be completed because what I was seeing was simple and so there were none. I did query the cost, only to be told that it wasn't really an issue because if I revalidated others I could charge a fee and recoup my own expenditure ten- or twenty-fold...

Re-reading this it has occurred to me that I have described an example of a threat but not offered any advice on how it should be met. That's because in cases with a wide impact such as this it really needs to be dealt with by the professional organisations, which should square up and immediately challenge such foolish political outbursts. On an individual or local basis it can be more difficult. When my rehabilitation unit was threatened for the third and penultimate time I took my team and some of my more articulate patients to a meeting with the health authority, outlined what we did, got the team to describe the outcome of closure and the patients to explain how it would affect them. It worked (the fourth time I was retired and gone, so it went ahead). Or you can discuss the issue with your friendly local (and occasionally national) journalists, who can plant some awkward questions and tacitly threaten bad publicity. This, however, has its risks. You need to be sure that your ace cannot be trumped, and equally sure that you will not find yourself in personal difficulty for whistleblowing – for despite all the comforting words about how whistleblowers will be loved, cherished, respected and whatever it is far from the case that they are, or will be... Who will rid me of this turbulent priest?

****

---

[57] On the surface Harold Shipman was a caring general practitioner, but in 2000 was convicted of the murder of 15 patients. He committed suicide in prison.

[58] In early 2017 the cardiac surgeon Stephen Westaby was told by his medical director that his revalidation process would not be signed off because he had not submitted a proper personal development plan. Considering that he has done more than anyone to promote thoughtful discussion on hospital process, and has devised several groundbreaking techniques, this seems to be a bit of an insult.

Who is in charge (2): Specialist or GP?

Forget the reform; the GPs are certainly in charge, which makes a change from the old-fashioned view expressed in the 1950s by Lord Moran that GPs were doctors who had fallen off the hospital ladder. In those days most hospital services were planned by hospital consultants and directors of public health. When I started my consultant career the Medical Staff Committee made decisions and expected the administrators to implement them. Now the managers make decisions and expect the consultants to do as they are told. Meanwhile the GPs, who ordered secondary care as required for each patient, are on the one hand saying that they can do a lot of what was deemed specialist care themselves (which may be partly true) while on the other introducing referral management mechanisms that impede hospital referral, largely cloaked under targets. While hospitals depend on the work they receive from general practice, general practice is limiting work – which will inevitably lead to major financial problems for the hospitals. Another oxymoron…

Of course, any attempt to offload hospital work onto general practice results in an outcry…

I am concerned that the powerful consultant voice has been silenced, and it has been. Although there are mutterings in hospitals about the problems of the way forward, objectives have been hijacked by managers, and those clinicians who have crossed to the dark side pay lip service to general consultation. The role of the once all-powerful Medical Staff Committee has been neutered; consultants work harder and harder to keep the hamster wheel turning and have no time to discuss things with each other, as well as no forum. Indeed I liken many to sheep, unlike the goats of a previous age.

I date this problem to a specific event – the closure of "Hospital Doctor", a weekly newspaper full of country-wide news, views, opinions and comment. It died when taken over by a new company which saw its financial security undermined by restrictions on pharmaceutical advertising (partly a response to the inability of such advertising to influence hospital staff tied to formularies). I declare an interest; I wrote for it often, and was reported by it more often. But it was a national forum; it encouraged competition (it ran a highly successful specialty Team of the Year competition), whistleblowing and uprising against authority. Unlike the British Medical Assocation's journal it carried no medicopolitical trade union type overtones. Its death was a disaster; revolution and dissent are made very difficult if communication is disrupted, as the Iranian and Libyan people found when their internet access and phone networks were shut down in 2009 and 2011.

The BMA's weekly newsletter had more about working conditions in Northern Ireland and Wales than about consultants working in England. On the other hand "Pulse", which is a similar journal to "Hospital Doctor" aimed at GPs, is flourishing and its power is obvious. It is treated with respect from without; one of my emailed rapid responses to a "Pulse" article was quoted by a national journalist and in 2018 its vigorous and prompt campaign led to the resignation of England's most senior managerial GP. It seems crazy that the whole hospital service can be suddenly disadvantaged by an event totally outside its control, but it happened, and I cannot see a way back without recreating "Hospital Doctor" – at great and probably unaffordable expense. Were I to win the Euromillions lottery I would consider it.

From a clinical perspective, despite the gradual erosion of power of the hospital specialists they are increasingly becoming the first port of call for patients with long-term disease (while hospital A&E departments become first choice of patients who cannot get a GP appointment promptly enough).

Patricia (not her real name) was on methotrexate for her rheumatoid arthritis. It was convenient for her to come to the cottage hospital for her bloods (to which results her GP had access). Methotrexate can rarely cause problems with blood cell production and liver function, so a "full blood count and LFTs" are done on a regular basis – if all appears stable, once every four to six weeks. One test came back showing a typical iron-deficient picture. Nothing to do with the methotrexate, just a shortage of iron. My secretary had a phone call to tell us this and ask us to sort it out.

If we are supposed to discharge all our patients after two appointments who will look after them? I have noted this before (see the new:follow-up essay). Some GPs have neither the time nor inclination to embark on yet more long-term disease management for which they are not trained. They won't look at bloods; they sometimes won't prescribe; they ask constantly for advice; they won't manage acute flares. We provided a responsive service which meets their needs. Why fix it if it isn't broken (except for the money thing, and there's a way out of that).

Despite much huffing and puffing on the sanctity of whistleblowers there has been, in parts of the NHS, a fairly ruthless suppression of dissent. I was threatened with disciplinary action when quoted in the local press expressing a view considered to be contrary to my hospital's policy, and subsequently ignored when I raised some serious matters of concern over a directive that would severely curtail my ability to prescribe (the GMC supported my contention that the directive was unacceptable, but the Trust took no notice when I sent it the GMC opinion).[59] I have seen overt and crude threats made against colleagues. When medical managers have made decisions about specialist services without consulting the relevant specialists it seems reasonable to me that these latter should protest, but on doing so one was told they would be removed from their clinical lead position if they continued to make a fuss.

Such suppression has echoes from the past.

> "The former social order was reversed. The "nobodies" of yesterday became the "big shots" of today. The former scum and dregs of society, such as ex-convicts, gentleman-crooks, swindlers and well-known failures became the new elite, riding high in official favour and power."[60]

"German and Japanese carpetbaggers who had achieved little status or respect in their own societies became proconsuls in their nations' new possessions" continued Max Hastings in his masterful account of the Second World War – and later, talking about the beginnings of Hitler's Final Solution for the Jews he writes "It was hard for victims, accustomed to lives in ordered communities, to grasp the implications of their absolute impotence."[61]

This is where the hospital doctors are today. Those Jews who foresaw their potential fate, and got out, were the lucky ones; those who could not conceive that such things were possible in a "civilised" society, and stayed on, reaped the whirlwind. My advice to hospital doctors with any sense of duty and morality who are faced with persecution or obstruction is either to resist (and, like me, face isolation – or punishment or a coronary) or get out.

---

[59] I expect there are many people reading this who are thinking "Thank God I didn't have to work with him" or alternatively wondering, on behalf of those who did, who might rid them of this turbulent priest.

[60] Chin Kee On, a Chinese Malayan citizen, writing on the Japanese occupation in "*Malaya Upside Down*", Singapore, 1946, p.190. Quoted by Max Hastings in *All Hell Let Loose*: London, Harper Press, 2011, p.499. Christina Lamb, a foreign correspondent, comments on a similar process in Afghanistan (*Small Wars Permitting*, HarperCollins, 2008)

[61] *Ibid*, pp 500-1. Frank Binder's novel "*Sown with Corn*" (Farthings Publishing, 2010) describes his own experience in Germany at the beginning of the rise of the Nazis in identical terms. As Christian Wolmar put it in his review in "The Oldie" (which prompted me to buy the book) "Hitherto insignificant local people, disaffected plumbers and penurious school teachers suddenly appear wearing a uniform and exercising power over their neighbours."

****

Who is in charge (3): Doctor, or patient?

For all that's written above, it should be the patient who is in charge. They are the ones who won't take their pills or insist on trying weird treatments like crystals and cranial osteopathy, and all you can do to try and persuade them otherwise is to say "What would I do if this was me?" The customer is always right…

****

Money, money, money…

Comparethemarket.con: The NHS sub-prime mortgage scandal and other matters monetary

I am rendered speechless by the complete inability of politicians, managers and, sadly clinicians, to understand the fundamentals of borrowing. The rule should be that you can borrow what you can afford. However the Labour government of the end of the 20th century turned a blind eye to the borrowing excesses of credit cards and mortgages, even changing bankruptcy laws to make it easier to write off debt and start without penalty with a clean sheet. So borrowing got generally out of control, both on an individual and a corporate basis[62]. And nowhere is this more true than in the NHS.

What is worse than a blind eye is the complete inability to see analogies. Some economists are now saying (or should I say more are now agreeing, for a few have been saying this for a while) that the euro is too big to be sustainable, and the default of one part of the Eurozone runs the risk of bringing the whole lot crashing down. In late 2011 it appeared that two countries in the Eurozone were indeed about to default on their government debt – Greece and Italy (and others may not have been far behind). Why? Because they borrowed too much on the one hand, and committed themselves to spending beyond their means on the other (for example, paying rafts of civil servants 14 months' pay for 12 month's work and allowing them to retire early on huge pensions). So they are bust. To save the euro the richer, more prudent countries were obliged to bail them out. Thus on the one hand we had the Greeks screaming about the unfairness of no longer being able to have that to which they had become accustomed, and on the other the Germans screaming at their chancellor for bailing out the profligate. And everyone else seems to be blaming the banks, though I cannot quite see how it is the fault of the banks if governments have actively encouraged them to relax the rules on borrowing.

How is this any different from the current NHS? Let's take a micro-analogy of borrowing.

---

[62] In May 2014 the new Governor of the Bank of England, Mark Carney, expressed his concerns over the overblown housing market, suggesting that if interest rates rose many folk would find themselves in deep financial doo-doo. *Quelle surprise*! In the same month warning noises were made in the NHS as the cumulative debt rose to nearly £250m. And it's still rising. It's somewhere in the billions now.

Many people have, or will have, mortgages. When my wife and I got our first we could borrow against our joint income on the basis of two and a half times plus one. Nowadays (at least until the crash of 2008-9 when banks almost went under for over-lending) you could get up to six or seven times your annual income. Low interest rates encourage folk to borrow even more. But a large mortgage requires big repayments and if interest rates climb these can suddenly become unaffordable, or the loan needs to extend. I know of some people who will have mortgages well into their 60s. Early retirement may not then be an option.

Yet all new hospitals are classic examples of trying to afford the unaffordable.

The Private Finance Initiative, devised by one political party and implemented by another, is probably the sneakiest and most damaging thing to have hit the NHS at the end of the 20th century. It is a system where government has offloaded its old commitment to capital finance onto the banks and other financial institutions which have ensured a reasonable return on their investment by setting up long-term repayments at attractive (to them) rates of interest. PFI for short has, it is true, resulted in the construction of large numbers of brand-new hospitals – but each now has to find, out of its revenue stream, the wherewithal to repay the debt.

A hospital of £200m capital cost will, at a rate of interest of 5%, cost £10m per year to service the PFI capital debt before it does anything else. In fact many current PFIs have higher rates than this. There is no income guaranteed by government for PFI; it must come from operating revenue. Then there is the service charge on top. And what a charge; nearly £100 to change a lightbulb in one place. What happens if income exceeds expenditure?

In my part of the NHS world, SE London, two of the three hospitals were PFI new builds. When amalgamation was first mooted a discussion paper written by the finance directors of four hospitals (one pulled out of the plan) pointed out that income could, under Payment by Results, never cover the PFI costs – an admission of technical insolvency.[63]

However the merger went ahead, despite repeated efforts by clinicians to raise this very issue (not least as the merger was driven by finance but "justified" on clinical grounds). As PFI repayments are legally binding, this placed the organisation in a bit of a quandary. It could not close the third,

[63] See AN Bamji, *Public Finance Indiscretion.* BMJ 2010; 341: c4295

non-PFI hospital, as there would then have been insufficient overall capacity to maintain clinical services. So now what?

Actually I can answer this. After three years of North Korean standard propaganda in which we were reassured that the deficit was being managed most satisfactorily and clinical services had never been better the Secretary of State declared that the Trust was bust and sent in an insolvency manager. It was interesting that the previous Chief Executive managed to jump ship to a safe haven before the falsehoods of his reign were public. The new troubleshooter embarked on a serious and careful analysis of the problems. He concluded that it was essential to write off the previous deficit (which had ballooned over the three years from £40m to nearly £200m) – and also write off all future PFI payments. Fancy that. To my amusement (or perhaps *schadenfreude* would be better, as one of my friends at the hospital that originally withdrew from the merger – Lewisham – was jubilant at their escape from the sinking ship) he also concluded that Lewisham should link with the Queen Elizabeth Hospital in Greenwich and lose its A&E department. As this had only just been refurbished at enormous expense (we are told £20m) the whole sorry saga exposed the short-termism of NHS planning as well as the financial catastrophes. Of course, the South London debacle was compounded by the refusal of Lewisham to play, on an "I'm all right Jack" basis. They went to court to overturn the report's (and the Secretary of State's) judgement and won. A triumph of anti-common sense.[64]

I raised the PFI issue when I met with the Chairman of the House of Commons Select Committee on Health. He said that without PFI there would be no new hospitals, and was that what I wanted? I replied that I would like to drive a Bentley. However I could not afford the interest payments were I to buy it on hire-purchase, so I drove something smaller.

Shortly after the South London Healthcare Trust collapsed I was on a train where two gentlemen were discussing NHS issues; from the conversation I deduced that both were high up either in NHS management or the Department of Health itself. It was impossible not to eavesdrop as we were all standing and within feet, even inches of each other. They alluded to the problems of Stafford, and then one said "Of course, PFI is a major issue. Look at South London Healthcare". Confirmation from the top? Well, well...

You buy the house you can afford. You build the house you can afford. If you cannot meet the repayments you have your home repossessed. This is

---

[64] Subsequently Lewisham merged with Greenwich, although each retained their own A&E department.

the rule for oneself, so why should it be any different for hospitals? Or governments (or nations).

The collapse of the banks, and their baling-out by government, has set the UK up with an astonishing debt. The newspapers publish revised estimates weekly. However they are lies. *PFIs are off the government's balance sheet.* Not only is there a debt, but there is this additional secret one – and it is, in many cases as in ours, not covered by income. Actually it is now less than secret, and amounts to about £20bn annually. If the PFI hospitals must be saved so they can pay for themselves then economies will be made by closing non-PFI hospitals, or by baling the whole shebang out. This of course makes a mockery of the whole purchaser-provider market concept, because if the set price paid by the one does not cover the other's costs, then the provider drops deeper into debt and yet cannot (in a hospital context) be declared insolvent and wound up because the political fallout would be overwhelming. Yet there is no obvious move for the government to be consistent and bale out hospitals as it did the banks. Neither has it occurred to politicians or managers that simply lumping together the various failing hospitals will not cause failure of the worst, but failure of the whole lot together.

Indeed government tried to make things worse. It suggested that it was cheaper to farm out stuff like outpatients "into the community" where it is cheaper. What it failed to realise is that if you asset-strip a business of its profitable lines, leaving only the loss-makers, then the residue of the business goes bust faster, or needs even more propping up. Of course if you can make people believe that less beds are needed (in 2009 it was being suggested that London could easily lose 6500 beds from 2010-13) then it might be possible to shut hospitals. But when you see the consequences of closing an A&E department just at night-time and then having to close the divert hospital because it is seething with norovirus, you really wonder what planet folk are on when they say less beds are needed. We didn't even get a swine flu epidemic in 2009. If we had, there would have been bodies on the streets (or perhaps in refrigerated containers in hospital car parks, or the cold storage facility at Dunton Green near Sevenoaks in Kent – don't smile – it has happened before) as well as an inpatient meltdown.[65]

---

[65] In early 2017 a series of programmes about St Mary's Hospital, Paddington and the others in the Imperial College group has made the effect of insufficient beds very clear. Most of those on the front line accept that an 85% bed occupancy is the maximum allowable for emergency spare capacity; many if not most hospitals are running at 95% or higher. The cold storage facility at Dunton Green is no longer an option for an overflow morgue; the site was sold and redeveloped for housing (so there are even more people for hospitals to look after, with ever fewer beds).

So PFI is the NHS's own sub-prime mortgage scandal. It is perhaps ironic that the government is effectively paying mortgage interest (over the odds) to banks that it has itself saved from collapse and in some cases actually owns – in other words, it is paying exorbitant interest charges to itself.

I wonder what NHS historians will make of this in 50 years.

There is another piece of government-speak you need to ponder, economics-wise. It tells us, in a rather puzzled voice, that it has poured more money into the NHS than any other before it and cannot really understand why the system has not delivered more as a result. Oxymoronic thinking. Let's look at where a substantial amount of the new money has gone.

PFI interest payments, as above, are the first. Millions of pounds for no additional productivity (not least because many new PFI hospitals are smaller than the ones they replaced, owing to the partly fallacious belief that lengths of hospital stay can continue to reduce; at this rate we can look forward to negative lengths of stay in 10 years). Also the PFIs contain a service contract element. If the figures I was given for my rehabilitation unit were correct, this is a total, mind-blowing, incredible rip-off.[66]

Next comes pay rises. New contracts for GPs and consultants have added many millions to the wage bill and while the extra pay has restored lost differentials to some extent (though they are way short of what was earned at the start of the 20th century) they were not and could not be tied to extra productivity. You cannot do more clinics than there are sessions to do them in. And if you see too many patients then the commissioners may not pay up anyway.

Next is the signing up to the European Working Time Directive. At a stroke trainee doctors had their hours reduced by one-third. The rota gaps were filled by employing more of them. The hospitals are the same size (or smaller, as above) so it is hardly surprising that productivity has gone down. Of course, many of the fill-in posts were filled-in by locums working for

---

[66] The unit cost £1.2m to build; the PFI recharge was listed as £650,000 per annum. I could believe that £60k represented the annual capital repayment but was unable to get anyone to tell me what the rest was for. I was simply told it was right. One of my patients likened this to going to Sainsbury's, doing the weekly shop and getting a non-itemised bill with a total plucked out of the air and being told it was correct. My repeated queries, on the basis that the sum meant the unit was loss-making, had one good result; the PFI recharge was amalgamated into the overall hospital PFI cost, so would not be attributed directly to the Unit. Where it went is not clear!

agencies that charged a lot. A serious lot; £3000 per shift, it was suggested in 2015.[67] I couldn't earn that in private practice.

Then there is taxation. People forget that employers pay tax in the form of employers' contributions to National Insurance. The NHS is not exempt. A 1% rise in NI results in a 0.75% rise in expenditure (75% of hospital costs are on staff). Every year I have been in the NHS the rise in allocation has not kept pace with all of this, and "efficiency savings" have to be even bigger to match the shortfall. There is a limit to how long one can go on becoming more efficient. We point all this out and still see politicians scratching their heads over why the "huge" increases in NHS spending are not matched by increased productivity (measured by activity per pound put in). It's perfectly clear that much of the money that goes in goes straight out again!

There is thus big money being spent on nothing to do with patient care before we even start to look at the increasing costs of new drugs. There is, you will by now not be surprised to learn, an economic blind spot over these. Ten years ago the treatment of rheumatoid arthritis was cheap; it wasn't much cop, because we had not learned the treat early, treat hard regime we use now, but the drug spend of a rheumatology department was well down the pecking order. Now we have biologics. Even though we are prevented from using these properly, because of their cost, the spend of an average hospital department is now probably higher than the oncology department spend. My small department looked after about 280 people on biologics at a cost of £9,000 per year each.

That looks bad, you may think, but it pales into insignificance compared to the cost of statins. Just think. Biologics and some of the new cancer treatments are high cost but low volume. Statins are low or sometimes moderate cost, but at astronomically high volume. While there has been debate about health benefit, some of it spurious, statistics-wise (see later for an analysis of this), people have forgotten that a small number multiplied by a large one is the same as a large number multiplied by a small one.

While here, I still have difficulty with the concept of spending ever-increasing sums on drugs to treat diseases when the underlying causes of those diseases are not dealt with. Many were the grossly overweight, still-smoking patients who wheezed their way into my clinic with osteoarthritic

---

[67] Although the then Secretary of State for Health, Jeremy Hunt, sounded off about locum rates in 2015, nothing was done. Market forces appear to have ensured that attempts to cap locum payments will fail (too little money for a shift to be worth doing, no locum at all).

knees and on four antihypertensives, a statin and a couple of antidiabetic drugs. What are we doing?

I also have little doubt that the increasing sophistication of data collection is driving up cost, as procedures and admissions are no longer slipping through the net uncharged. Reductions of length of stay mean that every admission is more action-packed with costly tests and procedures, not to be evened out by those in a convalescent phase requiring no expensive investigations.

That is another economic oddity about the NHS. One part is supposed to pay the other (the purchaser-provider arrangement) but if all the funding comes from government then it is impossible to understand how it can ever make a profit, and if it does what that profit is for. There is a set tariff for most procedures and consultations. If a provider (a hospital, say) makes a profit then it must be doing so at the expense of the purchaser – the PCT.

This has become explicit in some areas. In Stoke-on-Trent the whole musculoskeletal service was removed managerially from the acute hospital and transferred to the PCT, which could charge itself what it liked (and has made a saving by paying itself less than the tariff rate, but paying sufficient to cover its costs). The nonsense is extended by finding that some parts of an acute service generate a provider profit which offsets the loss made by other bits, and taken still further when PCTs refuse to fund an expansion of hospital work. This usually takes the form of paying a proportion of the tariff rate for cases over a set number, often the previous year's total. This provides a dangerous incentive not to admit emergency patients because the marginal rate paid on the excess is not sufficient to cover costs. Similarly GPs are questioned over referral rates. Those who refer too many are warned to reduce; personally, as I have said earlier, I am more worried about GPs who refer too few, as I think they take more risks. And something is eventually going to go horribly wrong because a GP has used up his quota of referrals and fails to refer someone who requires this. This is another example of the law of unforeseen consequences.

However, if we ignore the incomprehensibility of the system and concentrate on the income/expenditure line of a single hospital department, we can use some simple calculations to modify decision-making. Most finance departments will provide the necessary information for one to decide whether your service is a financial asset, or not. It is nowadays complicated a bit by the need to apportion some of the overall hospital costs to your budget, which can be obscure. However a simple understanding of the I/E equation can be useful.

A while back, as part of proposed budgetary savings, our department was threatened by the withdrawal of funding for its nurse specialist, saving some £40k on salary costs. We pointed out that there would be a substantial loss of Payment by Results income from such a move, as we would not only lose the follow-up income generated by the nurse-led clinic, but we would also have to share out the biologics monitoring work among the medical staff (two consultants with occasional trainee support). This was time-consuming enough to mean that the new patient numbers would have to be cut by 75% to allow space. The overall PbR loss was over double the salary saving. Our managers conceded the point. Sad to say we had to resurrect our defence document a couple of years later as all the hospital's nurse specialists were put "at risk". This happened only a month after we had appointed our much needed second nurse.

While on the profit/loss subject it's also worth reminding the financially less literate that if you have responsibility for a budget with many lines, the ones you need to spend time on are the big numbers. I queried the tax return figures my accountant sent me once because they had omitted an expense of about a fiver. They retorted that if they worked everything out to the last penny the cost of their fees would far exceed any tax rebate I might get. So if an equipment line is a couple of hundred pounds adrift at the year end it's not worth getting in a panic. If a line is a couple of hundred thousand adrift you need to understand why; the old adage is: if you owe the bank a hundred thousand you have a problem; if you owe the bank a hundred million the bank has a problem.

Got it?[68] Well, if you have, why haven't the politicians?

In mid-2011 a sad situation arose in which a company running a series of care homes, Southern Cross, slid into administration because the income from its residents no longer covered the costs. There was much concern over the risk of elderly people being turned into the street, and much anger at the reason for the company's collapse. Essentially it had sold the family silver by transferring its assets (the buildings) to outside investors, and then leasing back. Suddenly it found it couldn't afford the rent.

A story appeared in "The Times (July 12th, 2011) detailing what had gone wrong.

If one replaced "Southern Cross" with "NHS" and "care homes" with "hospitals" (and changed a few names) the story would have made complete

---

[68] Allyson Pollock has (and has for some time) but see A Pollock, D Price, M Liebe. *Private Finance Initiatives during NHS austerity*. BMJ 2011; 342: d324

sense in the context of the PFI catastrophe. Politicians have huffed and puffed over Southern Cross, but seem unable, in addressing the mote in this company's eye, of seeing the beam in their own.

Actually it seemed that, at last, politicians were beginning to see that PFI was a problem. A BBC "Panorama" programme aired on 28th November 2011 included a couple of powerful interviews from politicians; one, Margaret Hodge, was Chairman of the Commons Public Accounts Committee – but appeared to have forgotten that she was part of the Labour government machine that developed the mess, while the other, a Conservative, needed to do more to stop his health ministers from approving yet more sub-prime mortgages. Mind you, seven years on the things are still there.

I suggested to a friend with financial nous that the NHS could be spared huge cutbacks by writing off the PFI debt (this was before the SLHT administrator agreed with me). After all, that was the basis of the financial bailout for a whole country (Greece) and the situation is the same – an over-borrowed economy that cannot pay its debts. He pointed out that the UK's creditworthiness would be seriously downgraded if the government defaulted on contracts that it had underwritten itself. However one could perhaps suggest that banks were forced to reduce their interest rates on PFIs to a market rate.[69]

There is a commercial parallel. In June 2012 a banking scandal emerged in which a number of banks were found to have been artificially fixing the inter-bank lending rate (LIBOR for short) so profits could be maximised and bonuses enhanced. Hidden behind this was the spectre of a mis-selling programme in which large numbers of small businesses had been encouraged to take out large loans at fixed interest rates of around 6.5%, with the prophecy that rates would rise and thus that the deal would be advantageous (they were known as interest rate hedge policies). Of course the opposite happened and these businesses found themselves locked into loans that they could not repay, and found the rates were non-negotiable. Some went bust.

All of this has, predictably, caused a torrent of hysteria in the press, with ongoing gibes about why banks cannot be trusted, why directors should fall on their swords, lose their jobs as well as their bonuses, and how dreadful all the banks are. But let us pause to consider two things.

---

[69] AN Bamji, *Reduce repayment rates to 0.5%*. BMJ 2012;345: e4789

First – how could the banks have been so "irresponsible"? Could it perhaps be because the government changed the Bank of England's regulatory responsibilities to a "light touch"? I think so.

Second – what is the difference between mis-selling loans at exorbitant interest rates to small businesses and allowing loans at exorbitant interest rates to Trusts wishing to rebuild hospitals (aka PFI)? I cannot see any. So if, as the current hysterical backlash suggests, small businesses that go out of business will be compensated, then hospital Trusts should likewise be compensated for being forced to use PFI. All businesses are equal…

I was bewailing the state of the nation, and the NHS in particular, to my cousin in Australia. I told him we were ruled by Muppets. He said he disagreed. "Andrew," he said, "at least Muppets make you laugh".

Since I wrote this depressing analysis I learned of a brilliant piece of creative accounting that could possibly get hospitals off the PFI hook. One very large Trust, faced with an unsustainable PFI debt mountain, managed to refinance it. I often wonder whether its Chief Exec was simply very good, or whether he had read my letter in the BMJ. It appears that they approached the local County Council. Councils can, I gather (even if I don't understand quite how) borrow large sums of money at very favourable interest rates. So the Council arranged to borrow £100m, and lent it to the Trust, enabling it not only to write off the historic debt but buy back the hospital freehold. The interest rate charged to the Trust by the Council was 1% or so above the rate charged to the Council by its lender, but even this was substantially less than the 8% negotiated on the original PFI loan. So the Trust is very happy and the Council is making a profit. What's to not like?

Better than PFI?

I wrote this piece for "Hospital Doctor" in 1990. The debate over the rights and wrongs of euthanasia has raged ever since, but, bad dream or no, I cannot help revisiting it with a certain pragmatic feeling that we should, perhaps, not exclude any possibilities – as I suggested in an earlier essay…

Inheriting the benefits of efficient dispatches

Paul came into the dining room and flopped down opposite me.

"I did seven this morning," he said proudly. "The way things have been this last week we shall have enough for the new operating block and the wheelchair houses by October."

I was interested in the latter.

"Which wheelchair development – Erith or Welling?" I asked.

Paul grinned at me. "Would both do you?" he asked smugly.

I got up and poured more coffee. The full benefits of the white paper were yet to come, but there was no doubt that the hospital had changed significantly already. It had appointed three new paediatricians, expanded maternity, commissioned the combined rehabilitation unit and the MRI scanner and doubled outpatient capacity. The A&E helicopter was arriving in a couple of weeks. And with Paul's latest piece of news it would have 60 wheelchair-suitable houses to add to the two residential homes opened two years back. How different it was from 1990 – the days of overspends, scratching for every penny and constant cuts. Why, with the new theatres and the new urologist and orthopod, all the waiting lists would be down to three weeks. It was rumoured that the canteen was to get a second Michelin star and the Kent County Indoor Games were due to take place in the recreation centre in November. The cinema was also a great success. All in all, Sidcup was a good place to work.

Paul shattered my reverie.

"Of course if I do agree to be clinical tutor we will need another part-timer to cover euthanasiology, unless Laura will take it on," he said.

Laura was the most junior of the 12 physicians and had, I knew, done euthanasia as part of her senior registrar rotation. For ten years the Bodkin Adams Memorial Unit had worked well under Paul's directorship. Patients seeking euthanasia were vetted in screening interviews. In senile dementia cases, relatives – accompanied by a member of the coroner's office ethics staff – were vetted as well. If there were no clear objections a new will was drawn up, leaving half the estate to the hospital. After termination carried out with pentothal and potassium chloride the client's estate was realised. Each termination realised on average £75,000 for the hospital. As a result, capital projects were planned sensibly, equipment was ordered on demand, operations were almost never cancelled and geriatrics had ceased to exist as a specialty and had been reabsorbed into general medicine. Indeed, the needs of the ageing population had been met in a highly cost-effective way and the enormous burden on medical services of the frail and sick elderly had vanished.

Paul interrupted my thoughts.

"Laura won't like the idea, you know," he said. "She doesn't believe in inherited wealth."

"If her lot get in at the next election we won't have to worry, because they'll scrap the whole scheme," I said. "It will be back to under-funded pay awards, cancelled lists, dirty corridors..."

My phone rang – and then turned into an alarm clock. I realised I'd woken up...

In 2012 my nightmare (or dream) took a small step closer, with acceptance that life's inevitable end may in some circumstances be hastened to advantage (hence the Liverpool Care Pathway, though some folk have managed to find fault with that, failing to see that it was the implementation that was an issue, not the pathway itself) and a growing feeling, expressed through organisations such as Dignity in Dying, that maintaining sick, demented people with all the modern technology known to medicine is itself sick.

Just because you can do something does not mean that you should.

Ponder the following. My mother whose death I mentioned before was 94, partially blind from macular degeneration, mostly deaf, doubly incontinent (with a chronic and untreatable urinary tract infection, or UTI for short), had had a couple of mini-strokes, and was immobilised by hip OA and a severe scoliosis with osteoporosis and several old crush fractures. She had previously fractured each neck of femur in falls and had pins in both. She could no longer read or listen to music. She was admitted to hospital on the last occasion having fractured her shoulder in a fall – confused by her UTI, she had tried to get out of her chair to let in some imaginary visitors.

The orthopaedic team told us that their plan was to fix her shoulder, and while they were about it replace the worse of her hips.

Mother had been a GP and had signed an advance directive years before. She left us in no doubt that she had had enough.

Despite excellent palliative care, and fantastic nursing, it took her 11 days to die. She had Cheyne-Stokes respiration for nearly five days.[70] I even did a tutorial on it with a medical student brought up by the palliative care nurse. We sat by her bedside every day from 8am to 10pm. We ran out for sandwiches at lunchtime and returned briefly to the hotel for an evening meal, then back to the hospital. We extended our hotel stay daily. We bought new clothes as we ran out.

Her death was inevitable, and desired. She may not have suffered much (although she remained in pain despite a morphine pump) but we did. And of course she died in the night after we had returned exhausted to our hotel.

I would have given a great deal to have been there when she went. I regret and resent that I wasn't. I was for my father's death, which was at home. But the unpredictability of the final act of a terminal event conspired against me with my mother. This is, in my view, just the circumstance for assisted dying. Yes – it must be hedged around with all sorts of safeguards. But I think that to deny a person a convenient time for an inevitable death is more brutal for the relatives – and I was an only child – than almost anything.

That is why I cannot understand why opponents of dignified and convenient death completely ignore the psychological suffering of the relatives in their obsession with the patient alone.

NHS contracts and service developments

It was with some alarm that I noted in early 2014 that in Bedfordshire a five-year contract for musculoskeletal services had been agreed with a private provider. I only hoped that the tendering process was thorough and that all possible clinical governance problems had been flagged and covered. My own experience has been that some providers have a rather cavalier attitude to that side of things and may allow practitioners to exceed their competence (doing things they really need a lot of training for – for example, physiotherapists doing joint injections) or using unproven techniques often of the alternative medicine type.

However I have a more fundamental problem with this type of outsourcing. Consultants are appointed around the age of 35. This leaves them a

---

[70] This is an irregularity in breathing, thought to represent the near end of life. Breathing is shallow, and then stops. After a little the carbon dioxide concentration in the blood rises enough to be a powerful respiratory stimulant, and breathing recommences, only for the cycle to continue.

professional life of 30 years, possibly more. How does this square with a contract life of only five years? We can assume that during a five year cycle the first will be spent consolidating the agreed contract, the second and third bedding down, and the fourth and fifth winding up to renegotiate and reapply for the contract. This will not only be time-consuming, but also will be a time of great uncertainty. What happens if the contract is awarded elsewhere? Could the site in current use be closed? Will current senior staff be taken on by a new contractor? Could they be re-deployed elsewhere in the contractor's ambit? It will become impossible, particularly in the chronic disease field, for any long-term service planning to be meaningfully achieved. Rheumatology and orthopaedics cannot be treated the same.

I have seen examples of contracts not being applied for. One Trust I worked at had put together a comprehensive tender document to supply a primary care group with physiotherapy services only for a non-clinical manager to decide at the eleventh hour that the tender would not be submitted. I did wonder whether money had changed hands between the manager and the other bidder. The result was a need for significant and disruptive changes within the Trust's own service. It also created yet another "service interface", limiting opportunities for primary/secondary care communication, and caused significant damage to a well-established and effective back pain triage service.

Constant reorganisation and change is not just disruptive – it is demoralising. The setting of five-year contracts is not appropriate to medicine but is predicated on the assumption that all medical care is short-term. With an ageing population afflicted by multiple chronic conditions that is simply untrue. Furthermore the partition of general services may result in patients' care being fragmented. If one organisation runs the musculoskeletal service and another the cardiac service, patients will be shuttled about and clinical information may not be exchanged effectively.

Contracts and tendering undoubtedly focus the mind and may have financial advantages but there are substantial and risky downsides to the process. Short-term micromanagement based on money and not clinical excellence will replace long-term service planning. A further risk is that experienced staff subjected to these processes will examine options to relocate somewhere where this does not happen, and they will leave. The brain drain to Australia and New Zealand may speed up; I was alarmed, on a recent visit there, to see the horror and incomprehension on the faces of doctors, some from the UK, when I explained what was happening. They won't be coming back.

A further risk of contracting fragments of health care is that interprofessional communication will break up. In a hospital that provides all services it is easy for colleagues to seek quick opinions from other disciplines. For example, if a patient turns up in a rheumatology clinic with a ruptured tendon they can be whisked round the corner to see an orthopaedic surgeon, or if a patient is ill with breathing difficulties a chest physician can be consulted at once. This effective and rapid focus on acute problems becomes impossible when the services are scattered. I had a patient in my clinic who appeared to be in the middle of a heart attack. My hospital having no A&E thanks to reorganisation I suffered the indignity not only of having to ring for an ambulance to ship them out (there were no medical staff available to assess the patient, and no ECG facilities in outpatients) but wait over half an hour for the ambulance to arrive. My protests at the delay were met with a blithe remark that there was no rush as the patient was already in a hospital...

The break-up of the South London Healthcare Trust, and its consequences, also rang alarm bells. Of the three constituent hospitals, Queen Mary's was the orphan, being without any acute facilities, and it was transferred to the care of Oxleas Trust, the local mental health organisation which had a foothold by virtue of its acute psychiatry unit on the site and which could not spell Outpatience (*sic*). The clinical services were however transferred to Dartford and Gravesham Trust (itself the victim of financial difficulties, and in a failing relationship with yet another Trust, Medway). Then the local GP consortium (now known as a Clinical Commissioning Group, or CCG) decided to have a fiddle. It professed itself keen to get the best services it could by tender and asked for bids for the musculoskeletal service. Dartford bid – and lost. Musculoskeletal services are now run (very well, it would seem) by King's College Hospital. But we now have a curious, probably absurd situation where a hospital is managed by one organisation while its clinical services are managed by two different ones. Joined-up thinking? Easy long-term strategic planning? I don't think so.

By all means look at the advantages of contract-setting, but before starting out look also for the possible problems. Indeed I would go so far as to suggest that the problem-seeking should come first. It will be a disaster if these are glossed over, only for it to become apparent that they are insuperable and dangerous. And believe me, I have seen that happen too.

Single bedded wards and the nursing crisis

When our new rehab unit was built in 1998-9 we designed it to be fully wheelchair accessible and as safe as we could manage. Unfortunately our best efforts were obstructed by the politically correct who wanted to pursue their ideal of single-bedded rooms for all.

Sometimes I despair of policymakers who have no common sense and no ability to see past the end of their short book of dogma and commandments. I doubt many have been in hospital themselves; if they have, they have failed in one of my commandments – look not only at the action but its possible consequence – and indeed another: weigh the risk, and benefit, of doing something against not doing it. I think I have said this before.

Single rooms are lovely and private and can have their own washing facilities so people don't have to share toilets – nice when there's a lot of diarrhoea about and not many cleaners. But – they are lonely places and unsuitable for the really ill. Wards of single rooms require many more nurses to supervise them; bells and buzzers are fine if they are answered, but you cannot see when a patient collapses and neither can anyone else. And the James's of this world cannot work the buzzer, and the nurses don't like them shouting so they ignore them. If a patient on a Nightingale ward "went off" then all the other patients would raise the alarm. If a severely disabled patient was assaulted by a demented neighbour (this happened on my unit once) then help could be summoned. Suppose I shut you up in a single and featureless room, and the TV didn't work, you would rapidly go crazy; in a bay, or large ward, there is someone to talk to.[71] Patients can help each other, even do things for each other. And they can make carping comments about staff hygiene, as they can watch whether handwashing takes place.

All of these arguments were raised by our own patient group who were very unhappy, given their heavily dependent state, to be confined to single rooms. Shouldn't they know best? But worst is the apparent assumption that a ward of 20 beds requires the same number of staff to manage safely irrespective of its configuration – an assumption that is patently untrue. And in these financially straitened times it is nonsense to design single-bedded wards when it will then be impossible to run them because the staff cost is unaffordable. Once more the economic argument must be deployed. Can we afford to be fully touchy-feely and if not, how will we compromise?

Another aspect of the strain in hospitals is the feeding issue. For years there have been stories of disabled patients who have had their food put in front of

---

[71] When I ran a high-dependency unit in Bath, patients who were flat on their backs had nothing to do except try to count the holes in the acoustic ceiling tiles, which sent them mad. Try it. All credit to the genius who suggested – and implemented – the placing of nice pictures on the ceilings – think Chatsworth's Painted Hall, by Louis Laguerre. Plenty of action to hallucinate over.

them and either been unable to eat it (because they cannot reach or see it, or are very slow). Nurses' patience seems to be shorter, so the trays are removed, usually with a comment such as "Don't you want it, dear?" and the patients gradually starve.

Recently a government spokesman suggested that if relatives were concerned about the nutritional state of inmates then they should come in and do the feeding themselves. If this does nothing else, it underlines the staff shortages in hospitals. Of course such practices are common in Europe, but two problems are immediately apparent.

The first is that many if not all wards have a notice on the door banning visiting during mealtimes.

The second is that if a relative does manage to slip through and do some feeding, the reaction of the nursing staff is not to say thank you but to suggest, often with a gay laugh, that perhaps they would like to help with some of the other unfed patients.

Oxymoron!!! This is not good.

Toilets and contracts

We are constantly told that NHS procurement is poor, and that we would do better to order in bulk from one supplier than have multiple types of the same thing from several.

This is largely cost driven.

Consider toilet paper and soap. Each time the hospital decides to re-tender, and each time it chooses a different supplier, you end up with a different wall dispenser. The walls of the toilets are riddled with bug-collecting holes from the various devices. Someone has to fix the new ones and take away the old. In my hospital this happened five times in ten years. Is this really cost-effective?

And, if it worked, why do successive governments, at roughly ten-year intervals, tell us that procurement is poor, and we would do better (*D.C. al fine*).

Look after the pennies…

In my old hospital it became apparent that we were missing out on income because we were not coding activity properly. I have no objection to chasing money if it is a consequence of better (or more ordered) practice. But things can get out of control.

In 2009 it was finally agreed that procedures done in NHS outpatients could be charged for. It was also decided that it was necessary to devise a new outcome form to take account of the 18-week target for completion of treatment. So a form was created, on which all the new relevant information could be entered.

Now with targets there were certain subgroups of outcomes. A repeat follow-up patient need not be counted, so that required a box. There are several outcomes that "stopped the clock" – for example direct admission, first appointment default, discharge – and there were others that left the clock running or started a new one.

The new form appeared.

It was printed in colour.

Each of the clock groups was in a different colour which bore no relation to the goodness of the outcome – thus a stopped clock (which we didn't have to worry about) was in red. The colour was in large blocks.

Now I know a bit about colour printing as I do some at home. It is quite expensive, even on an office laser printer. So I thought "Why the hell are we printing these forms in colour? The colours mean nothing. They are expensive. The outcome sheets are discarded once the information has gone onto the computer, so if we are seeing 200,000 outpatients a year we are throwing away an awful lot of money."

I had no idea how many outpatients were seen across our three hospitals, because no statistics had been provided, but if every one of my colleagues saw what I saw then my figure is probably an underestimate.

So I wrote to a manager asking why the forms had been printed in colour. I was not given a direct answer, only told that it wasn't that expensive (4p per sheer) and would easily be covered by the extra income that the forms would facilitate.

The cost of a black and white sheet might be at most 0.3p. So we were wasting over £7400 per annum in unnecessary costs, but it didn't matter as we would get it back.

Actually, to be fair, someone saw sense, and the forms were changed to black and white – a good two years after I made a fuss.

However I then discovered that the forms were accumulating in an office because there was no-one to enter the data…

When is a deficit not a deficit?

Being retired I don't often meet Health Service managers, but merely snipe at them from the sidelines. However I met some at a funeral of a much-loved clinical colleague and sniped face to face about the impossibility of squaring good clinical services with "good" financial management. I pursued my usual line of "If every acute Trust is in deficit then it's not the Trusts that are wrong, but the system."

Well. I was put right on that. The Trusts you had to worry about, they said, were the Trusts who could not explain their deficits. In some cases these had sort of appeared out of the blue, and the managers found it most puzzling, but from outside you could see it coming so they had a problem. "We have a £40m deficit" they said, "but it's not a problem *because we know exactly why*".

Oh boy.

I thought that perhaps if I were to go to my bank and say "I have an overdraft of £10,000 but it's not a problem because I know exactly why" then, adopting this principle, the bank would say "well, that's all right then". Somehow I don't think that's very likely. A deficit is a deficit. It may be nice to know why it's there but if it cannot be sorted (or written off) then I for one think that it is a problem.

More on laundries: an expensive whitewash

When I started as a consultant I was based at the Brook Hospital in Woolwich, originally a fever hospital and designed, as mentioned in a previous essay, with widely separated wards and fireplaces in each. It was slowly slipping down the side of Shooters Hill, and is now largely demolished and replaced by yuppie apartments. The Brook was part of a group with Greenwich District Hospital (a 1970s concrete-cancer ridden monstrosity full of asbestos, and structurally unsafe because the cross beams were too long, and so sagged in the middle a bit and didn't rest squarely on their supporting corbels), the Victorian St Nicholas, Plumstead, the Dreadnought Seamen's Hospital (where the upper limit of normal liver function was raised to allow for mariners' propensity to drink, and where I was the last consultant ever appointed), The Memorial Hospital, the British Home for Mothers and Babies (no prizes for guessing its function) and little Eltham Hospital. All of these were eventually closed, but the large number of sites was a giant financial problem, and rationalisation was inevitable. Even then cost-saving, and income-generation, were on the agenda. So one of the managers came up with the wheeze of redeveloping the Brook laundry (at considerable expense) and thereby enabling it to serve a number of other surrounding hospitals, and earn lots of wonga.

Soon things were in full swing.

Unfortunately the laundry staff got a bit behind, and dirty washing began to accumulate in the pre-wash area. Spring was turning into summer, and the staff were plainly not gardeners.

Gardeners?

Medics are good at confusing punters with lateral thinking, so if you turn up in A&E with swollen legs you may be surprised to be asked if you get breathless lying flat. We know why that happens, but if you don't have a grasp of physiology you may be forgiven for thinking your doctor has gone very off track.

Back to gardens. Think compost. You make a heap of organic material, and it begins to decompose, in the process getting warm. A compost heap can get very hot indeed.[72] So imagine what happens when you have a giant pile of wet, uriniferous and faeculent sheets sitting in the summer sunshine. The pile gets warm. Then hot. Then even hotter. And then it spontaneously combusts.

Thus the Brook Hospital Laundry, pride of the management, income-generator to balance the books, was reduced to a charred heap, with the

---

[72] We had a load of manure delivered to our house – several cubic yards of it. Through a bitter winter the heap was free of snow even when there was eighteen inches on the grass, and it steamed satisfyingly. Once we had spread it there was a large depression in the drive.

92

(uninsured) loss of over £100,000 worth of equipment. That meant not only could we not do other people's washing, but we couldn't do our own. A replacement service was frantically sought, and found. In Birmingham. So our laundry chugged back and forth up the M1, polluting the atmosphere with diesel and, no doubt, bugs falling off the back of the lorries.

None of this, of course, reached the ears of the public. Neither, for that matter, did the cost of removing asbestos from the between-floor voids of Greenwich District Hospital. £6m was a lot of money in the early 1990s. I never did find out where it had come from. Mind you it may have saved money in the end. When the whole place was razed ten years later they didn't have to worry about it.

Conditioned behaviour (or, save every discussion paper you ever write because you need to learn how to be a parrot)

This essay overlaps with others, in that it bewails the loss of institutional memory (again).

Some years ago I was asked to sit on a working party to develop chronic disability care in a seamless way between hospital and community. This was long before everyone started talking of interface relationships and Teams without Walls – in fact it was in 1987.[73]

We set up a joint Working Party between the Health Authority and Social Services and made enormous progress. Everyone was engaged and there was lots of blue-sky thinking and other such jargon that had not been discovered yet.

Then the Chairman, a really sensible chap from Social Services, got another job. There was a hiatus before his successor arrived. When he did, we had to start all over again as he had different ideas. We got about halfway, but it had become quite unsatisfactory. Then he left.

I recycled the document at least four times (the original, which I still have, was printed on a dot-matrix machine). I rarely had to change anything except the costs.

---

[73] The title of a paper published by the Royal College of Physicians and published shortly before I stopped being a Council member in 2008 – without any direct input from me it encapsulated numerous arguments I had been making both in Council and outside

Email tale

Seen it all before? A play in one act

Narrator (tone: narratorly): The scene is my hospital. The cast are the senior staff. The time is the end of January 2009. The play is written entirely in email.

Senior medical manager (tone: anxious bordering on frantic). Will all consultants do a ward round immediately to clear beds. There are 7 patients waiting in A&E

Chief Executive (tone: ponderous and impressive, with overtones of coercion): It is very important that we implement our draft plan for speeding up discharges which I know will work because I have successfully implemented it elsewhere

Medical consultant (plaintive): It doesn't help when beds are blocked by patients waiting for nursing home placements

2nd medical consultant (annoyed): I have 3 patients where the relatives are refusing to agree the discharge plan

3rd medical consultant (irritated): I have already been round and identified 5 patients who can't go because social services haven't sorted it out.

CE (brisk and efficient): it would be even more helpful if we knew the names of these patients. As for the relatives issue we have powers to deal with them and enforce discharges. (switches to Prime Minister-speak) I will do all I can to help.

Social services head (plaintive, aggrieved even): It's most unfair to blame it all on us because we're understaffed and people are off sick and the doctors aren't filling in the panel papers and (etc)

Rheumatologist (who has nothing to do with acute takes, but possesses the hospital's institutional memory, for it is I): It would be wise to be very careful in using special powers to get rid of patients as we will get nasty headlines about our cruelty, generated by the troublesome relatives who will go straight to the papers.

3nd medical consultant (petulant): I stand by what I said.

4th medical consultant (smug, with a touch of schadenfreude): I
have just been round to identify the patients and here is a list of
those we cannot get out (there follows a list of 55 patients, all named
and listed by ward and consultant).

Exeunt omnes

Narrator: The hospital started to have problems with overcrowding
in the late 1990s, coinciding with the turning over of a medical block
to psychiatry. Up to then acute admissions were manageable;
thereafter, trying to find beds became a nightmare. Perhaps it is no
coincidence that the change resulted in the loss of 56 medical beds.
The problem of placement is thus simple; in those days elderly
patients were kept in a holding pattern on the wards, and the
shortage of residential and nursing home places was not a serious
issue. Now it is – and nothing has been done to address it. There is
not even an epidemic of anything (yet). We are not alone; all around
the A&E departments are full to overflowing, and ambulance delays
result because the crews cannot decant their cargoes into the
departments and so cannot go out for the next collection. All around
patients in A&E await a bed. Yet the plan is to close ours.

Could this also be a hospital near you?

As a follow-up to this piece, which I wrote some years ago, I can report that
the A&E did close, so creating enormous pressure on the three surrounding
ones that remained open. Two (part of our Trust) thought they would cope
by moving all their cold surgery into the A&E-less site, forgetting that not
all of it could be moved as the intensive care facility had also been shut,
which meant that "serious" surgery was unsafe. So "step-down" medical
beds were created.

Thus an acute patient is admitted to one hospital, shunted to the second as
soon as it is thought to be safe, and *then* the planning for discharge has to
start (unless, of course, they weren't safe and had to be shunted back). And a
proportion of those having cold surgery, despite being selected for safety,
developed complications and had to be shipped off. Some 70 patients
required this in the first two months. Lengths of stay went up, although as
this was divided between institutions it appeared to be going down. What is
the matter with these people?

Private medicine: the monopoly issue

When I started doing private practice my fees were determined by what my colleagues charged (if they would tell me, which wasn't always the case) and what the British Medical Association suggested was the going rate. Having been doing a bit for a bit I was surprised to learn that the private insurers had suddenly taken the BMA to task on the basis that their suggested rates amounted to the development of a monopoly, which was unfair (in fact it was a little more complicated, as one insurance company, BUPA, also set indicative rates, so the issue was whether this amounted to a complex monopoly). The BMA defended its position and lost.[74] There appeared to be some satisfaction that the medical profession's hold on private fees had been broken.

Within two years it became apparent that, far from allowing a free market, the private insurers had banded together to set suggested rates themselves. I thought this was rather a case of the pot calling the kettle black, but the BMA failed to react. Slowly the insurers developed their pitch. First they began to refuse to pay more than the rate they suggested. Then one (BUPA) instituted what I thought amounted to a bribery system within which, if you agreed to stay within their recommended rates, they would pay you a yearly bonus. As a matter of principle I refused to sign up – not that my fees grossly exceeded the new limits (for follow-ups and procedures they were well within them) but because I saw no difference between them setting limits and the BMA offering guidelines. The bonus thing only impinged on my consciousness when it was reported in early 2010 that doctors would be pursued by HM Customs and Revenue if the taxman was suspicious of under-declaration of tax, and all the advice lines told all doctors not to forget to declare their BUPA bonus. They also pointed out that HMRC was prepared to backdate claims for 20 years – odd, given that the requirement to keep documents only goes back for 7.

Next I was told by a couple of patients (with different insurers) that I was not on the companies' "recommended specialist" list. Indeed one patient had telephoned one of the big insurers to check her cover and gained the impression that the advisor not only insisted that I was not on the recommended list (and therefore she might have to pay something) but also that they could recommend another specialist who was on the list. And yet another patient reported that if they came to see me, and the fees I charged

---

[74] See
http://webarchive.nationalarchives.gov.uk/20111202183914/http://www.competition
-commission.org.uk/rep_pub/reports/1994/348privmedical.htm#full for the report by
the Competition Commission. (Accessed 7th September 2018)

were outside the recommended limit, they would not pay anything – not even up to their limit.

This might be seen as odd, as I am a past President of the British Society for Rheumatology and therefore not exactly low profile. They had paid me up to now; could it be that they too were penalising me for not staying within their rates?

Why on earth the BMA never counter-claimed I do not know, but their "monopoly" had been quietly replaced by another. Somehow I think this is all wrong. But perhaps I have missed something.

Actually, 16 years later, the BMA woke up to this, and tried to get it looked at again. Better late than never. But I am not sure anything came of it.

Private medicine and Muppets

Quite apart from the above, private insurers are getting very strict about follow-up. Many companies in the UK started refusing to pay for follow-up visits for so-called chronic conditions, and so patients who have been happily (and needfully) attending for some time were suddenly told they wouldn't be covered any more. Michael Moore's film "Sicko" illustrates the end result of such policies.

Worse than that, they insisted on the supply of clinical data – they seemed unable to take the word of a doctor for a diagnosis – and some of their criteria were completely wrong.

I was told by one company (it was a big one) that they would not accept my diagnosis of rheumatoid arthritis unless I could produce X-rays that showed joint erosions. Modern rheumatology is not only at the point of treating hard and early, so as to prevent erosions (which show that serious joint damage has occurred) but even considers treating *before* the onset of signs and symptoms in patients who have the "at-risk" ACPA antibody (the citrullinated peptide antibody – the acronym changes periodically). It took three letters before the company grudgingly accepted that this patient, with classical disease and positive ACPA and rheumatoid factor at very high levels, but no erosions (yet) actually had RA.

Ignorance is not bliss. It is shocking, particularly when, as here, treatment might be delayed significantly. Anyone who comes across this should encourage patients to threaten to sue.

****

Making the workplace work; planning, targets etc

Charity may begin at home, but no longer helps hospitals

Doctors need to watch their charitable funds very carefully.

Many hospitals have Trust funds, small and large, into which grateful patients pay donations, relatives leave legacies and drug companies pay money for clinical support, or staff to run trials. If you have one, watch your statements like a hawk. If statements stop coming, demand them.

One of my friends discovered a few years ago that his entire departmental fund had been sequestered by the hospital finance manager to help reduce the overspend. After 18 months of fighting to get it back he was forced into a compromise – but not before his health had suffered and his entire research base had been threatened (he had a fairly standard self-perpetuating system whereby funds came in that paid the research team and they did more research that brought in more funds).

Just before I retired all the signatories to our hospital funds got a letter saying that as the general Trust fund was low, all the others were going to have 45% of their content removed. They felt sure we would understand.

Not. After a battle this decision was, in part, reversed. I approached the Charities Commission; it said that the practice was legal, if unusual and not in the spirit of things (heard this before somewhere? Something to do with tax evasion?). It also pointed out that if donations were made to a fund for a specific purpose then these are untouchable.

Moral: if you have a fund and get a donation make sure you have a letter stating what you are to use it for. Or spend it before anyone can steal it. Sadly this scenario resurfaced. One of my erstwhile colleagues at SLHT phoned me to ask what they should do having found that their hospital fund, to which they were a co-signatory, had been systematically denuded of 80% of its content by a manager who had become a signatory without anyone else being told. Effectively the fund had been misappropriated. I advised, and await the outcome, but as seven years have now passed and I have heard nothing I doubt it was a happy one.

I find it sad that people who do this sort of thing seem to escape without punishment. However the ill-educated and appalling Mel, a contestant in the 2010 series of "The Apprentice" on BBC1, may in her rage at being expelled have come up with the ideal phrase. Slagging off the two young men she thought had ganged up on her (and for lack of insight she has to take a gold medal) she growled in the taxi taking her back to oblivion "They will suffer karmic retribution". A phrase I shall use often (not least as Carol Midgely in "The Times" the following day was very rude about Alexandr Orlov, my favourite meerkat – "Simples!"). I have a little list of people who should suffer karmic retribution. If I had my father's confidence I would apply a curse, as he used to do.

2011 and the Lansley plan for the NHS

The Secretary of State for the coalition government elected in 2010 introduced yet another "reform" to the NHS which placed general practitioners in charge of commissioning. Initially there was silence from much of the medical profession, with a gradual swell of revolt ranging from GPs who didn't want to do it, but just get on with their jobs, to hospital specialists who were surprised and hurt to find they were barely mentioned in the plan.[75] In our locality, which was a "pilot", the GPs elected as their head someone who was avowedly against hospitals – the same Dr Stoate who wrote the Fabian Society pamphlet "Challenging the Citadel: breaking the power of NHS hospitals". I thought this could be interesting. Were the barbarians at the gates of Rome? It was curious, and worrying for hospital doctors, that the Bexley pilot was lauded by the Secretary of State for Health as an excellent model.[76]

The law of unforeseen consequences

You need to develop a sharp eye for detail if people are planning things. You might not think a little change will affect you but it could. There are two classic ways of looking at this; the traditional one of the butterfly fluttering its wings in Brazil that sets off a tornado in Texas, or the difference between space rockets and chess, as above.

When my hospital was threatened with downgrading as part of a reorganisation it was decided that, instead of it retaining a "step-down" medical unit (which had been the original plan) all medical work would move off site. The unforeseen consequence was that this instantly put my rehabilitation unit at risk as there would be no day-to-day or out-of-hours

---

[75] See A N Bamji , *Health Bill is a step towards privatisation of NHS.* "The Times", 18th January 2011)

[76] I now live in the centre of southern England's only hilltop walled town. The area is known as the Citadel but we have our own challenges

junior staff cover. No-one doing the planning had thought of this. I spotted it in time but for want of a nail the battle was almost lost.

Actually it turned out that no-one had properly planned the medical bed numbers, and at the eleventh hour it was found necessary to retain "step-down" beds – about 80 in number, which is not insignificant. We waited eagerly to see how many patients who were not really fit for moving to the step-down beds ended up being shuttled back; as I wrote this the whole of the South-East was paralysed by snow, which I thought would bugger up everything. Actually it didn't, exactly. However after the snow had gone there was chaos. Our A&E was now shut, so all acute work went to the other two sites, which silted up everywhere. On one day 65 patients were awaiting admission overnight; there were delays to be seen in A&E of up to 10 hours, and waits for patients in ambulances of up to two hours actually to get into the A&E department.

The A&E closure was forced through on the grounds that it was safer for patients to be seen in bigger, better staffed units. Because, in advance of the closure, ours had lost its educational recognition, it was no longer possible to re-open it. Indeed although the initial closure was billed as temporary, the department was immediately emptied of all its equipment. But is it better, or worse, to go to a big unit and not be seen for hours than to go to a slightly understaffed unit and be seen on time? I think the jury is still out.

The only way to beat a target is to cheat

If we want to increase our new:follow-up outpatient ratio we can:

- Count bone density (DEXA) scans for osteoporosis as new referrals and not as tests
- Pull all the simple stuff under the rheumatology label (eg all the back pain patients who go straight to our physio service – after all, we supervise it)
- Book requests for earlier appointments as new patients (after all, it's a new letter!)
- Abandon the "SOS" ("give us a ring in 6 weeks if it's not better and we'll see you again") system which patients love and is highly effective – and get the GP to re-refer
- Discharge everyone and ask the GPs to refer them back – which they will have to do

If we want to meet 18-week targets we can:

- List patients awaiting tests as "watchful waiting" (which stops the 18 week clock) rather than "awaiting tests" (which doesn't)

I am aware of many who play such games. It's sad that we waste our time inventing ingenious ways of beating the system instead of relaxing at home, doing research, weeding the allotment or writing letters to "The Times".

Medical records and the Cloud

Computer illiterates (and they are getting fewer by the day) will not know that the Cloud is the place where you can store your data without requiring it to be on some unreliable hard disk in a desktop computer. Basically it is a global collection of servers; your stuff could, in truth, be anywhere, and that is what has, perhaps, underpinned opposition to the development of an electronic patient record (EPR) system for the NHS (along with the fear that someone inappropriate will nick the data and find out you have AIDS, thereby changing your chances of getting life insurance).

I don't personally have much of a problem with this (and no, I don't have AIDS, although I did once perform a procedure on a colleague who had failed to reveal he was HIV-positive, so I had myself tested – negative of course). In fact I used a secure Cloud service to keep my correspondence, so I could access it at will from any one of the sites I worked at. After all, vast amounts of data on you are already held by your bank or banks, mortgage lender, financial adviser, eBay, Amazon and any other retailer from whom you have bought online. It's spooky, even knowing that, when you get emails suggesting things you should buy which are based on past purchases. It's even more spooky when you discover that your car insurance renewal date appears to be common knowledge among all car insurers, and a dozen or so letters and emails turn up suggesting you might like to consider switching. (I did actually pursue one such quote, which turned out to be uncompetitive, and then gave reams of personal information so they could quote for my house insurance also, only to find that the level of contents cover I had was several times their maximum.) Spookiest of all is when you go to Sainsbury's in Hastings and an hour later Google asks you to review your experience…

Medical data is fragmented. Your GP has some, maybe almost all. The various hospitals you have attended will have more. You may yourself have copies of letters about you, and a repeat prescription list. But it is very irritating for physicians to meet a patient for the first time and find that a vast swathe of necessary information is unavailable to them.

When my hospital merged with two others there was the devil's own job trying to marry up the different IT systems and databases.[77] It was 18 months before I could view X-rays and scans done on the other sites, so the best way to provide a one-stop service was to repeat the investigation. Not cheap, and not terribly good for the patient.

Perhaps the answer lies in the data stick. Everyone who has a computer, near enough, will have one (or more – I have about 12 – they used to appear as conference freebies) or seen one. They can be encrypted and can hold many gigabytes of data. Or you can put a memory card of large capacity in your smartphone and use Bluetooth to let it talk to the desktop terminal. So let's give every patient a personal stick on which can go all their medical history, drug list, allergies, correspondence, investigation results etc. The patient can present it at their next consultation, the health professional can plug it in, enter a password and get access (perhaps even at different levels). Simples![78]

Of course, there will be much blathering about what happens if you lose your stick, it gets flushed down the loo, eaten by the dog (don't laugh –

---

[77] The cost of integrating all systems in S London Healthcare Trust was put at £12m – which, as it had a deficit at the time of around £40m, was not exactly affordable. I forget how many incompatible systems they had, but it was over 20.
[78] For those who do not watch commercial TV channels in the UK a website called comparethemarket.com is advertised by a meerkat in a velvet jacket called Alexandr Orlov (that is the name of the meerkat, not the jacket) who points out the difference between this site and comparethemeerkat.com. The second site is worth a visit; then you will understand the significance of the catchphrase.

when I was in the mobile phone shop a lady came in with a terminally chewed BlackBerry and mournfully reported that this was the fourth the dog had ruined) or run over by a lorry. Listening to the hysteria there has been over the Electronic Patient Record, or EPR, you would believe the world would come to an end. So why don't people have the same approach to credit cards? Everyone has lost one or had one stolen or knows someone who has. You might even have your bank account emptied. But the general reaction is to shrug shoulders and say, "It happens". What's special about a medical data stick, or card? The plus side is you will never again encounter a doctor rolling the eyes heavenwards and bewailing his lack of information – or the missing notes. Turn up unconscious in a distant A&E department and the staff will know your past history and drug regime, which may help quick diagnosis. And if the stick, or stick shaped as a credit card, or SIM card, does go missing we can create a new one from the master data in the Cloud.

Electronic communication is now the norm. We have emails, text messages, Twitter, Facebook and others. So why does communication between GP and hospital consultant interpose a raft of paper?

My secretary typed a letter from a tape I dictated and stored it on her computer and in the Cloud. She then printed a copy, stuffed it in an envelope and sent it to the GP by post. The GP staff opened it, scanned it into their computer and shredded the hard copy.

Let's cut out the middle man and email the letter. No paper, no post, no delay (indeed it would be even better with voice recognition software, so we could do away with the tapes, which always get scrunched up or separated from the pile of notes they refer to – but the last time I tried this the program wouldn't recognise methotrexate and kept printing "me though treks eight" however hard I tried to train the bloody thing).

Oh no. Blather, blather, the internet isn't secure, confidential things could go to the wrong people etc. As if the postman delivers everything to the right address, assuming they deliver it at all…

Planning clinics

This may not apply to every doctor but the statistical lesson is an interesting one to doctors and patients alike.

Many folk in specialties set up subspecialist clinics to deal with particular conditions. Thus in rheumatology you can find early rheumatoid arthritis clinics, lupus clinics, combined clinics with orthopaedic surgeons or paediatricians etc.

There is a nice PowerPoint presentation which proves that this should be avoided if you wish to be efficient.[79] Subdividing your work will increase your waiting lists and you will end up with some underbooked clinics. This is queue theory at work.

I was never afraid to overbook clinics. There has been repeated blathering about the problem of patients who fail to attend their outpatient appointments. The Department of Health wants us all to stop patients not attending, because it is wasting the NHS £700m per annum. Actually a "Did Not Attend", or DNA for short, costs nothing.[80] People overbook their clinics to compensate for DNAs, just like the airlines do; what's good enough for EasyJet is good enough for me. If everybody does turn up you have a hell of a clinic but it doesn't happen often, and a no-show saves a lot of investigation, and no-one is actually charged for them (it would be different if they were).

Anyway – why do patients not attend? I audited this about 30 years ago and doubt much has changed. Many never got the appointment in the first place (sent to the wrong address, postal failure etc). Some cancelled, but this did not get through to the clinic. A tiny number forgot. Many had some other pressing commitment, such as a family funeral, a relative in hospital somewhere else, a childcare problem. Or the car broke down. Or they fell over getting on the bus, and ended up in A&E. I feel these are all quite reasonable excuses. Given the overbooking bit there is no need to spend vast sums on armies of clerks who are going to chase the patients up the day before, whether by phone, email or text message.

However there is a curious DNA issue which I call the endless loop syndrome. Let's suppose a patient cancels and the clinic doesn't know. What happens next is as follows:

- Let's say the patient rings to cancel the day before the appointment (January 30th), and is rebooked for 5th March
- The patient doesn't appear in clinic on January 30th but their name is still on the clinic list, so the clinician, not knowing of the cancellation, completes a DNA form, which generates another

---

[79] See www.steyn.org.uk for some demand management presentations, including queue theory (accessed 29th August 2018)
[80] A.N. Bamji *Did not attend.* "The Times", 18th December 2010

appointment booking. However this takes a day to process, so this re-book is for 12th March as the 5th is full

- Patient receives the letter confirming their own rebooking for 5th March
- Two days later they receive a second letter generated through the DNA, for 12th March. The letter says "Due to unforeseen circumstances your appointment with Dr Bamji has been changed to the 12th March"
- The patient thinks this change refers to the appointment they made for the 5th, but this remains on the system
- On 5th March the patient doesn't appear in clinic but is still on the clinic list, so the clinician completes a DNA form, which generates another appointment booking. However this takes a day to process, and is for 27th April
- The letter confirming this is received by the patient on the 11th March, and they assume it refers to the appointment the following day, so they don't turn up
- On 12th March the patient doesn't appear in clinic, so the clinician completes a DNA form, which generates another appointment booking. However this takes a day to process, and is for 9th May

And so on. At least until the patient phoned my secretary and asked what the hell is going on.

Moral: If a patient fails to attend make sure that there is not some later extant appointment. Eventually they will complain at being continually postponed and wonder what they have done to offend you

Cutting working hours makes for safer medicine

Maybe it does, because doctors won't make so many mistakes because they aren't so tired.

Maybe it doesn't, because doctors make more mistakes because they no longer pack in the same experience as they used to (and they don't share experiences over lunch). Furthermore if you have to cover the same overall time, cutting down the hours each doctor can work necessarily means you have to appoint more (perhaps 30% more). The bed numbers and theatre time remain the same, so no more work can be done. Thus productivity per doctor falls (by 30%) and then the government wonders why. We have been here before. Or the doctors get more stressed, go off sick more often, end up covering blank shifts because the hospital can't get an emergency locum (either because there is no money for one, or no doctors available), and then make mistakes because they are exhausted.[81]

In mid-2010 the incoming President of the Royal College of Physicians, Sir Richard Thompson, commented that the European Working Time Directive was a "complete disaster" as far as trainee doctors were concerned. This view was echoed by Raymond Tallis in a "Comment" piece in "The Times" (August 9th 2010), who suggested that the move had not really changed the work-life balance and that actually trainees wanted to learn by packing in experience[82]. He was concerned, though, that attitudes among trainees were changing and that increasingly there was a clock-in, clock-out mentality.

This is nothing new. When the first move was made on trainee hours, some ten years before, I arranged to admit a patient with severe and undiagnosed back pain whose GP had phoned me mid-afternoon. I rang my trainee to tell him to expect the patient, clerk her in and I would contact him when I had finished my clinic. He was on call so that was fine. By the time I had done all the paperwork and sorted out the day's phone messages with my secretary it was half past six, so I phoned and asked my trainee to meet me on the ward. An urgent MRI was indicated (one had been done two weeks before, and was apparently normal, but everything pointed to osteomyelitis – bone infection – of the spine, as indeed it turned out to be). We dusted everything down, dotted some I's and crossed a few T's and I prepared to go. It was after seven. The trainee turned to me and said

"Dr Bamji, can I ask you a question?"

"Of course"

"Why are you still here?"

"What do you mean?"

---

[81] The 2018 case of Dr Hadiza Bawa-Garba is a case in point. Suspended by a GMC medical tribunal for an identification error, scapegoated in the courts and convicted of manslaughter, and then struck off when the GMC asked for the tribunal's decision to be overturned, there was in my view a miscarriage of justice. The tribunal heard the background of overwork and understaffing, which it appears the criminal court did not, so one might argue her conviction was on the basis of incomplete evidence.
[82] In 1977, while a medical registrar in Bath, I was responsible for the trainee rotas and devised a new rota that meant there was full cover, but no long working days or rolled-over days where folk would work for 3 days in a row without a break. I thought it was brilliant. Those affected protested, because it would reduce their extra-duty payments and they would be financially quite a bit worse off.

"Well, don't you go home at five?"

There followed a brief outline of why I thought it was better to tie up loose ends than go home worrying that a failure to do so might result in disablement or death. I could see he was unconvinced.[83]

I can see the attitude becoming more prevalent and as today's trainees turn into tomorrow's consultants it will indeed become the norm. However, what horrifies me more is that today's consultants seem to have lost the will to criticise and just let it happen. I am not advocating a return to 104-hour weeks (which I started with) but this lack of concern, and continuity, is worrying, and may put more patients at risk than a tired doctor.

I have not seen any clinical trial testing the hypothesis that lack of continuity is more or less dangerous than doctor fatigue. However – bear in mind that if you depart on the dot of five leaving things undone they will haunt you all evening (and night).

Neither does it help when patients are seen by successions of doctors working shifts, so that no patient is seen through from start to finish. This is exaggerated when teams rotate, and you end up doing things in a great hurry.

Remember the parable of the two bulls. The young bull came dashing up to the old one and said "Hey, Jim! The farmer's left the gate open, so we could go and have some fun with the cows. Let's gallop down and do a couple of them!" The old bull looked at him, winked and replied "No, my young friend. Let's walk down and do the lot".

One of my friends, the ebullient Gordon Jackson who was a consultant at Lewisham Hospital, suggested that when we were trainees we worked all the hours God gave us so the consultants could get off at five, but once we were consultants we worked all the hours so the trainees could get off. Of course, with everyone now off at five, or working shifts, more doctors are needed just to be there, yet politicians wonder why productivity per doctor has gone down. Simples! And on that note…

Lunch

Time was when doctors met for lunch in the canteen (and before that in the postgraduate centre dining room). It was sociable and you found out what was going on, devised policy and so forth. Nowadays we all snatch a

---

[83] Adan Kay makes the same point in *This is going to hurt*.

sandwich in our office (I understand this is called eating *al desko*) and browse the internet, communicating in grunts (called emails).

We have lost something, just as we did when living-in was abolished for trainees except when on call. Work hard to get it back.

History matters

The PCT decided it was going to build a new Child Development Centre on our cottage hospital site in Erith. The outpatient consultants got wind of the plan. It required demolition of the existing 1960s department (which instantly raised questions about where outpatients might be seen during the rebuilding, as spare capacity in the main hospital was non-existent).

However the proposal also demanded the demolition of the X-ray department. This is opened yearly under the London Open House scheme which allows public access to interesting buildings that are usually inaccessible; the department is housed in the only surviving underground hospital in the UK built in case of major attack from the air and was completed just before the outbreak of the Second World War.

Those planning its demolition were unaware of its significance. I assumed that it was a listed building, which would have knocked the whole plan on the head (car park spaces sufficient for the new proposal could not be provided without flattening it). I did some homework, and found it wasn't. So I asked the Department of Culture, Media and Sport (once known as the Department of the Environment), by way of a detailed submission, which ran to a dozen or so pages, with pictures, to spot-list it.

It did. Curiously the CDC planners, once hell-bent on destruction, suddenly became enthused by this historic building they now had to care for and cherish.

But a sense of history is important – likewise joined-up thinking. Some while earlier a proposal to consolidate three Bromley hospitals picked a site on Green Belt land. The outline plan cost about £8m. Perhaps unsurprisingly, for it appeared that no-one had thought to run it past the DoE as it then was, that department turned it down.

When my rehab unit was being constructed there was a delay, as the builders struck water unexpectedly while digging out the foundations. Ah, I said, that's because you are building over the old ice pond that belonged to the big house in whose grounds the hospital sat. They knew I had the estate plans in the archives, but nobody thought to consult them. My colleague Peter Savage reminds that is not the only reason; the hospital lies on a geological interface (the Boya Hill gravels, Lambeth group and Thanet Sands), so there are also springs under the hospital which caused long-term problems in the tunnel linking the main hospital with the maternity block.

In all these cases you might detect a sense of *schadenfreude* on my part. However each one underlines the fact that doctors are trained in analysis and if their analysis is better than anyone else's then they will win. It is likely to be the case in many such instances (I confess the planning rules are well-known to me because my wife and I are serial NIMBYs who have objected to numerous planning applications near our various houses – not all of which we have won). But the principles are – know your facts, rely on your experience, look for every possible fault and consequence of any particular action and think not about what is necessarily best, but what is least bad.

There may be some managers reading this. I have met many good ones, though too many of those have become disillusioned by the constraints and bureaucracy and have left the NHS. But there is a rule for you, too. By all means pursue a firm agenda, be it related to service change, cost or political direction. But do not under any circumstances forget that if you do not carry your troops along with you, then you are lost. Too many plans and diktats are imposed without proper consultation and those who feel they should have been consulted will be those who will try to undermine you and even bring you down. Doctors, particularly consultants in the hospital setting, have longevity. Although there is increasing mobility many consultants will stay for 20-30 years. Managers, in comparison, are here today and gone tomorrow. You may resent the inertia of such a system but the only way to change things is to ensure that no-one will feel excluded from the decision-making (or worse, come up with an immutable reason for no change). So. Consult. Then, if you must, make the decision you were going to make anyway.

Now I am out of it all I can let you into a secret I was entrusted with by a friend. I was always impressed when, in meetings, he would preface a plan by saying "I have consulted with a number of people". How thorough, I thought. Then one day he came out with a comment about something that would have involved him consulting me, but he hadn't. After the meeting I asked who he had consulted. He winked. "Andrew" he said, "zero is a number".

As a corollary to this, sometimes you can achieve results by frightening people. Write a letter, and indicate it has been copied to various influential folk (chairmen, MPs and the like). There's no need to send the copies.

Stand up to politicians. You may think you know best (and probably do)

The NHS has been a political football for ever and a day. Plans for "reform" are often a smokescreen to divert people's attention away from the deficiencies by distracting them into planning change.

Join management and you may be infected with a religious fervour that blinds you to common sense and humanity and you go over to the dark side.

Ask why the changes are needed and you get all sorts of rubbish about the need for change, how reform will "transform" services and why the public want change to make things better. The public may want things to be better but to date (from 1948) organisational change has not made much of a difference, and it is remarkable how many "reforms" get undone years later. I am reminded of the medical school curriculum I helped design while still a student, which was implemented with much pride. I returned to the same hospital some six years later to discover the current medical student body didn't like it and a further review had just started (which came up with something that looked very like the original one we had demolished, whereupon I suggested we should rotate the two schemes every seven years – long enough for institutional memory to be blunted – and everyone would be happy all the time).

Who, then, would you ask about how to reform the NHS? The public, or the staff? The well who have never used it, or the sick who have? The affluent and articulate, or the disadvantaged chronic sick?

Sadly the NHS has lost sight of its patients. There are too many examples of where NHS planning has become a management exercise (often facilitated by the inappropriately-named management consultants). If a company wants to sort out its organisation it asks the workers and does not rely solely on outside advisors. If it wants advice on how to deliver goods it asks its customers, not those who will never buy. It will then ask its staff whether the plans are practical.

Let us therefore get rid of all "focus groups" that comprise the middle-class well who have no idea what it's like to be poor and ill and are the last people on earth who should be planning healthcare. Ask the patients – they will understand what they need. Ask the staff – they will understand how to deliver it (or explain why it cannot be done).

And another thing. Just because government says we must do something it doesn't mean that it is right. I have made my case on care in the community – a divisive and inefficient way of providing specialist care which will be cheap because it will be bad, or vice-versa. I am fed up with managers (and medical politicians) who whine we must do things the government's way because it's the only way we will "move forwards". Maybe they want their gongs and such. But if it's wrong it's wrong.[84] The disastrous implementation of a new medical training programme and jobs system (MTAS) was a prime example. Interestingly a pressure group called Remedy UK tried to bring senior NHS doctor/managers before the General Medical Council with the idea of seeking reprimands for their behaviour. The GMC refused to act (and were backed up in the High Court) on the basis that doctors were immune from GMC action if they were following public policy.

I have pointed out that this argument would have resulted, in the aftermath of the Second World War, in no doctors being brought before War Crimes tribunals for killing people during experiments on concentration camp inmates, as they too were following public policy…

2010's new UK government sprung yet another reorganisation on us. Oh dear. It had obviously been some months, or longer, in the making, judging by its detail.

James Heathcote, a Bromley GP, wrote in the local Faculty Newsletter in May 2006, as follows:

> "2005-6 (the "best ever" year for the NHS) found me working for the PCT as co-chair of the PEC and I witnessed for myself the chaos and pain that PCT managers suffered in trying to manage budgetary shortfalls, yet another threat of total reorganisation and a deluge of new policies – perhaps sensible in themselves individually, but completely bonkers when tipped out of the box altogether."

A nice turn of phrase, I thought, but *plus ça change, plus c'est la même chose*, as Alphonse Karr put it (in 1849); worse still there was yet another reorganisation, as noted above. Although in mitigation the development of NHS England has resulted in the new head of the NHS having a considerable amount of independence – except when he tries to exercise this the politicians start screaming foul.

It really is extraordinary that managers will not learn from experience elsewhere. Many is the time that I was summoned to a meeting about some

---

[84] Likewise, facts are facts and if the theory doesn't fit then it's the theory that's wrong. Read Benoit Mandelbrot and Richard Hudson's book *The (Mis)Behaviour of Markets* (Profile Books, 2004) for an exposition in the world of economics.

new initiative to hear that it is the "latest thing" from the USA. Indeed I have been offered free trips to the USA to see it all in action and I have read the accounts of those who succumbed to temptation, and went. Now you would think, reading this, that I have made a mistake – that managers are at the cutting edge of enquiry about new methods. But there is a problem. What they want to tell us about is not actually that new. Worse, if you go to the clinicians in the States, they will tell you (often) that they implemented the proposals ten years ago, and just as our managers are getting excited by the possibilities, theirs are discovering that they don't work. I have heard this from two rheumatologists, some 20 years apart. The last one was looking at getting a post in the UK to escape what he saw as the diminution of clinical care and the priority of making money in the USA, and was disheartened to find that in another five years he might be back where he began, management-wise.

When threatened, respond with facts

When I was President of the British Society for Rheumatology I was telephoned by a colleague at another hospital who told me that their department was to be closed, as the local PCT had decided not to fund patient referrals.

I paid a visit. I asked for some departmental statistics, like numbers of new patients, follow-ups, casemix and so forth. They had none. Surprised, I asked how many patients were on biologic agents for rheumatoid arthritis (at that time all such patients were being entered on the newly created BSR Biologics Register).[85] They didn't know. By now appalled I suggested that they needed to get this information, and pretty damn fast, for otherwise they had no way of defending themselves.

I myself kept some sort of database since the day I started as a consultant, beginning with an exercise book noting names of new patients, their diagnoses and GP. As a result I was able to provide myself with some simple statistics, and indeed a collaborative paper came out of it.[86] I stopped

---

[85] The Register provides a classic example of the value of extensive and complete data both in assessing side-effects and complications and generating research questions. Needless to say it was set up by the BSR without any input from NHS managers and runs as an independent unit

[86] AN Bamji, PA Dieppe PA, I Haslock and ME Shipley, *What do Rheumatologists do? A Pilot Audit Study*. Br J Rheumatol 1990, **24**, 295-8

recording when it became apparent after 10 years that the casemix was not changing much (although that itself was to change later). By now sensible computers had come along, so I ditched my BBC B computer, onto which I was entering the stuff from the exercise book and migrated a follow-up database onto a machine in the hospital's Respiratory lab. Its data capacity was gigantic. It had a hard drive of 20Mb! This was 1985… Later still when Microsoft released Excel and desktop machines came to outpatients I developed a follow-up database which listed patients by name, birth date, date first seen and date most recently seen (to calculate follow-up duration), and drugs used and date to next appointment (to calculate follow-up interval). As part of this I was able to check the mean methotrexate dose, biologic exposure and all sorts of other things. There were separate sheets for little projects such as reviews of new patients and their outcomes (useful for assessing who was to be followed up or who was "one stop"). Three further presentations followed.[87] [88] [89]

But the bottom line was that when any managers came by asking me to change what I did, or asking – usually with a furtive grin that suggested they knew I wouldn't be able to answer their query – I had all the information at my fingertips and could provide better and more useful statistics than the hospital database. Mostly they slunk away with tails between legs to lick their wounds.

The moral of this is that if you want to win battles you need to prepare for them better than the opposition. I have suggested to medical students that two important books that will come in useful are Machiavelli's "The Prince" and Clausewitz's "On War".[90] Bernard Montgomery (of Alamein) was a great proponent of the sand table when planning battles. Presentations should be well prepared and rehearsed. No data, and no background, and you are dead. One of my wise senior colleagues once said that if you have read the minutes of the last committee meeting once you are ahead of 50% of the attendees; if you've read them twice that goes up to 95%.

---

[87] A Litwic AN Bamji, *Follow-up or discharge? A new patient outcome analysis.* BSR Annual Meeting 2008, Abstract 417
[88] AN Bamji, J Lane, *Impact of a community-based rheumatology clinic on a hospital department.* BSR Annual Meeting 2010, Abstract 96
[89] AN Bamji, *New: follow-up ratios: Dogma or Design?* BSR Annual Meeting 2011, Abstract 59
[90] I was accosted by a trainee while I was collecting some stuff from the Postgraduate Centre after I had retired. He asked if I was Dr Bamji, and on my confirmation told me how he had been much influenced by the after-dinner talk I had given in Cambridge four years earlier, and both books were now in his library. I was much flattered.

The meaning of reality

Reality is not fixed. Some years back I invited an old medical school friend to give a lunchtime lecture. He had begun his career in public health medicine and had switched to the Department of Health and Social Security, as it then was (we called it the department of Stealth and Total Obscurity). He began his talk by saying that when he crossed the divide from us to them he believed that people in the department had no grasp of the reality of the NHS. He realised, he said, that he was quite wrong. They had an excellent grasp. The problem was it was a different reality.

Don't let wool be pulled over your eyes

…or maybe not.

Our Trust decided it was going to have another round of back-office cuts to try and meet its deficit, so it set off by telling all the over-65 staff that they were to have their contracts terminated (there was a bit of a rush with this, as the law was to be changed to forbid this, to be enacted some 6 months later). We lost a senior orthopaedic surgeon, some of whose patients were so angry they followed him into the private sector, but we also lost two of our valued and hard-working clinic receptionists, who had spent the last 15 years or so manning the desk for the rheumatology and orthopaedic clinics.

I was sad at the manner of their exit but returned the following week to discover that the reception desk was empty, and that my patients (many quite disabled) had to walk 60 yards round to main outpatients, queue for ages and then return to the rheumatology waiting area. It transpired that the reception staff had been cut by four. Two desks had been abandoned, and the remaining staff were tearing their hair out trying to cope with the large numbers of patients, who at peak times would be queueing almost 50 yards down the main hospital corridor.

I complained to our Medical Director who, Pilate-like, washed his hands of the matter. Well – I suppose the hand-washing set a good example on the *C.Diff.* front.[91] After several other complaints directed at those to whom he had directed me I finally got an answer – which was that the restructuring had only lost one full-time equivalent post and implying that the reception manager was falling down on the job. Having seen her, in tears, trying to cope a week before, I was not impressed so summoned her to ask if the figures were true.

She told me they were. However, the staff numbers included two receptionists based at the cottage hospital, and one member of the pre-admission team, who could hardly be classed as main hospital receptionists either because they worked somewhere else or because they did another job entirely. None of them had previously been in the reception staff budget.

It got worse. My secretary was suddenly phoned by an anxious senior manager, telling her that she now had to collect a huge pile of outpatient outcome forms (the ones in colour, which had been accumulating as described above), book the follow-up appointments and code the details. Otherwise, she was told, the hospital would lose oodles of money because it couldn't claim for the work done. Guess who normally did this work. The receptionists they had just disposed of.

It is very sad when managers not only try to delude others but appear to delude themselves. If you are faced with an improbable scenario, or offered

---

[91] And norovirus, and E.*Coli,* and other transmissible bugs. *C.Diff* causes awful diarrhoea in antibiotic loaded patients.

some rumour, check it out and get the facts. Preferably in print. Then you can screw the bastards back.

I must try not to be rude about managers. Some of ours were absolutely excellent; analytical, full of common sense and very charming to boot. None of these lasted very long before they were shafted.

Whatever the rewards, you can only bang your head against a brick wall for so long

My NHS hospital, Queen Mary's in Sidcup, was built in 1974 to replace an old WW1 hospital (of considerable importance, but that's another story) which had been run up in 1917 with the standard construction of asbestos sheet.[92] When it was demolished the spoil was removed from the site.

Or so it was thought. When the old site was being surveyed (probably, though I am not certain, when it was thought ripe for development that would fund a growing deficit – though not for long) it became clear that something was up, as the entire area was suddenly fenced off and notices appeared warning that the site was contaminated.

I enquired further and discovered that test borings had revealed the existence of substantial quantities of asbestos which had obviously not been removed, but had been ploughed in.

The hospital archives contained a wealth of material about the redevelopment and without much trouble I found the original contract for demolition. It was written in black and white that any hazardous material was to be taken away. Clearly this had not happened.

I wrote to the Chief Executive pointing this out. I had established that the contractors were still in existence and suggested that they be sued for the sum now required (several million pounds) to clear the site properly.

Nothing happened.

I wrote again, and to the legal department suggesting that as the contract failure had only just come to light the statute of limitations would not apply.

---

[92] You can boost my royalties by reading my book *Faces from the Front: Harold Gillies, The Queen's Hospital, Sidcup and the origins of modern plastic surgery* (Helion Press, 2017)

Nothing happened.

Notwithstanding the land being possibly Green Belt, and thus unusable anyway, the opportunity to clear up properly was passed up. I gave up.

Accidents will happen

The retrospectoscope is a very accurate instrument. However the futurescope is not. Consider the following. It has been in the newspapers, so is hardly a confidential story.

The hospital received a call from the police that a dead baby had been found at the local laundry in a sheet that had come from us. This had caused quite a stir there. What had happened was very simple; stillbirths went down to the mortuary and were kept in the bottom drawer of the mortuary fridge until the paediatric pathologist could come in to do the post-mortem; this was a very limited service, so the bottom drawer could fill up. The remains were usually carefully wrapped in a shroud (a sheet to you and me). This day the pathologist had come, and one examination was to be made. The assumption was that another bundle fell from the drawer and, being wrapped in a sheet, was mistaken for an empty sheet which was put into the linen basket that stood next to the fridge. So the sheet, with remains within, tootled off to the laundry where unsurprisingly the quality control person had hysterics.

The Chief Executive went to the mother's home to offer a personal apology. The father created a huge stink, threatening press exposure if he didn't receive a seven-figure sum in compensation for the distress caused.

The failure of the hospital to pay had an interesting sequel. Press publicity was huge. The CE then got a phone call from a lady identifying herself as the mother of the baby's father to the effect that he was a lying git, having abandoned his wife and kids up north and failed to pay maintenance. The baby's poor mother headed back to the continent, whence she had come, having been confronted by this hidden side of her partner.

The internal enquiry resulted in the entire procedure for stillbirths being revised so that the remains were put into specially labelled plastic boxes. The linen basket was moved to the other side of the mortuary.

When the head of pathology dropped by to check all was well, he found the basket back in its usual place. The staff said its new position was inconvenient.

Words matter

I wrote this piece back in 1994. Once again, you can change names and find parallels now. Choice of words is very important. A corollary to this piece is of course that officials with not enough to do will start filling their time with trivia.[93]

1.   And the Lord looked on the National Health Service, and saw that not a lot had changed since He last took a peep.

2.   For lo, the Ministers had not harkened unto him, and the scribes and accountants had misinterpreted His instructions to Abraham.

3.   For verily had He said "Go forth and multiply", but he had meant in a mathematical sense.

4.   And an plague of bureaucrats had descended, worse even than those plagues which He had deliberately visited upon the Egyptians, and their children, and their children's children, and (*Get on with it— Ed*).

5.   And the bureaucrats were Muppets, save that according to Coz Soli the Contractor, the Sage from Sydney in the South, at least Muppets make one laugh, and the bureaucrats did not do this thing.

6.   And the Lord was troubled, as most of these Muppets had so little to do that they were inventing projects to keep themselves busy.

7.   And the Lord went even unto Global House, and saw that the "housewives from Hayes" who ran Bromley Health were Muppets.

8.   For they were running a campaign to promote safe sex in the borough, and verily they had devised posters to advertise the "morning after" pill in cinemas; posters like film posters. And lo, the first draft had a huge banner headline:

9.   **Coming Soon!**

---

[93] Global House was the HQ of the then Bromley Health Authority

10.   But the "housewives from Hayes" could not understand why everyone fell about laughing, while the Lord thought anyway that in this circumstance when the coming had already come, an abbreviated condominium might be better.

11.   And the Lord saw that the next draft had a new banner:

12.   **Now Showing!**

13.   But the Muppets got very fed up when everyone fell about again.

14.   So they decided they should set up an counselling service to make couples' relationships more satisfactory, by teaching people how to be more sensitive to their partners' needs. And they saw that it was good, and decided that it needed a snappy name as part of the marketing strategy.

15.   So they called it PART, which stands for

16.   **Partnership Awareness Raising Tool**

17.   And lo, they were sore dismayed when everyone fell about again.

18.   And the Lord thought that if there was partnership awareness, then the tool might well be raised. And He said "Nation may speak unto Nation, nay verily, about the Health of the Nation, but in the end these Muppets will go on wasting money.

19.   "For as a camel may pass through the eye of a needle, so shall darkness and rationing cover the earth, and the secondary care facilities will wither, and as in Adam all die."

20.   And the Samaritans and the Doctors wept, and lifted up their voices unto the Lord, and said "We shall not slumber nor sleep, but shall drink ourselves into oblivion, and end up with Varices, never mind Pharisees.

21.   "Why can't the Muppets wither instead?"

22.   And they went up to the White Hall, even to the Major, who Curry favoured, and who sat in the lee of a Bottom[94], but he had hardened his heart towards them, and awarded their pleas no merit, never mind merit awards (please).

23.   And God saw what they had done.

24.   And even He wept.

Note: Muppets make you laugh (vide supra)

Signs matter

I have mentioned the Outpatience department, where one might expect to spend a lot of time waiting. My friend John Styles, magician and puppeteer extraordinary, told me a salutary tale for patient peace of mind. He was having a heart attack. He found it not entirely reassuring to be whisked past his local hospital (A&E now shut) and ferried up to King's College Hospital, where he found a doctor at the door waiting for the ambulance; he was wheeled rapidly up to the cardiac unit and had his stent within minutes.

He was extremely impressed by the whole process – a tribute to the sense of placing the superspecialist work in one place. Except for one thing. As his trolley hurried through the corridors, he spotted a notice.

It said: "**Warning!** Thieves operate in this area"

"Andrew," he said, "I was hoping to get a surgeon to operate on me!"

Emails matter, too

When I retired it was a relief to escape from endless emails, many of which were "global" and were not relevant. It is tempting, when you have a computer with two screens, to leave the email program open on one so you can respond at once to anything important.

DO NOT DO THIS. If it's that important someone will phone, or even turn up at your office door. The temptation to respond instantly to a stupid email

---

[94] Virginia Bottomley was Health Secretary in John Major's last government; Edwina Currie MP had a surprising fling with the said PM

120

is overwhelming, but you will often regret the hasty response for various reasons:

- You think of something you should have put in half an hour after you have sent it.
- It may cause offence (well OK, so did the original you are responding to, but there's no need to sink to their level)
- You haven't got your facts right
- You pressed "Reply all" by mistake

By all means construct a response but sit on it for 24 hours. Then first decide if you really want to send it, and if you do then check the facts, add the missing bits, remove the expletives, and so on.

There's nothing worse than the wrong person hearing the message. Many years ago I was chewing the fat with a friend after a very boozy wedding party; we were happy, relaxed, off our guard and, to be honest, drunk. We were sitting at the top of an outside staircase enjoying a warm summer evening and disparaging the social relationship of a colleague, about whom I vaguely remember we were quite forthright (rude, in other words). There was a break in the conversation. It was not an angel passing over, for suddenly, from below, the disembodied voice of the subject of our analysis floated up.

"I heard all of that."

Charity could begin at home (with a bit of thought)

Like many doctors I filled in large numbers of forms for patients who wished to claim Disability Living Allowance (the majority are ineligible, but I would fight like a cornered rat to help someone deserving who had been turned down; you must make sure you assess the patient properly and fairly, write a letter in their support and remind them that their self-assessment should be based on their worst level, not their best.). Sometimes I got a long spiel about how poor they are. Some of my disadvantaged patients expressed concern that they wouldn't be able to afford their usual fortnight in Lanzarote. My father always used to say, when he was in general practice in the 1960s, that it was amazing how many people claiming to be broke had big cars and colour televisions (we had a black and white one, rented at that) but I have a way of stopping this whinge in its tracks.

Often the perpetrators have had a quick fag before they came into the hospital, and one can smell it. So I say "You know, there is a very easy way to increase your income by 40%".

They look interested.

"Stop smoking" I say, and before they have a chance to protest they only smoke occasionally, and only roll-ups, I add "How many do you smoke a day? 40? 50?"

It's important to overestimate, then you get the real figure as they say "Oh no, Doctor, nothing like that, 20 at the most."

So 20 a day could be £42 a week.[95] Benefit of £120 per week – well, you can do the maths.

Sometimes I get caught, as they slyly said they bought them cheap from a friend that went to France with an articulated lorry, but it is a salutary thought, and akin to powerboat racing, where you stand, effectively, in a freezing shower that crashes 6 feet up and down every ten seconds, all the while tearing up £20 notes.

By the same token spending £25 weekly on lottery tickets diminishes the value of one's state pension by a quarter. I suggested to one nice old lady who bought this amount that she would help her Raynaud's more by setting the heating a bit higher – which she could afford if she abandoned her Big Draw Numbers and scratchcards – and she looked at me as if I was mad.

And I haven't even started on the cost of maintaining status dogs, such as bull terrier crosses, Rottweilers and the like. Observe a very large person in a tracksuit or similar with two supermarket trolleys and you will often find that one is loaded to the gunwales with pet food. Poor? I don't think so. But these days it's wrong to point this sort of thing out. For some reason.

Flags

When Queen Mary's Hospital at Sidcup was rebuilt in 1974 there was considerable pride both in it and its appearance, and the main block was dignified by a flagpole from which flew the hospital flag, designed by one of the staff and lovingly created by the needlework room (most modern folk won't have heard of such a thing, but all hospitals had them before laundry

---

[95] More now. I wrote this in 2010. 20 Benson & Hedges Gold were priced at £11.24 in Tesco in August 2018. Nearly £80 per week.

was outsourced). This began to fray as flags do. One day I came in to find that an anaemic replacement, based on the headed notepaper, had been hoisted in its stead. I was able to rescue the original but the new one had such small print that it looked like a white flag of surrender – perhaps prophetically, in view of what was to happen later. We designed a replacement in the hospital green, with a smart and distinctive logo, and hoisted that.

Here it is. I am hoisting it with the Director of Nursing, Rosemary Robinson.

For a few years all was well. Then the NHS decided it was going to rebadge itself, with what most people will know as the italic white on blue NHS initials, typeface prescribed down to the last point size, templates for every eventuality (except flags). So all the hospital signs were taken down and replaced with identical ones only with a blue rather than a green background – and to my horror our flag came down, replaced by a horrid blue and white NHS one. Which said "NHS". Nothing else. As if one didn't know that the hospital was part of the NHS…

Anyway after a long and eventually acrimonious discussion we were able to restore our green flag, in the face of dire warnings that any visiting NHS bureaucrat would order its removal. This never happened. Then we were told that our respectful practice of lowering the flag to half-mast for the death of a staff member must stop, as it might upset relatives who might think it was for a patient (of course it would have been at half-mast every day in that case). Then we were told that the flag must not be flown at all. There was a further fuss. The flag stayed up.

But management remained unhappy. So when the car park was resurfaced they used it as an excuse to remove the flagpole because it was in the way of the repairs (which it wasn't). No flagpole, no flag. I believe the pole is still lying in the works yard.[96]

Gardens

When I was Clinical Tutor and responsible for the hospital's Postgraduate Centre I thought it would be appropriate to plant up a weedy flowerbed outside the front entrance as a miniature Physic Garden and so bought a few plants to realise this – rosemary, feverfew, periwinkle (vinca) and some others. A few months later a strange plant appeared in the bed and I was about to pull it out when I realised it was *Belladonna Atropurpurea* – better known as deadly nightshade – but it seemed such a splendid medical addition that I didn't.

Some months later as flowers were turning to seeds I was forwarded a letter from a member of the public, who had written to the managers insisting it was removed as it was a risk to children. As it was tucked in a discreet corner down a road reserved for staff there should be no children there, so I replied to this effect, pointing out that it was a fine specimen of a medicinal plant and highly appropriate in its setting.

I heard no more, but the following year the landscape contractors came by (equipment a three-gang mower, hedgetrimmer and strimmer). Slashed to bits, my deadly nightshade was no more. Nor were all the other plants.

Dumping syndrome

This is a medical term, not that one sees it any more because patients with ulcers no longer get major gastro-duodenal surgery,[97] but hospital closure can produce some odd effects.

---

[96] See A Bamji, *Flying the flag*. BMJ 2002; 325: 501.
[97] After such surgery, often involving removal of part of the stomach, food would rush through the much-reduced stomach too fast, hit the next bit of gut (the

When the Queen Elizabeth Military Hospital in Woolwich was closed in the early 1990s we wondered what might happen to the local civilian caseload that it had accumulated. The answer was not long in coming; we had a circular letter letting us know that the rheumatology department, which had three consultants, would shut and that local GPs had been advised to send all the follow-up patients to the nearest NHS hospital. Accordingly I started to get a stream of letters re-referring these patients, of which there were over 200.

No extra resources were available to manage these patients, until suddenly a chink of light appeared. The government of the day decided to help the employment of those who wanted to work part-time and invited applications for posts that would meet a clinical need.

I set up an application. Not only did I have this extra workload to manage, and pointed out our locality had just lost the equivalent of 2 whole-time consultants, but one of the QE consultants, already working part-time, was keen for a similar post locally and suddenly saw that she could pick up where she left off and continue to treat all her old patients, not to mention crack our own waiting list problem.

The application failed. I was surprised; I thought we had an unstoppable case. A post in rheumatology was created – in Peterborough. It could not be filled. So my local friend started to commute to do some part-time work in Peterborough, seeing new patients who would then have to be followed up by someone else.

I learned about six months after my retirement that the replacement for my own post was far from guaranteed and that the current locum was likely to go elsewhere given the uncertainty. He asked me what he should do with the patients he had inherited from me. I suggested that if there was no-one replacing him then he should write letters to all the local GPs explaining that without consultant supervision these patients were unsafe, and that they were being discharged so that the GP could re-refer to a consultant still in post.

---

duodenum) and create a rush of insulin which was too much for the amount of food, provoking a drop in blood sugar and a feeling of horrible malaise and faintness. There is an interesting moral here. Many years ago two preparations were used as treatment of ulcers – a drug called carbenoxolone and another marketed as "De-Nol", a bismuth preparation. One of my bosses, Ken Gough, swore by the latter. No-one could explain why it worked, but in recent years the underlying cause of ulcers was found to be infection with a bug, *Helicobacter Pylori*, and De-Nol inhibits its growth. So he was right – moral: just because you cannot explain something doesn't mean it's not true.

In other words, I was telling him to do exactly what had been done to me. The difference is that rather than there being 200 patients there are 1200. There could be trouble ahead, as the song says…[98]

What's in a name?

This is the corollary to the above tale. Shortly after this fiasco we suddenly had the opportunity to appoint a part-timer, funding for which arrived by another route (or magic). My friend had got another job by now, so (sadly) was no longer interested in ours. It went to advert and we had one application from an Associate Specialist from Crawley looking to upgrade.

There was, however, a problem. I am Dr A Bamji. Our applicant was Dr A. Bhanji.

Asgar is a delightful man and would have been an excellent colleague. However, we had to face (probably politically incorrect, at least these days) reality. If we had two consultants with such similar names the potential for confusion and error was immense, even risky. Indeed even when he was in Crawley we would get each other's correspondence. With reluctance we decided it was impossible. He was good enough to understand, and agree, and I am pleased to say he got a job elsewhere.

Hospitals need attention to their naming, as well. The new Dartford Hospital took its naming from its geography; overlooking the valley of the River Darent it called itself the Darent Valley Hospital. However, its reputation was suboptimal and it is now popularly known as Death Valley. Naming it the New Dartford Hospital would have been so much more sensible. Likewise I learned from an old friend that she was glad to live near the Conquest Hospital (think history, and you will realise if you don't know already that it's in Hastings, and actually also has tales spread about it) so she doesn't have to go to the brand new Kent & Sussex, which is apparently now known as the Kent and Snuffit.

At my own old hospital, the now closed (and demolished) Kent Women's Wing is quite pleasing, until you think about the potential double-entendre immortalised by James Naughtie on the "Today" programme on Radio 4,

---

[98] As a postscript to this gloomy scenario I learned from my secretary that an advertisement for my substantive replacement was finally agreed – five years after I had left

introducing the then Culture Secretary Jeremy Hunt.[99] After all, what do Maternity Units deal in?

S&M: the NHS version

The strangling red tape of NHS bureaucracy has extended into the training environment. However the abbreviation may have a different connotation in the nightclubs of our great cities; here it means "Statutory and Mandatory" and refers to various essential training protocols that have to be completed.

In the old days much of this was treated in a fairly light-hearted way. There was a requirement to attend a fire lecture once a year, for example. In our hospital this was delivered at a ponderous pace designed to accommodate the most stupid employee (although some of those delivering the talk were pretty stupid themselves). Now I own a house and a car, and therefore am well aware of how to put fires out (and with what) largely because I don't want my house to burn down while I wait for the Fire Brigade. So I didn't go. But the powers-that-be decided that an enforcement process was required. This began by incorporating the lecture into a postgraduate meeting. Fortunately on my first attendance I was called out (my secretary thought dealing with a clinical problem could not wait. Bless her.).

Then it was decided to put the entire S&M repertoire onto the hospital intranet, so it could be completed electronically. This included such things as moving and handling, anger management, ethnic diversity training (vide infra), hand washing training and, of course, the fire training.

I decided to be a good boy, and signed into the system. Oh boy. Whoever wrote the modules was not only stupid but illiterate. And patronising. I lasted all of ten minutes staring at this drivel before giving up with a headache. And by this time I really needed the anger management module.

What I had not reckoned on was enforcement. When I put in a claim for study leave expenses it was turned down. Someone had checked the system and discovered I had been a bad boy and failed to complete sufficient modules to qualify. I argued that the stress of trying to learn from this rubbish was quite intolerable for educated folk, and I was not going to complete anything at least until it had all been re-written in proper English.

---

[99] Broadcast on 6th December 2010. He replaced the H with a C. Don't know why. So, take Kent and replace the e with a... got it?

It was (I take credit for that; everyone else just whined). I tried again. Trouble was, when I came to do the MCQ at the end I always failed. But IT came to the rescue. The IT department had decided that the hospital's desktop monitors had not got sufficient resolution to display the new X-ray imaging program and told me it was going to upgrade my screen. Except they had no process for disposing of the old one. So I had two screens, and they kindly set up my workstation to use both at once.

Magic! I opened one intranet window on one, and a second on the other, thus displaying both module and its MCQ together. Easy peasy! But I reluctantly concluded that all I was doing was completing a tick-box exercise with no benefit to myself, or my patients (I calculated that to finish the lot would take a whole working week) so I stopped. Not wasting my time was worth all of the £700 or so that I couldn't claim for my annual rheumatology update (and anyway I could set it against tax on the private practice side). But is S&M really worthwhile? I think not.

It is interesting to note that another example of the same thing has surfaced in my new home town. One of our best restaurants failed to gain the required public health five stars, while the burger van on the road by Rye Golf Club did. It was the paperwork that was not in order and nothing to do with the kitchen. The paperwork was completed, the stars appeared and no-one thought more about it.

Paranoia

Remember; paranoia is when you *think* people are persecuting you, not when you *know* they are.

Ethnicity and anger

I had a polite note from an NHS organisation which shall remain anonymous, reminding me that I had not replied to an earlier circular on ethnic and cultural diversity training, requesting my own origin on the tick-box form and suggesting that I would be removed from a list of eligible people for some task or other unless I replied.

Now if there is one thing that really makes me angry it's this ethnic diversity thing. However hard I try, I seem unable to convince bureaucrats and others that I do not require any further training. My whole bloody life has been ethnic diversity training – which is, when you think about it, inevitable for the product of a mixed marriage and a foreign name. My mother got cut out of a will for marrying a black man (even though he wasn't); when family came they would gabble happily in a mixture of English and Gujerati and my mother and I would get lost. My mother's sister married into a family of secular Jews. The family was thus pretty multicultural. I would walk into a class at school and the whole lot would go (there was a TV series at the time with a Batmobile, and Robin) "Da da da da, da da da da, BLACKMAN!!!" Sadly there was no-one called Robin in my class to team up with, so we played Biggles instead. I was Algy. My father invented the Tebbit Test at my birth (1950) so I learned none of his Indian languages and his religion was a specialist subject.[100] As I wrote above I knew enough to outsmart my smart Hammersmith boss. Father was irritated when I reported that I always ended up being India at break, playing "Howzat", though I found it quite amusing to point out that two of the then team, Engineer and Contractor, were Parsees like him (and anyway I often won). [101] He suggested I would continue to suffer discrimination unless I changed my surname that sounded English but was still a Parsee name, like Cooper. He was right there. He said I would never reach the top with a foreign name, but there he was wrong, and anyway there is of course an eminent rheumatologist called Cyrus Cooper, which could have been confusing. Perhaps I would have had less mis-spelling of my name, which is another irritation, as we get everything from Anglicisation (Barry, Bambridge) to Hindu (Banerjee, Bhanji, as with Asgar previously mentioned) to the downright ridiculous (Famjsi, Bongo). And as one branch of the family anglicises the name as Bamjee anyway, matters become even more complicated.

Once, in my clinic, I was writing up the notes of one patient while the next was being weighed in the ante-room. Suddenly my concentration was broken as the patient decided to get a problem off his chest. "Ere", he growled to the nurse "This Bamji bloke. Is he one of them… black doctors?" Tempting it was indeed to switch into a fake Peter Sellers accent, isn't it (and, lest you think that is politically incorrect cultural appropriation, my father used to go into hysterics when I did this at home, and I polished up my act to the extent that I can be northern, or southern, or Irish (north and south) or Welsh, at will). And South African (see below). I struggle with Geordie and learning Brummie polluted my hitherto excellent Scouse. I have even addressed the

---

[100] Norman Tebbit, right-wing Conservative politician, when talking about immigration famously commented that you could decide if someone had integrated because they would support the English cricket team. This should now of course be called the Bamji Benchmark.
[101] A table cricket game, involving rolling a lozenge with runs (including byes, wides and no-balls) marked on the faces; one is marked "Howzat" if it comes up then a second lozenge is rolled to determine whether out (and how) or not out. Scores are kept in a proper scorebook.

haggis in passable Glaswegian (should you have the need, there are several excellent video recordings of Burns' verse on YouTube).

The lesson I learned, and in this my father was influential and decades ahead of his time, was that if you flaunt your separateness you find yourself bullied, boxed in or pigeonholed. The best way to get on is assimilate and keep your head down. The Americans have learned through bitter experience that to promote equality it is sensible not to teach Hispanics in Spanish. Once again we are years behind our American cousins. The only good thing is that there are now so many people with foreign names in medicine that no-one really notices much any more, not least as many of them, being second-generation and public school (like me) speak unaccented English.[102]

Of course, with a name like mine you get circulated with oddities. I have more than once been asked if I would like to join the Overseas Doctors Association. I stood for an election once and had a charming letter from someone who said they would vote for me because I was a Parsee. I wrote what I hope was a charming letter back pointing out that I was in fact baptised a Methodist, but had turned C of E, and actually wanted people to vote for me because of my policies, not my name or putative religion.

Anyway, to get back to the tick-box form. I am White British, because of my mother and as I said my father wasn't very dark. I could be White Other, because my father took a while to become British, but that's another story. I could also be White Asian (Mixed). Or even Asian (other). So what the hell *do* I put? Am I bothered? Why should anyone else be?

Then there's the cultural diversity bit. Just you try ignoring cultural diversity in a public school, called Bamji, with parents who were once communists and who have brought you up to support the Labour Party. With about three others. We were always candidates at mock elections because there was no-one else (I might add at this point that I do not recall Charlie Clarke, once a Labour Home Secretary and the year below me most of the way up the school, being one of us then, though his ears stuck out just as they do now). We got slaughtered regularly.

Many of my hospital colleagues were more overseas than I. We seemed to get on fine. Our cleaners all seemed to come from West Africa, and they

---

[102] In a speech on February 5th 2011 the Prime Minister, David Cameron, expressed his view that multiculturalism was a failure. About time. The fourth programme in the "Hospital" series broadcast at the beginning of 2017 from St Mary's Hospital, Paddington in London named some 20 participating doctors, only one of whom had a British-sounding name – and he was Welsh

130

were lovely. I appeared, however, to be one of the few doctors who acknowledged their presence; courtesy costs nothing, does it? My sister-in-law is from Mauritius. And the worst discrimination I have seen is when you put Asians over Africans or, in one classic departmental dispute, pitch in two Muslims from different parts, one a gent and one a peasant, a high caste Hindu and a lower-caste Hindu woman. Omigod. What a mess that was. Individually all were <u>very nice, but</u> put them together and it was like tipping hot water onto a bottle of washing soda. Boom! There is no doubt that if you come from a different part of the world then your attitudes and approach might seem alien, especially if vernacular English has passed you by. I recall the most delightful and brilliant paediatric registrar, of Indian origin, who plotted a wheezy little six-year-old on the Tanner height and weight charts when his mother ventured that he was not very well made. She told his mother that he was normal. That wasn't, of course, what she meant. I took his pants down later (he was fine, actually and I expect he has had a stonking sex life unless the asthma caused trouble on exertion).[103] And I once saw a psychiatry trainee from West Africa making a diagnosis of low intelligence because he asked the patient if he had ideas of reference and the patient looked completely blank. Well, wouldn't you? I even came across a doctor, years ago, who could not get a drip up on an exsanguinating patient and walked off, saying there was nothing more he could do and if the patient died it was the will of God, Inshallah. And some of my patients venture, in a most embarrassed way, that they have not understood a doctor because their accent was impenetrable. I sympathise, because I have had the same problem. But I don't have a thing about race, ethnicity or anything. Admittedly I don't take kindly to illiterate circulars and CVs but then government and Department of Health documents were pretty dreadful in that respect. So forget training in diversity. I have been there, mate. In no trumps, not even spades.

When we were constantly exhorted to cut costs it went against my grain to be invited to celebrations of diversity in the hospital, and discover that good money was being spent on steel bands and eminent speakers while we could not develop new services. Indeed, I got quite angry about it. And about all the Improving Working Lives stuff. Stuff that. My Working Life would have been Improved by having two extra physiotherapists on my rehabilitation unit, a second rheumatology nurse specialist[104] and a third consultant.[105] So I seethed over these vapid newsletters and course advertisements from various

---

[103] Lest you have led a sheltered and non-vernacular life I should explain that being "well-made", if a boy, is a euphemism for being – well-hung, up to scratch in the men's department, big thing. Large penis in other words.
[104] Actually we got this, and my Life did Improve.
[105] When I retired my post was reduced from 10 sessions to 6. Same workload.

project teams that seemed to be doing nothing productive. But the one that made me really angry was the course (apparently compulsory), lasting a whole day, on… anger management. Except it was called Management of Stress and Challenging Behaviour in the Workplace just as lorry drivers are logistics operators and window cleaners are transparent wall maintenance engineers.[106] But heat cannot of itself pass from one body to a hotter body, so I'll go off and do some entropy, man.[107]

Midwife-led units: safe, or silly?

Suppose you are on a flight. The intercom crackles to life and a voice says "Hello! I am Boris Johnson and I am piloting your flight today. I thought you would like to know that I have been fully trained except in the details of what to do if an engine fails or there is a major fuel leak. But I am pleased to say that my senior colleague, who does know how to deal with those, is waiting at the end of a telephone in case of an emergency".

Would you happily take off? Change the words appropriately and ask yourself whether you would like your sister, wife, daughter to fly in a midwife-led unit.

I thank my good friend, now sadly departed, gynaecologist and legal eagle Julian Woolfson, for this parable.

Drugs, and why (not) to prescribe them

I don't intend to embark on a discussion of overprescription and the use of dangerous drugs in an inappropriate way (although I did read a piece that incensed me, about why patients with RA should not request or receive methotrexate because we rheumatologists dish it out with dangerous gay abandon, which we don't). Rather I want to discuss why some drugs are denied to patients by non-clinicians (or non-specialists) because of financial considerations alone.

---

[106] In the NHS the delivery of goods was contracted to a newly invented subunit called NHS Logistics, with lots of brand new lorries all logoed up. Just recently I saw one of these, but the unit has been re-badged – at God knows what cost – and now appears to be called NHS Supply Chain.

[107] From "*The Laws of Thermodynamics*", a song by Michael Flanders (and of course it is the Second Law): Heat can't pass from the colder to the hotter, you can try it if you like, but you'd far better notta, 'cos the cold from the cooler will get hotter as a ruler, and that's a Physical Law!

In my long experience of dealing with applications to use drugs – and these are always for highly specialist things that almost always cost lots of money – I have encountered managers and clinicians who fall into two groups. There are those who take a pragmatic, and to my mind sensible approach, which is that if a clinician submits a detailed application there must be a good reason, and thus they err on the side of agreeing. There are also those who are jobsworths, and shelter behind detailed guidelines to find any excuse to avoid allowing use of something expensive while not always having any reasonable clinical argument to back up their decision.

Certolizumab is a case in point. It is a biologic therapy – a tumour necrosis factor antibody used in the management of severe rheumatoid arthritis. Because it is one of a family of TNF antagonists it has been treated as identical to the others available (infliximab, adalimumab and etanercept). A deal done by the manufacturers offered a free three-month trial of certolizumab; as a result, some GP managers and therapeutics committee members decided that it should be the first choice TNF antagonist because of the cost saving (also it was presumed that TNF failure at 3 months was the end of the line for that particular treatment).

However this decision failed to account for several factors.

1. The mechanism of action of the TNF antagonists is not physiologically identical, and there is therefore no reason to believe they should produce identical clinical effects. Antagonists ending in "ab" are antibodies against TNF but the human immune system can and does produce antibodies against them. Those ending in "cept" are fake TNF which blocks the receptor sites on cells.
2. There are differences in side-effects (not fully detailed, but it appears that the "ab's" have more serious respiratory side-effects than the "cepts")
3. It is never clear whether new "me-too" drugs will have exactly the same profile as the old ones, either in efficacy or side-effects
4. It's all very well comparing two drugs each against placebo and inferring they have similar efficacy, but without a head-to-head trial the verdict remains not proven, as the Scottish courts would have.

So one must conclude that the evidence on which a decision was made to use certolizumab first, even though there was much less clinical experience of it, was not clinical evidence. Cost was the prime mover.

Another example was the use of Infliximab in Behçets disease – an uncommon but disabling condition characterised by nasty skin lesions (including involvement of the mucous membranes of the mouth and genital area) and an arthritis. I had one such patient whose disease responded dramatically to Methotrexate, but she developed serious side-effects. So we had to terminate the treatment and she had a major relapse.

She had already received all the standard starting therapy, so we were at a dead end. I was not going to use thalidomide, for which there was trial evidence of benefit, because of her age and the possibility of her becoming pregnant. There were two case reports of dramatic benefit from Infliximab given as a short course.

I applied through the local vetting committee for permission to proceed. It refused on the grounds that there were no clinical trials and that anecdotal evidence was not good enough. I could however use thalidomide…

So I was faced with a patient in serious trouble, but forbidden to use a safe drug and offered the ridiculous option of a seriously dangerous one that was, it seemed to me, mad to consider in a young lady. I fear I lost my temper as well as the battle. The patient moved away, having lost her job because of her disease, so I don't know what happened to her. However in the intervening three years – guess what? Following up on the anecdotes a trial was done. It confirmed benefit. For the want of a nail…

At the end of 2012, some four years after this irritating episode, I learned at a rheumatology meeting some of the details of a new scheme to develop specialist centres for Behçet's patients. All a country rheumatologist now has to do to get authorisation for infliximab (which unsurprisingly has now been shown all over the place to work like magic) is discuss the case with one of the centre specialists and they will rubber-stamp it. There's nothing worse than being ahead of one's time.

And there was a third shameful jobsworth episode. A patient of mine with ankylosing spondylitis had, off her own bat, got herself funding for residential rehabilitation at the Royal National Hospital for Rheumatic Diseases in Bath. While there she had been entered into a trial of TNF blockade and had been on treatment for three years. At this time the biologic drugs had not been approved by NICE for use in AS, so when the trial came to an end I applied for individual funding from her Primary Care Trust. This was refused. She was devastated as she saw that her condition would slide inexorably backwards. The refusal seemed to me to be both uncharitable and stupid. I knew that NICE had already issued draft approval and it was only a matter of time before full approval was confirmed. After that the PCT would be legally obliged to cough up. But it stuck to its jobsworth principles, claiming that draft approval wasn't good enough. Having had considerable experience of NICE decisions I knew that the only ones that got disputed were those that NICE had turned down. For the sake of a few weeks, maybe months, the PCT was prepared to make my patient suffer.

However she did not take this lying down. Instead she went to the regional television news, made her case, got the media firmly on her side (I was turbulent again, but added a bit of gravitas), caused a major public fuss and got her treatment. I still find it hard to understand the inflexibility of the PCT in the circumstances, but it all caused her, and me, considerable annoyance and inconvenience. At least on the plus side it also caused great irritation to the PCT.

What nurses will do, and what they won't

I do not mean to generalise but it is a poor show when a student nurse refuses to give a sick patient a bedbath "because I have already learnt how to do it and don't need to do another for my book".

It is also a concern when you find that the only nurses who can do manual evacuations are the very senior ones, as the procedure isn't taught any more.[108]

However some nurses go the extra mile and are wonderful. At least I think so, but that's probably because they have the same old-fashioned values that I have and treat nursing as a vocation and not as a rather grubby job.

The Department of Health is not a Happy Place...

I attended a committee meeting in Skipton House at the Elephant & Castle in London, one of the Department's office blocks. It was a regional Clinical Excellence Awards committee,[109] and the previous day the Department had

---

[108] For the uninitiated, a Man Evac requires one to put a hand into the rectum and remove the faecal masses by hand. It is not a job for the faint of heart and it's advisable to wear two pairs of gloves; cost-cutting means that all too often gloves tear at the fingertips. I feel slightly nauseated just writing this. I would add that I have done this procedure myself, as have many colleagues of my vintage.

[109] Clinical Excellence Awards are given to senior hospital staff who have – excelled. Folk can nominate themselves and have to complete a fiendish form detailing their exploits (which has a set number of characters in each section box, so

published a discussion paper on the future of the awards, so I turned up having studied it with a magnifying glass off my mobile phone on the train, fully expecting a debate in committee once we had established who would and would not be recommended for awards in 2012-13. To my surprise I was the only member of the committee who had read it.

But I digress. After business was concluded the Bamji bladder required relief, so I headed off to the facilities. As I stood in growing comfort my aim was disturbed when I spotted a large notice on the side wall. It said, "Are you a victim of domestic abuse?" in large letters, and underneath gave some illustrations of what such abuse might constitute, and instructions on how to seek help.

Two thoughts crossed my mind.

1. It's pretty sad if Health Department civil servants are coming to work battered and bruised
2. It's even more sad if they are men.

I almost had to go outside and check I was in the right sex room (except there was a urinal in the corner, so I didn't).

..but a hospital can be. April Fool!

Sometimes one must lighten the atmosphere as an antidote to the overwhelming frustration of working in the NHS, or wading through treacle, which amounts to the same thing.

We had a particularly boring hospital general manager who was very keen on managerial innovation. Team Briefing was his first move, momentarily derailed by one of my colleagues, who left a pair of Y-Fronts on his desk labelled "Team Briefs".

It was before email. Christmas had passed and I was in poetic mode, and suddenly I had an idea. Thus it was that on April 1st a circular letter arrived in all consultants' and senior nurses' pigeonholes (you can see this was pre-email) over his moniker. The letter noted that he had been examining morale-boosting measures in industry and had discovered that in Japan factory workers sang the company song before starting their day. "I have

---

you cannot write a long essay) and there must be support from colleagues both clinical and managerial.

composed two songs" it continued "which are attached, and I would be grateful if you would indicate on the tear-off slip which you would prefer".

It was a devil to disguise origin, but I used standard issue NHS re-addressable envelopes and created false trails for each.

He had 16 replies, one accompanied by a serious letter about the lack of evidence of efficacy in Western culture.

I wish doctors (and all other staff) every success in similar endeavours and would love to hear about successful ones. Mind you, you will probably get a written warning for misusing the email system…

Fraud, Wolves and the Eleventh Commandment

As well as being utterly honest one should not cry wolf. Thus there are two vital things to be sure of; firstly, if you wish to reveal a story you should be absolutely and incontrovertibly certain you are in in possession of the facts, and secondly if you wish to conceal one you should be absolutely and incontrovertibly certain you will not be found out – the eleventh commandment. I have myself made the mistake of passing on unfounded rumours but I only did it once – lesson learned. However I have heard of instances where colleagues have been hounded, or even questioned under police caution, as the result of some attempt to "get" them for a perceived misdemeanour. Much as I am in favour of the NHS stamping out fraud I fear that the process is dangerous.[110] On the one hand a false accusation causes enormous distress to the accused (and to their families, as I discovered when I was sued) and may poison relationships ever after, while on the other the accuser will end up discredited. Later revelations may not be seen in the same light if the whistleblower has cried wolf before. Documents or witnesses are vital. I have related previously how a manager's attempt to dodge blame was belied by the email trail. I was angered to find one day that my car had been scraped in the car park by a consultant colleague reversing out of a space. He flatly denied responsibility until I produced statements from two staff who had witnessed his departure (and photos, taken by the hospital photographer, of the scrape on his car and the matching paint smear

---

[110] It amazes me when, on occasion, I hear of goings-on at the General Medical Council reporting serial misdemeanours over many years – in one case I was aware of the problems over all that time, and thus even more amazed that the revelations had taken so long to surface.

on mine). When I did the same thing to a different colleague I walked straight back in, found him, told him what had happened and suggested I would pay for the damage. He never took me up on the offer. Honesty wins respect.

Regrettably some of those involved in the management of wrongdoing have, in my opinion, adopted a Gestapo-like attitude which has on occasion verged on personal revenge, with improper processes, harassment, and serial attempts to force an issue when previous ones have failed for lack of evidence. My advice to those in charge of discipline in such instances is – back off and wait. We suspected a therapist of falsifying expenses – difficult to prove, but eventually they were tripped up when they called in sick, and the secretary had a phone call from another institution where they were moonlighting asking where they were. If an issue is real then another opportunity will arise. The appearance of threatening notices around hospitals, or waves of emails detailing how to shop one's colleagues, is somehow rather sinister but I think may contribute to the perception that we should be watching colleagues more closely than our patients.

That said, the large-scale removal of copper cabling by some maintenance staff from a redundant part of my old hospital might have been judged not unreasonable, not least as it might all have gone on a skip and to landfill otherwise, but it was somewhat foolish of those involved not to ensure that all their efforts to remove it through a basement corridor were not captured in almost every detail by the hospital CCTV system…

Reinventing wheels etc

In the British Medical Journal of 23rd April 2016 were listed the finalists for the BMJ Neurology team of the year awards, which included the Multiple Sclerosis team of University College London Hospital (UCLH) for its integrated service.

Reinvention of the wheel? Failure of institutional memory? Left hand not knowing what right hand is doing? All three possibilities came to mind when I read the nomination which "to everyone's surprise" showed that urinary infections were the commonest cause of admission in patients with MS.

I am certainly surprised it was a surprise. Indeed when I read it I was almost speechless. I have known and taught this for nearly 30 years. I took over a Young Disabled Unit in 1985. Over the next ten years I and my multidisciplinary team turned it from a long-stay unit with 15 residents to a dynamic rehabilitation unit with some 300 clients, the majority of whom had

MS. We provided a regular inpatient respite service, a helpline and regular outpatient review, which was supplemented in later years with bladder ultrasound. The superb nursing staff were also alert to admissions of our clients to acute beds, from which they would be extracted as soon as possible – or at the very least they would make a trip to the acute ward to advise. I taught all the trainee doctors that patients presenting to A&E with a sudden deterioration in their MS had an infection (usually urinary, but sometimes chest) until proved otherwise. While deterioration was rapid, so was recovery if effective treatment was instituted rapidly. I might add that, as a clinical point that will save some lives if anyone reads this, some patients with an acute infection regularly developed severe hyponatraemia (low sodium) which we attributed to acute adrenal insufficiency, and recovered with hypertonic saline and hydrocortisone; whether this phenomenon was related to previous high dose steroid treatment for relapses we never did determine.

Just to remind y'all, James fell through this net.

We also provided an effective pressure sore service. Regular physiotherapy helped prevent contractures and maintain mobility. Occupational therapy home visits were a *sine qua non*. Our service was entirely integrated. Our local district nurses involved in home care regularly exchanged information. If a patient "went off" suddenly then infection testing was arranged at home. Not infrequently I would write the antibiotic prescription sight unseen. Unit emergency admissions were organised not by GPs but by family or the district nurses by direct contact. In this way we actually kept MS patients out of acute hospital beds. All of this was done without any input from neurologists.

To return to my opening paragraph it appears to me that the UCLH team had reinvented the wheel. I regret that my teaching in a suburban district general hospital never permeated to the centre to provide a lasting institutional memory, but perhaps the most damning indictment is that, until relatively recently, it was rehabilitationists who dealt with long-term MS patients and not neurologists, who concentrated on diagnosis (once made, there was little treatment, so many, though not all, lost interest). So the crossover of information from left to right hand was as limited as in a patient whose corpus callosum has been transected.[111] It is thus encouraging to see the

---

[111] Right and left halves of the brain communicate through this central structure. Divide it, as was done for some severe cases of epilepsy, and you cut one off from the other. Then show coloured discs to the right side of the brain (left visual field). It knows the answer but cannot tell the speech centre on the other side, so this has to guess. If it gets it wrong the right side gets agitated, which creates enough electrical

growing interest and enthusiasm of neurologists in integrated long-term management.

Rehabilitation takes time, as anyone who is involved in neurological work will tell you. Like with buses during the Second World War, whence this poster:

REHABILITATION

59,750 windows in trains, buses, trolleybuses and trams were damaged by enemy action, apart from those on totally blitzed vehicles. The wartime substitutes are being replaced by glass—but

IT TAKES TIME

Though our model was highly effective, and much appreciated by patients and their families, it was expensive. The Unit kept afloat as much through my political lobbying as through its care success. Within a year of my retirement it had been closed down.

****

activity for the left side to realise it has erred, and then gives the alternative, correct answer.

Following the evidence base is excellent – or is it?

Evidence based medicine or EBM as it is commonly known, is self-explanatory. You base decisions on evidence. However, many management decisions are made on no evidence – or, to be fair, bits of evidence that do not add up. Furthermore there are numerous examples of clinical trials which have produced good evidence that cannot be relied upon.[112] If, for example, A leads to B, and A also leads to C, that does not necessarily mean that B leads to C. Statins (A) reduce cholesterol (B). Statins appear to reduce coronary artery mortality (C). But it's wrong to assume that reducing cholesterol reduces coronary artery mortality because statins also have an anti-inflammatory effect (D) and so it could be D that leads to C.

Two examples in my own specialty come to mind. In one case a lack of anatomical knowledge prejudiced the outcome (also true of the second) and in the third a failure to understand exponential data meant that like was not compared with like.
Bear these examples in mind when you look at any clinical trial. And don't believe a word of those fancy adverts for cosmetics that quote "trials" which turn out to be a survey of 30 people.

Do you know your anatomy (1)

Colleagues in a neighbouring Trust performed a sequential audit on the benefit of steroid injection for frozen shoulder – technically known as capsulitis, and basically a severe inflammation of the joint between long arm bone (humerus) and shoulder blade (scapula) – the glenohumeral joint. The injections were administered by a single practitioner, and the results suggested little or no benefit. The conclusion was that frozen shoulder injection was a waste of time. But - the injections had been given by the lateral approach, which enters another part of the shoulder mechanism – the joint under the tip of the shoulder blade (subacromial joint). This and the glenohumeral joint are quite separate unless the main shoulder muscle, the rotator cuff, has torn – an anatomical fact not appreciated by the study sponsors, probably because rheumatologists don't read orthopaedic textbooks and have never sat in orthopaedic clinics run by the doyen of shoulder surgery, the late Lipmann Kessel. So, as one can reasonably suppose that injection of one joint will only rarely have any effect on the

---

[112] For more examples, see Malcolm Kendrick's *"Doctoring Data"*

other because the joints don't communicate unless there is a muscle tear, if the wrong joint had been injected as here the study was useless.

This failure led to some debate. It became clear that there was disagreement on the management of shoulder problems that extended further to the actual accurate assessment of them. We set up a little study which showed that even experts did not agree on an anatomical diagnosis even when they saw the patients together.[113] There are a number of published trials which have fallen into the same trap – but are still adduced as evidence when people attempt to assess the efficacy of joint injections. The first thing you must do is ensure that you are actually treating the part that needs treating.

LOLA © Todd Clark. Reprinted with permission of Andrews McMeel Syndication for UFS. All rights reserved.

Do you know your anatomy (2)

People are still treating sacroiliac joint strain. This is supposedly a cause of low back pain and diagnosed by finding – pain over the sacroiliac joints. Injection treatment relieves symptoms. QED.

I am not so sure. A registrar in our department at the old Middlesex Hospital, when I was a senior registrar, came to me asking my views on this syndrome. He could see no logic in it. Inflammation and infection – yes; you can see changes on X-ray and scans and intrinsically you know that pain could result. But how do you *strain* a rigid joint – so stable that if you are in a dreadful car accident the pelvic bones are more likely to fracture than the SIJ disrupt? Also, despite the book descriptions of how to inject the joint, he was not clear, anatomically, how it was possible to get a needle into it. So if injections seemed to work, how could this be?

---

[113] AN Bamji, CC Erhardt, RP Price & P Williams, *The Painful Shoulder. Can Consultants agree?* Brit J. Rheumatol 1996; **35**: 1172-74

142

He set up a little experiment. He decided to do a traceable injection. Taking a series of corpses (necessary permissions were obtained) he performed injections by marking out the surface anatomy as per the books, and then injected under X-ray control using Indian ink. Then he dissected down to see where the ink was.[114]

He did not get into a single sacroiliac joint. The ink was everywhere but. Interestingly some got into the venous plexuses and spread up in the vertebral veins but most spread out over the surface of the pelvis under the attachments of the gluteal muscles.

Could it be, therefore, that sacroiliac region pain is actually a gluteal strain syndrome? This little piece of evidence suggests so.[115] If pain is in a particular area that has more than one anatomical structure, one should beware of deciding it comes from one and not another.

I devised a simple scheme based on experience for trying more accurately to diagnose back pain (it's not perfect but it will do). It depends on a simple list of questions shown in the table opposite. There may be some unfamiliar terms to the lay person; a spondylolysis is where there is a fracture in the vertebral ring, and a spondylolisthesis means that the lysis (or break) has slipped. Ankylosing spondylitis is an inflammatory condition in the spine. Osteoporosis means the bones are thin, and more likely to fracture or collapse. Osteomalacia results from Vitamin D deficiency. Cauda equina claudication is a potentially life-changing condition where something is pressing on the lower lumbar and sacral nerve roots. Untreated this can lead to paraplegia and incontinence; if symptoms are in this column it's an emergency.

Tick the boxes and then you can apply treatment more scientifically – although, as I have said, much back pain requires nothing as a treatment. Applying treatment appropriate for a disc prolapse won't work if it isn't a disc prolapse. Etc.

That said I developed sudden, acute and incapacitating back pain and applied my schema to myself. It didn't fit.

---

[114] This was before the development of ultrasound examination which enables you to see where the needle is.
[115] To my everlasting regret he never wrote it up

Seven questions to help identify the cause of back pain

	Disc pain	Facet joint pain	Iliolumbar ligament strain	Gluteal muscle strain	Spondylolysis/ listhesis	Ankylosing spondylitis	Cauda equina claudication	Osteoporosis & osteomalacia	Malignancy
Where is the pain centred?	Central back	To one side	Back: to one side (focal)	Buttock	Central back	Back	Leg (root distribution)	Back (diffuse)	Site of secondary
Where does it go?	Down leg; root distribution	Into buttock and down leg; referred	Into buttock	To hip and down leg	Referred into buttock	Up and down	Root	Up and down	Remains local
How does it go?	Shoots; associated parasthesiae	Diffuse, ill-localised	Vague spread	Vague spread	Worse with exercise	Vague	Slow onset with exercise	Vague, severe if crush fracture	Sickening ache
What makes it worse?	Flexion, coughs and sneezes	Extension, rising from sitting, prolonged standing	Exercise, twisting	Exercise, getting up in the morning	Flexion, exercise	Rest	Walking, especially uphill	Constant	Constant
What relieves it?	Rest (lying)	Rest (lying), rest, flexion, walking	Rest	Rest	Rest (lying)	Exercise, NSAIDs	Stop walking, flexion	Exercise (unless crush)	NSAIDs, potent analgesics
Is it bad at night?	Sometimes (if spasm ++)	Yes	No	No	Sometimes	Yes	No	Often	Always ++
Is there morning stiffness?	Not a lot	Yes	Little	No	No, it's usually the best time	Yes ++	No	No	No

You may not be clear if a drug is working...

...but if you stop it, and everything goes haywire, then you can be sure that it was. This is sometimes the only way to persuade a patient to stay on their pills.

The converse applies. If a patient appears to have side-effects, and you stop a drug, and everything returns to normal, you can be fairly sure of cause and effect – and make certain by a re-challenge that produces the same problem. I did this with statins. More fool I.

You may not be clear if a drug is working (2)...

...and you rely on the evidence as is. However the evidence can change. My biochemistry professor used to say that medical knowledge had a half-life of seven years, so by that time half of what we had been taught might be wrong. Only we don't know which half.

There are dozens of examples of this with drugs. Take bisphosphonates and osteoporosis. There is no doubt that you can prove that their administration may stop the progression of bone loss. However as time goes by other things surface; thus there has been a significant scare over osteonecrosis of the jaw, and undoubtedly there are many patients who have significant side-effects, either with dreadful indigestion or worse (hence the instruction to wash it down with lots of fluid and then stay upright for half an hour) or acute allergic reactions to the infusions designed to get round this. Reports have appeared of an increased risk of unusual site hip fractures in people on bisphosphonates.[116] So the drug you give causes the very thing you are trying to stop. Not good. By the same token the elderly patient (more prone to fracture) has been put on blood pressure pills. So when he or she stands up suddenly they pass out and fall over. So before starting, ask why (actually with the blood pressure thing you may be risking trouble, as narrower vessels need a higher driving pressure, so you might be at greater risk of a stroke, or coronary, if the pressure drops too far.). The owner of our local dry cleaners worked that one out so it's odd that doctors cannot.

---

[116] S Agarwal *et al. Risk of atypical femoral fracture with long-term use of alendronate (bisphosphonates): a systemic review of literature.* Acta Orthopaedica Belgica 2010; 76 (5): 567-71

Clinical trials: fact or fiction?

Let's follow on from that and gently hum "As Time Goes By". Most
newspapers will report the results of clinical trials as if they are gospel.
Remember MMR and the Wakefield research? Not just report but total
hysteria. And it took a while before the whole thing was debunked as fraud,
after which there was more hysteria, except this was mostly from the papers
that had shouted loudest to start with and had been shown to be gullible
fools. [117]

Beware.

Many years ago my friend from medical school now a Professor (in those
days I think most people would have thought I would end up as the Prof, and
he as the medical politician) analysed a series of trials of non-steroidal anti-
inflammatory drugs, showing that the methodology of most of them was
flawed.[118] In the same year (1982) I went to a company symposium abroad
launching a new drug; this was not the ill-famed Orient Express trip, but
much gin was tasted, as the meeting was in Amsterdam.[119] This may not be
quite as bad as it looks, because it was cheaper to fly all the British
rheumatologists to Amsterdam than it was to fly the much smaller number of
worldwide experts to London. The pharmacodynamics of the drug had been
tested on, I think, eight normal subjects. Seven were very similar in terms of
the plasma half-life. The eighth was quite different. In the presentation the
pharmacologist blithely told the audience that the outlier had been ignored in
the analysis of the data. I got up and asked how it was scientific to exclude
over 12% of the sample; perhaps the wayward subject had some genetic
difference that meant they metabolised the drug differently. He couldn't
possibly assume that this one was unique and, if they had done another

---

[117] See Brian Deer's articles in the British Medical Journal (2011:342:c7001)

[118] JR Kirwan, *Clinical Trials: Why not do them properly?* Ann Rheum Dis
1982;41:551-552

[119] For those not in the know, a group of rheumatologists were treated to a trip on the
"Orient Express" to Venice as part of a new drug promotion. This was exposed in a
"Panorama" television programme and commented upon – adversely, unsurprisingly
– in Parliament. See https://api.parliament.uk/historic-
hansard/commons/1983/jan/27/opren (accessed 9th August 2019). David Crouch,
MP for Canterbury, said "The programme also described the apparent junketing of a
company—not this company, but an Italian company—taking the Orient express to
Venice to talk to doctors, rather than talking to them in Manchester—as I think one
of the doctors said could have been done, although he added, with a smile, "I don't
think that I would have gone to Manchester, rather than to Venice." Even so, it
stretches my credulity to think that a junket on the Orient express is the way to
promote an idea among rheumatology consultants. It is a pity."

hundred tests, who was to know whether another 11 subjects would have produced the same result? Much muttering and harrumphing went on. I ignored the rest of the programme and went sightseeing. You cannot analyse only the data that fits your model, and similar selective data manipulation has been exposed in other large-scale trials. Indeed it now appears that the whole heart disease-cholesterol hypothesis may be based on inappropriate data selection. I look at statins in some detail later, but the original study underpinning the cholesterol – heart disease hypothesis done by Ancel Keys concentrated on data from seven countries. In fact the study looked at 22 countries, but Keys chose those that fitted his hypothesis. Had he chosen others, the results would have shown the complete opposite.

We now know that there are a number of drugs whose metabolism may be different in some people, sometimes as the result of enzyme differences and sometimes because age may alter response. A classic example of the latter was benoxaprofen, launched with great fanfare as a new non-steroidal anti-inflammatory drug in the early 1980s. After a short while it became apparent that elderly patients were dying from liver toxicity.[120] This had not been picked up as a risk, partly because the problem was uncommon. Think about this. If the risk of a serious side-effect is 1 in 1000 you may need to treat 3000 patients or more before you twig that something is up. Any individual clinician will probably use a drug like benoaxprofen in a hundred, max, so will only have a 1 in 10 chance of seeing the effect once. But in fact elderly patients were never included in drug trials at the time, so the risk of accumulation went unrecognised in the pre-launch trials. The drug was withdrawn, with as much press hype to kill it as there had been to launch it.[121] One might suppose, though, that the initial excitement led to considerable numbers of patients being given the drug in a short time, which reduced the lag time to discovery of the adverse event.

In similar vein thalidomide, which caused an epidemic of birth defects, was never tested on pregnant women (in case it might have caused birth defects, perhaps). Babies take nine months to appear; thus many pregnant women got thalidomide before any of the effects on limb development appeared – and of course there was a further lag time before astute clinicians put two and two together. Just because there is no evidence does not mean it won't appear later. Strangely thalidomide would probably have been withdrawn anyway because it was found to cause significant peripheral nerve damage at a

---

[120] HM Taggart, JM Alderdice, *Fatal cholestatic jaundice in elderly patients taking benoxaprofen.* Br Med J 1982; 284: 1372.
[121] Oddly enough I wrote a letter to a medical journal warning that the hype was overblown, and that longer-term use might reveal a hidden downside. The editor refused to publish it, even though nearly the entire department had signed it.

higher-than-acceptable level. Which raises the interesting question of whether limb development in utero is dependent upon properly growing peripheral nerves…

You cannot take heterogeneous groups and lump them together for data crunching. A trial requires statistical power – that is, you must have enough subjects in the trial to be sure that what you demonstrate cannot have happened by chance. So it may be tempting to get numbers quickly and do a trial of a so-called disease-modifying anti-rheumatic drug in rheumatoid arthritis by collecting patients at all stages of disease, from onset to late stage. However this is unreasonable, especially if you pick an endpoint or measure that may not be the same for each group.

In RA one of the measures used is the rate of progression of joint erosions, which you can see on X-ray as little holes in the bone ends of small joints. These represent inflammatory changes that have eaten the cartilage joint surface and extended into the bone, as the graph overleaf shows. However their development, which starts to occur after about six months, follows a pattern of a steep start that tails off. It follows that the slope of the curve (ie the rate of change) is much higher early in the disease than late, and the natural history alone determines that the rate of progression between 6 months and 3 years is higher than at 10-20 years' duration. See the graph. So if you expect the rate of change to be modified by a drug, you cannot lump together people with early RA, where erosions increase significantly, and those with longstanding disease where the natural rate of change may have dropped almost to zero. Patients in this latter group will exhibit no change whether you treat them or not. But a large number of trials did exactly that and are thus useless. This has been recognised in recent years, although I have been going on about it for 30 or so. But many early trials are still quoted.

Of course modern imaging has rendered X-ray erosion counts largely irrelevant, as one can see much earlier changes in the cartilage and joint lining (synovium) using MRI or ultrasound scans. But the principle is what matters here.

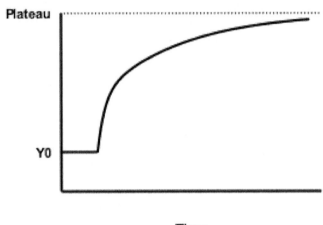

Exponential decay curve. Time is plotted along the bottom, the number of erosions seen vertically. The flat start represents the first six months of disease, when erosions don't normally appear. The slope at the top (the rate of change) approaches zero. Patients taken from the right-hand side, with longer disease duration, have a natural rate of progression much less than on the left side. If you are trying to decide if a drug alters the rate, and it doesn't alter much anyway, you will find no effect

Even today the problem persists. Biologic agents (which are special antibodies, or stick to sites that important inflammation-producing chemicals stick, so blocking them) have revolutionised the management of rheumatoid arthritis. But they are very, very expensive. They compare well to existing treatments – but in fact the comparisons are not all they seem to be, as the comparator treatments are themselves suboptimal. To compare a biologic against methotrexate, when we know from lots of research that methotrexate alone is not as effective as in combination (with hydroxychloroquine, sulfasalazine and steroids) is to guarantee that biologics look better than they are. People (including John Kirwan, who started the whole critique of trials) have been batting on about this for years, but some new trials still pay no attention.

Another fault is in a misunderstanding of comparative sequential trials. In these, a plot of each patient is made on a graph depending on whether drug A is better than drug B, or vice-versa. A plot enables one to tell, and you can change the confidence limits, when one is better than the other. However, if the graph continues and fails to show a difference, it doesn't mean there is no difference, merely that you have failed to prove a difference. Many such trials are interpreted, however, as showing no difference.

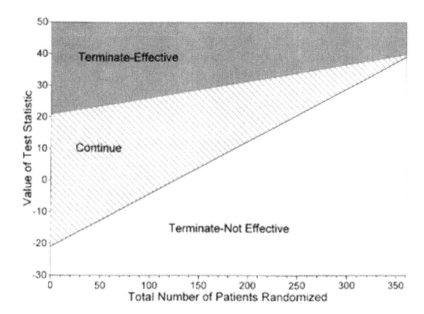

Sequential plot. Each time drug A performs better than drug B (here a placebo) the plot moves up, and if B is better than A it moves down. As soon as the plot crosses one or other of the marked out boundaries then statistically one (in this case A) is better than the other. If it doesn't, you have not proved there is a difference, but neither have you proved that they are the same; carry on long enough and it may cross the line later (from M Ross Bullock *et al*, Outcome Measures for Clinical Trials in Neurotrauma: Review of Outcome Measures in Clinical Trials: http://www.medscape.com/viewarticle/439169_2 (Accessed 7th September 2018)

As I have said previously, medicine and science are littered with trials that are redone and later found to be false. At worst this is due to fraud, at best to some unrealised problem; in the latter case a substantial body of research in the late 1970s, on which several PhDs were based, suggested that rheumatoid arthritis might be due to Epstein-Barr virus infection, until further work proved that there was a contaminant in the assay the researchers were using. There is good evidence that positive trials are more likely to appear in print than negative ones, and in recent years some drug companies have been taken to task for ignoring or even possibly concealing adverse events found in trials. More recently – and the concept was aired for a lay audience on BBC Radio 4's "More or less" programme (13th May 2011) – some folk have cottoned on to Nicholas Taleb's proposition that by probability alone a run of success may be followed by a run of failure. Hence the "Past performance is not an indicator of future performance" that tails every financial advert. Similarly people have begun to see that, just because five trials show a drug has benefit, there is no guarantee that the next 30 will do the same. Indeed some nasty long-term side-effects may emerge as well.

It is often difficult to get to the raw data in trials. The British Medical Journal began a campaign to ensure that drug company trial data is widely available, and unredacted. Ben Goldacre has written a book about this and other issues with trials.[122] Likewise it is not always clear (though more recently journals insist on a conflict of interest statement) whether researchers have any vested interest in the trial they are doing. If they have, they may be less receptive to negative reports. Sometimes this can lead to long delays in the release of information that requires a product to be withdrawn.[123]

Back in the 1950's it was discovered that if you irradiated the spine of someone with ankylosing spondylitis (an inflammation in the small joints and ligament edges causing back pain and stiffness and ending up with spinal fusion) you could significantly alleviate the symptoms. The treatment was used a lot. Then it became apparent that patients seemed to be at high risk of developing leukaemia.[124] The treatment was rapidly abandoned. However in the early 1980s the then Professor of Oncology at the Middlesex Hospital, Roger Berry, thought it might be interesting to review those patients treated at the Middlesex – some 1500 in all. We also reviewed the fatal cases reported by Court-Brown and Doll.[125] What was interesting was that a significant number appeared to have been misdiagnosed. AS tends to present in the early part of life and burns out. A number of patients had another condition, diffuse spinal hyperostosis, which is not due to inflammation; these patients tended to have treatment later, and it was apparent from a review of the leukaemia sufferers in the Court-Brown and Doll study that the risk of leukaemia induction rose significantly with the age of first treatment. Furthermore it was possible that another treatment, phenylbutazone (a powerful non-steroidal anti-inflammatory drug known to produce blood dyscrasias) could have been responsible for some of the reported cases. One might conclude therefore that if you excluded the late receivers (who either did not have AS or had "burned out") and adjusted for phenylbutazone exposure the risk of blood disorders was actually quite low – and that perhaps a valuable treatment had been abandoned too early and for

---

[122] Ben Goldacre,. *Bad Pharma*. 4th Estate, 2012

[123] A good example is discussed by Deborah Cohen (*Out of Joint*. BMJ 2011; 342:d2905); this also raises questions about the regulation of devices, which is different from drugs, and needs tightening up

[124] WM Court-Brown, R Doll, *Leukaemia and aplastic anaemia in patients irradiated for ankylosing spondylitis.* HMSO, 1957, later (!) published as a scientific paper (J Radiol Prot. 2007 Dec;27(4B):B15-B154). Patients from 81 centres were surveyed.

[125] AN Bamji, RJ Berry, B Windeyer, *The treatment of Ankylosing Spondylitis with radiotherapy: report of a long-term follow-up study.* Brit Soc Radiol congress, April 1982; RSM Rheum Section 1983

spurious reasons. Certainly our reviewed patients were happy with their results. That said, in the Middlesex patients nearly a quarter had developed skin cancers within the irradiated area along the spine, and that alone might have been enough to stop use (although the particular cancers are not fatal). One could also argue about other possible confounders, such as lifestyle issues – smoking in particular.

Lastly there is deception in the reporting of trials. Benefits are reported as relative risk reductions, while side-effects are reported as absolute risk reductions. I will enlarge on this later, but in essence such recording overplays benefit and underplays risk.

The moral of this discussion is that you should treat trials with caution. Have they been well done? Is the sample big enough to prove the point? Has the right statistical analysis been done? Is the raw data available for independent review? If one starts to be critical, evidence-based medicine starts to look a little flaky.

That said there can be little excuse for practising "medicine" for which no evidence of efficacy exists at all – at least, not any that can be specifically attributed to the modality. Much of so-called alternative medicine falls into this category. Proponents of homeopathy cannot exactly explain why nothing can work, and it is possible that it's the time devoted, and kindly approach of practitioners, that does the trick. But reflexology, iridology, crystal therapy and so forth are nothing but mumbo-jumbo and a false understanding of them (or belief in them) may delay sensible and even life-saving "conventional" therapy. I have had many such patients. It is quite terrifying – and in the most part there is no comeback when someone comes to harm by delay. As Margaret McCartney suggests, we must purge medicine of its quackery. [126]

Statins are bad for you[127]

As a rheumatologist, my job was to help people with joint problems and arthritic complaints. So it was with some irony that I diagnosed myself with tenosynovitis - a severe tendon inflammation I often treat in my patients.

---

[126] M McCartney, *The scam of integrative medicine*. BMJ 2011;343:d4446

[127] This is a slightly adapted version of a piece that appeared in the "Daily Mail" in 2009. Following it I had a deluge of letters describing similar experiences; not all, clearly, were statin problems but all railed against the difficulty of getting their doctor to listen and understand that there really was a problem.

But the greater irony was that this chronically painful problem had been triggered by the statins I'd been prescribed to lower my cholesterol. The very pill that was supposed to be improving my health was actually making it worse.

Statins are the 'wonder drugs' enthusiastically prescribed for people whose cholesterol is considered to be significantly raised. Yes, it's generally accepted that if you've had a heart attack, statins are an important tool in preventing another. But the problem is that these drugs are being handed out willy-nilly, with very little apparent benefit.

Yet many patients face debilitating side-effects in return for the marginal protection statins can offer against heart attacks. And it's time that the medical profession recognised this.

Put simply, though people are put on statins for a reason, is that reason in any way *reasonable?*

I discovered the link between statins and rheumatic side-effects quite by chance. My attack of tendon inflammation occurred at the front of my shin - a highly unusual place for tenosynovitis - so I decided to do some research into what could have triggered this. I was amazed to discover the only other similar case was linked to a patient on statins.

Following a high cholesterol reading of 9.2 a couple of months before, I'd been put on the drug. Intrigued by the connection, I decided to stop taking my statin to see what happened. Within a couple of weeks, the pain had gone. I went back to my GP and, over successive months, tried various statins. Each caused terrible problems, including night cramp, muscle pain and general fatigue. In fact, I became so tired I couldn't lift anything when I was gardening or even walk the half-mile from my home to the centre of town. Yet whenever I halted the medication, my symptoms disappeared within a few weeks.[128]

I began to realise many of my patients with musculoskeletal conditions such as polymyalgia - pain, stiffness, and tenderness in the muscles - were on statins. When I advised them to stop taking their medication, their problems went away.

---

[128] Years later I have realised that the debilitating effects took a good three years to disappear completely.

Was this reckless? Not at all. Statins only marginally increase protection for the heart - but that protection comes at a price. It is commonly stated that statins reduce coronary risk by 50%. Fake news – because this reduction is in *relative* risk. If a patient has heart disease and high cholesterol, the chance of their dying from a heart attack over four to six years is about 6 per cent. A reduction in risk of 50% if they're given a statin every day equates to a new risk of a heart attack of roughly 3 per cent. That is a gain of three per cent, not fifty. What matters is *absolute* risk. If the payback is a life of musculoskeletal misery, is it worth it? And what about the idea that most elderly people should be on statins? By their very survival, they have proved they are the fittest. Should they be given pills to prevent a condition they don't have, nor are likely to get?

The much-quoted JUPITER study found that daily treatment with rosuvastatin cut the rate of heart problems and deaths by 44 per cent. Crucially, the study involved those whose cholesterol was healthy and so would not qualify for statin treatment in the UK and many other countries. But all those who took part had high levels of a protein (C-reactive protein, or CRP for short) which is linked to heart disease.

This study was pushed as evidence that our own drug watchdog, NICE, should bring down its risk threshold for statins. This would mean millions more would be put on the things. In fact, JUPITER suggests that rather than raising the numbers of statins, we should be looking at the role of CRP. Furthermore, where is the evidence to show that if your cholesterol is seven and you lower it by two, you dramatically reduce your risk of heart attack? There is none.

Branded cholesterol drugs cost the NHS between £10 and £25 per patient per month.[129] I know that money could be better spent treating the millions who are actually ill, including the many patients with rheumatoid arthritis. They are being refused treatment with effective medication such as anti-TNFs because it is too expensive. Of course, if you take statins without any problems then there's no reason to abandon the treatment. But the idea of their widespread prescription, given the cost, minimal (and questionable) benefit and potential side-effects, is just nonsense. As a patient who has thrown his statins away, I'm happy to take my chances.

---

[129] A new class of injectables which dramatically lower cholesterol costs thousands per year. Interestingly, while they cause the cholesterol level to drop substantially, there is no evidence that this reduces heart attacks. Which makes one wonder about the whole rationale of cholesterol-lowering drugs – see later.

Statins of course get co-prescribed with antidiabetic medication and anti-hypertensives. So it's not unusual for patients to pitch up on five drugs (blood pressure pills are like the No 73 bus – they come in threes). Which makes for a big drug bill. So it is satisfying to learn that recent evidence suggests that many people are receiving completely unnecessary blood pressure therapy because they have what's called "white-coat hypertension" – that is, they get anxious about going to the doctor to get it checked, and so it goes up in the surgery. It's cheaper to use expensive 24-hour monitors as it saves substantially on the drug bill. I can remember being asked to see one of my arthritis patients who had been admitted as an emergency with episodic loss of consciousness. Many investigations had proved negative. I was, of course, only supposed to be dealing with his arthritis, but he volunteered that it was odd, wasn't it, that he always seemed to "go out" when he stood up. His chart indicated he was on the usual three BP pills. I measured his blood pressure lying down and it was at the low end of normal. When I stood him up it disappeared. The technical term for this is postural hypotension. We stopped his anti-hypertensives and he never fainted again.

This is another example of how treating to tickboxes causes problems. Those that do need to bear in mind, as I have said many times, that guidelines are just that, and new research may completely overturn practice. Hysterical and slavish behaviours can cause harm. Another example is the cardiovascular risk from non-steroidal anti-inflammatory drugs (NSAIDs). They do increase the risk but double a very small number is still a very small number (relative versus absolute again). And if the "risk" of not using NSAIDs is that the patient cannot function then you may have reduced one risk by increasing another. I fear that pharmacists are to blame for much of this behaviour; rightly they want patients to follow the rules, but wrongly they do not have enough insight into patient care to understand that their well-meaning interventions may not only be dangerous, but interfere with the trust between doctor and patient.

Advertising for dietary measures recommended to lower cholesterol borders on the ridiculous. One series of adverts had patients (or actors, more likely) describing how taking product X has lowered their cholesterol from 4.12 to 3.68, or similar. They go on to describe how much safer they feel. I am not aware of any laboratory that routinely measures cholesterol to two decimal places, and the reduction spoken is from within the normal range to within the normal range. So they aren't really any safer, and the precision of the results is spurious. I thought about complaining to the Advertising Standards Agency but suspected they wouldn't understand. Anyway for some reason the ads have vanished.

It amuses me that we are enjoined to eat less butter. Fair enough if it is just butter (probably not, but let that pass). Take a look at your tub of spreadable butter and you will discover it contains a lot of rapeseed oil, which is why it spreads. And the so-called "lighter" spreads contain even more, and quite a lot of water to boot...[130]

Meanwhile you might like the cartoon by Randy Glasbergen, below...

"With this new drug, cholesterol forms *outside* of the body, where it can't clog the arteries."

Statins are probably not very good for you, either

Following my adventures with statin side-effects I discovered that there is a group of Galileans THINCS, as on the last page) who have been questioning the research into heart disease at a fundamental level. We have met with much opprobrium, because our views are not mainstream. Indeed we have been compared to the disgraced Andrew Wakefield, whose work that put fear into parents over the combined measles/mumps/rubella vaccine was found to be fraudulent. Go to the Internet and read the works of Uffe Ravnskov, Malcolm Kendrick, Aseem Malhotra and Zoe Harcombe. All that they and I have done is to pick holes in the cholesterol – heart disease hypothesis, which I will abbreviate as CHDH, on the basis of a number of *facts.*

---

[130] Visit the website of the International Network of Cholesterol Skeptics (THINCS for short) to keep up to date with the growing evidence that lowering cholesterol is a waste of time,

156

Be reminded that facts are facts. Also that if you come across an *observation* that contradicts a *theory*, it is likely that the *theory* is wrong if the *observation* is irrefutable.

Let me start with a few facts.

1. Statins have a small effect on mortality from heart disease
2. There are potent cholesterol-lowering drugs which have no effect on heart disease
3. The original findings of a link between cholesterol levels and heart disease were based on a study that selected only the observations that fitted the theory. Had another subset of the research work been used, there was minimal effect
4. The proponents of the CHDH rubbished the work, and destroyed the reputation of a careful clinician, John Yudkin, who believed that sugar, and not fat, was important in generating increased mortality. As cholesterol is produced in the liver from carbohydrate his belief had a scientific background
5. Many proponents of the CHDH have had their own research funded by drug companies that make statins
6. Despite new guidelines requiring researchers to release trial data for independent analysis, some proponents of the CHDH who have done trials have refused to release their data
7. Many of the early trials relied on in study reviews have flaws in subject selection, randomisation, allowance for confounding factors or a combination of these. Meta-analyses that include such studies, but are widely quoted, are thus useless
8. The CHDH relies on a supposition that the coronary artery plaque seen in heart disease, and made of cholesterol, is there because there is a high level in the bloodstream, and thus that lowering the blood level will cause such plaques to be dissolved. That a large molecule like cholesterol cannot pass through an intact blood vessel wall has been ignored (if it could, it ought to be found in veins as well as arteries, but it isn't)
9. However it is increasingly evident that cholesterol plaque deposits result from inflammation of the vessel walls, with damage to the inner lining (intima). The body's healing process is less than perfect and cholesterol deposition is a consequence of inadequate or imperfect healing. A major factor for vessel blockage appears to be due to irregularity of vessel walls, which cause blood flow turbulence and in the presence of low-grade inflammation results in small platelet clots forming, which provoke further healing attempts that eventually block the vessel completely. This may be aggravated if calcium is deposited in the plaque

– the reason why this happens is not clear, but probably has nothing to do with cholesterol

10. Inflammation in general is a risk factor for heart disease. Thus in rheumatoid arthritis the risk of developing heart disease is very high – but drops back towards normal if the arthritis is treated successfully. However, when this is achieved blood cholesterol levels rise. If the CHDH hypothesis was true, this is an inexplicable oxymoron
11. Statins appear to have a small anti-inflammatory effect
12. Ergo, any small reduction in coronary disease mortality is likely to be due to this effect, not least because new (and expensive) substances that precipitately lower cholesterol have no effect on mortality. In fact (although it is difficult to prove, because the big pharma trials testing it were terminated early and abruptly without explanation) it appears possible that mortality in patients given the drug was higher.

It is apparent therefore that there is a shedload of contradictions that render the CHDH an impossibility and a large number of trials are badly flawed. Yes, statins reduce cholesterol, but this is an epiphenomenon unconnected to their real action, which is as an anti-inflammatory substance. A leads to B, A leads to C, but B does not lead to C. Cholesterol-lowering drugs that do not have that anti-inflammatory effect *do not work*. Some artificial fats may be villains – but because they provoke inflammation. Overall the major risk factors for coronary artery disease are smoking and obesity – which latter is not due to vast fat intake, whether "good" or "bad" but to too many calories, most of which in the seriously obese come from carbohydrate. What is worse, if you eat lots of fat your appetite is suppressed; if you eat lots of carbohydrate you get an insulin rush which hangs over, and you feel hungry quicker, so you eat even more. You can try this for yourself. Eat a large bag of potato crisps and see how long it is before you want something else. Then drink (or eat, if it's thick enough) the same number of calories in a pot of double cream. I bet you will feel full for a long time.

As I have said, any hypothesis is only valid if there are no facts that destroy it. There are now so many facts in the way of the cholesterol-heart disease hypothesis that it must be consigned to the dustbin. What did I say my biochemistry professor taught us? Half our knowledge will be found to be wrong – but we don't know which half.[131]

---

[131] For a full (and readable) exposition of this brief diatribe see Malcolm Kendrick, *The Great Cholesterol Con.* 2007; P Rosch (ed) *Fat and Cholesterol Don't Cause Heart Attacks,* Columbus Publishing, 2016; or look at Zoe Harcombe's website (www.zoeharcombe.com).

HAMBONE by Mike Flanagan

I CAN'T SLEEP !

I ADVISE YOU TO EAT SOMETHING BEFORE GOING TO BED.

BUT A MONTH AGO YOU ADVISED ME NOT TO EAT BEFORE GOING TO BED !

MEDICAL SCIENCE HAS TAKEN GREAT LEAPS FORWARD IN THE LAST FOUR WEEKS !

You will note that I haven't even started on the side-effect issue. The risk of side-effects is thought to be grossly overestimated by the statin purveyors. I retain an open mind; all I know is that my side-effects were severe, and they were not the result of thinking myself into them, as has also been suggested. Initially I had no idea that statins could do what they did to me. But what I find particularly difficult to handle is the approach of some doctors whose patients have thought they have side-effects and have told their patients that if they stop they will die of a heart attack. Apart from being complete rubbish it is a closed-mind phenomenon; they have guidelines (flawed, but there they are) and the guidelines matter more than the patient in front of them. Not very holistic if you ask me.

You may recall I mentioned the major difference between reporting absolute and relative risk reduction. Triallists tend to report side-effects using the latter. They may also ensure bias by excluding from analysis some groups of subjects; if for example, you have a run-in period then anyone developing side-effects in that period are not analysed. Deceit? I think so.[132]

Risk, benefit and the four-way analysis

Why the four-way analysis? You must look not only at the benefit and risk of *taking* a drug (two) but the benefit and risk of *not* taking it (another two). Makes four. For any drug:

1. It works
2. It doesn't work
3. It doesn't have any side-effects
4. It has side-effects

[132] see David Diamond & Uffe Ravnskov, *Historical Perspective on the Use of Deceptive Methods in the War on Cholesterol*, in Rosch P (ed), *Fat and Cholesterol Don't Cause Heart Attacks and Statins are Not the Solution*, Columbus Publishing, 2016

Obviously the pairs are mutually exclusive but a simple understanding of maths indicates that any patient can be in any one of four groups:

Drug works; no side-effects	Drug works; side-effects
Drug doesn't work; no side-effects	Drug doesn't work; side-effects

And it doesn't take an idiot to work out which is the best and which is the worst. The trouble is that we cannot reliably predict for any individual patient which box they will be in.

So doctors have to invent a third dimension – themselves. There may be a number of drugs that one could use for a specific condition. As you cannot predict, for example, whether one non-steroidal anti-inflammatory drug will cause a rash, or headache, or whatever therefore you cannot make a rational choice for your patient, and what they get given is down – not to them, not to the range of drugs – but down to you. What might influence your choice? An advert that you saw in the BMJ? The name on the Post-it notepad (I currently have a pad stamped "Movelat", a rub-on cream I never prescribed)? Your ballpoint?[133] Which rep you saw last? What side of the bed you got out of? A puff in a national newspaper that caught your eye? Actually it might be your local drug committee that has a recommended first choice, often as not based on price, but these can change (and you can never be entirely sure that a generic will have exactly the same effect as a branded version)[134]. So you can see that prescribing is nothing to do with drugs or patients but is entirely down to the doctor.

You can take a horse to water…

Or – what part of "No" do you not understand?

---

[133] My pen pot currently contains three drug company pens, one from the Royal College of Surgeons, one from Qatar Airways, one from a holiday firm, three from hotels, one "NHS60" souvenir and a pencil from "Le Shuttle". It also has two drug company pointers, one gift ballpoint, one ballpoint inherited from my father in the 1970s, one from a furniture restorer in Lewes and one from Syed Kamall MEP.
[134] Even now patients will remark on differences; see "The customer is always right" later on. For a review of the issue see J Lindenbaum , *Bioavailability of digoxin tablets*. Pharm Reviews 1973; 25: 229-237. Also, see F.Bochner, W.D.Hooper, J.H.Tyrer & M.J.Eadie, *Factors involved in an outbreak of phenytoin intoxication*. J Neurol Sci 1972; 4: 481-487. Recent fake statins underline the point

I went to a meeting convened by the Multiple Sclerosis Society, taking all my rehab unit senior staff. It was just as well, as one of the miniature screws in my glasses fell out, the frame sprung (sprang?) apart and the lens was neatly caught by the unit sister (who then grovelled in my lap for the screw but enough of that). The meeting was attended by a mix of professionals, patients and carers and was at a time when many health authorities were not providing funding for a new therapy, beta-interferon. We were treated to an expert exposé, based on a long-term trial, of the failure of beta-interferon to halt disease progression, or alter severity, over a fourteen year study period. The graphics were excellent and the statistics sound, though depressing. I was about to offer my opinion that, given these results, we were better off diverting funding for the drug into things with tangible quality-of-life benefits, such as physiotherapy to prevent contractures, equipment and nurses to prevent pressure sores and so forth when a carer at the front of the hall caught the speaker's attention.

"My wife has been refused beta-interferon!" he exclaimed. "I know of lots of people who have had it and what I want to know is – when is she going to get it?"

I said "When are YOU going to get it? We have just spent half an hour listening to an expert tell us IT DOESN'T WORK!". But I only said it to myself. Science can be very difficult to grasp, and statistics are worse.

A last word on drug trials

I like to think that this cartoon represents one of the first trials ever done.

"Be positive! At least now we know that being able to fly
has got nothing to do with having
a pointy head!"

****

Alternative medicine: the facts

To digress briefly, here are my short thoughts on various so-called alternative therapies. All are based on the false premise that doing nothing is not an option; you must do something. The so-called evidence for most alternative therapies is based on hearsay, magic and witchcraft and relies on the placebo effect and the gullibility of the recipient. Even so-called traditional Chinese medicine, usually in the form of evil-smelling herbs, is dubious. Some of the preparations contain large doses of steroids, so of course they work; some contain active ingredients in un-measured quantities, and some are frankly toxic. How the hell are you supposed to know that Guan Mu Tong, which is the main constituent of Fen Qing Wu Lin Wan, is aristolochia, a potent kidney poison? Even if the label on the packet is printed in English, which it probably isn't.[135]

Less is more

> When asked for my view on homeopathy
> I retort that it means almost nothing to me.

---

[135] See ZI Shaohua *et al*, *Fatal renal failure due to the Chinese herb "GuanMu Tong" (Aristolochia manshuriensis): autopsy findings and review of literature.* Forensic Sci Int. 2010 Jun 15;199(1-3):e5-7. doi: 10.1016/j.forsciint.2010.02.003

Putting your foot in it

Reflexology, not pills,
Tickles the fancy of some folk
They say it can cure all your ills
And do so at a stroke.

Other nostra they may tell;
("Diet: You are what you eat")
But tickling toes to make you well
Is quite a clever feat.

The Eyes have it

I find it very difficult to see
Eye t' eye with iridology.

Pulling and pushing

Manipulation of the spine
Is nearly always, mostly, fine.
But should your bones be full of cancer
Osteopaths sure ain't the answer.
But it might be still worse a tactic
To resort to chiropractic.
T'would be a sad twist to the tail
That brought a lawsuit in the mail.

Sniffy Niffy

Aromatherapists eschew
Cod liver oil. Yes, that is true
But still their touchy-feely care
Is rather fishy, I declare;
You cannot cure the gout, or boils
With myriad essential oils.

Pins & needles

Consider, would you, at this juncture
What I think of acupuncture –
Meridians, yin-yangs, even Qis
Promulgated by Chinese.
There is some science, it is true,

Endorphin rush may well come through
But no. I'd purse my lips, and frown
I'd not agree to be pinned down,
I truly do not wish to be
Given Hepatitis C
Down some dark back street, where I knew
The needle'd done some thug's tattoo.

Let it be clear that I am not alone in my scepticism.[136]

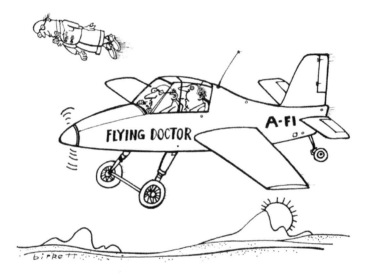

"It's that bloody flying faith-healer again!"

On the other hand… if there is no evidence, it may be necessary to invent it, as the famous plastic surgeon Sir Harold Gillies did when starting sex-change surgery in the late 1940s in the UK, and earlier with facial reconstruction. Doing nothing because no-one has done it before may be the least bad option for individuals, but it would be a disaster for innovation.

That said there is no need to reinvent it constantly. Iain Chalmers has pointed out that vast sums are wasted by the repetition of clinical trials;

---

[136] See Edzard Ernst and Simon Singh, *Trick or Treatment? Alternative medicine on trial*, London, Bantam Press, 2008; also by Ernst *SCAM: So-Called Alternative Medicine*, Imprint Academic, 2018

164

assessment of benefit is often clearly shown within half a dozen or so, and the next 40 serve no other purpose than to get authorship of papers – assuming those first trials were large enough to capture rare side-effects. But even then such effects will come out in the wash. Furthermore there has been a lot of work that has been done in one piece but sliced up for better impact; this is known as divided or "salami" publication.[137] My best experience of this was the report of a study of Vitamin D; a hypothesis was generated and the paper showed it was false. A year or so later a second publication appeared looking at the same hypothesis, but this time suggesting that a different form of Vitamin D (1, 25 Hydroxy rather than simple Hydroxy) should be tested. The result was the same; the hypothesis was false. The original work had actually looked at both, as the author rather shamefacedly admitted to me when I accosted him after the meeting where the second study had been presented, but it was implied that two papers were better than one. Many journals have cottoned on to this but rely on reviewers to notice, not least as there are now so many journals it is easy to submit somewhere else and so cover one's tracks.

****

---

[137] For a good discussion of this see E Huth, *Repetitive and Divided Publication*, in *Ethical Issues in Biomedical Publication*, ed. A Hudson Jones & F McLellan, Johns Hopkins University Press, 2000

Life and death

Saving life?

Ben Goldacre's other book "Bad Science"[138] – not just recommended reading but essential reading – pokes fun at the press for its uncritical acceptance of strange claims that have no basis in science. But we are sometimes just as careless in our use of words and phrases. The statin issue is a classic example. You may *reduce* the risk of a coronary by 50% but if you look at the data the other way about you only *increase* the chance of *not* having a coronary by 2%. Strange, that. Read Uffe Ravnskov's analysis of this to get the full picture, and if it doesn't make you wonder why we are using statins at all it may at least make you think[139]. I could reiterate my belief about lowering the cholesterol level being an epiphenomenon[140], but enough of it. What about other new drugs and how they come to market (or rather to media)?

You have all seen the headlines: "New drug will save lives"; "New op may save hundreds of lives"; "Advance in cancer treatment will save thousands of lives" etc.

We must understand quite how the lives will be saved. Then we must learn how long they will be saved for. It becomes clear that if a new cancer drug increases life expectancy by 6 months then this new advance is not doing a great deal (other than, perhaps, giving the recipient enough time to rewrite their will and leave their money to the donkey sanctuary instead of cousin George "who once said I was too mean to even mention him in my will – Hello, George!").

There is one overwhelming, crushing, irrefutable certainty about life. Death. I am unaware of any immortal being on Earth, irrespective of what operation or drug they have at some stage received. On this basis there is nothing that

---

[138] Ben Goldacre, *Bad Science*. London, Fourth Estate, 2008. This is an adapted compilation of his contributions to "The Guardian".

[139] He writes "Tell a patient that his chance not to die in five years without statin treatment is 85.4% and that simvastatin treatment can increase this to 87.1 %. With these figures in hand I doubt that anyone should accept a treatment whose long term effects are unknown." (BMJ 2002; 324: 789) and also see http://www.ravnskov.nu/cholesterol.htm. It's a bit polemical but has my brand of healthy (?) scepticism

[140] Oh all right then. See AN Bamji, *If facts do not fit theory, the theory is wrong*. BMJ 2012;345: e6584. For more recent analysis, again I recommend Malcolm Kendrick, *Doctoring Data*, Columbus Publishing, 2014

saves lives. There are lots of things that postpone death. But that is neither quite the same thing, nor quite so exciting for the newspapers. However, it is a lot more honest.[141]

What is more, if you reduce the likelihood of death at an early age from one disease you will increase the likelihood of death from another. Why is the death rate from cancer going up? Less people are dying of the alternatives. Simples.

What death actually is

Most people are confused by death because they don't know what it is, on the one hand, and confuse the actuality of death with the process of dying on the other. There is also a failure to understand the difference between death of the organism as a whole, and death of the whole organism. Thus, if you believe that death occurs when the heart stops you will have to confront the oxymoron of decapitation; if someone has been guillotined, their heart will beat on for a while, but it can scarcely be believed that the organism is alive. If the brain is dead, then so is the organism. Thus a patient with irreversible and severe brain damage, who has also lost the capacity to breathe because the breathing centre in the brain stem is dead, cannot be deemed to be alive; while the brain is still connected, its function is no less separated from the rest of the body than if it was physically separate. Brain stem death represents the point of no return. If a body can breathe, its physiological operations still function, and thus an intact brain stem in the presence of a compromised cerebral cortex will still sustain life.

Making the diagnosis has three stages; there are essential preconditions, with the identification of irreversible brain damage, exclusion of possible reversible cause of coma such as drugs and the results of specific tests of brain stem function that show conclusively that function is absent. Thereafter, if all the conditions are satisfied, one is ventilating a corpse.

My neurology boss, Chris Pallis, was dragged into the public gaze by a BBC television "Panorama" documentary which implied that in the UK patients' ventilators were being switched off while they were still alive because organ-snatchers wanted kidneys. It was based on the resurrection of four patients treated in the USA but careful analysis indicated that the criteria for brain stem death had been met in none of them.[142] Pallis, together with the

---

[141] Iona Heath recently expressed the same argument (*What do we want to die from?* BMJ 2010;341:c3883)

[142] See Bamji AN. *An appalling "Panorama"*. BMJ 1980; 281: 1028

neurosurgeon Bryan Jennett, convinced the BBC that a follow-up programme was required to set the record straight and clear the air. I too was pulled in, with the presenter trying (unsuccessfully) to get me to appear. It took half an hour out of an evening to get him off the phone ("What part of No do you not understand?"). The follow-up was made into a debate, where those who did not agree and did not understand were trounced. Their case was not helped by tendentious reference to criteria for death in a European country – but they had picked the wrong one (do your homework).

Nearly 40 years later the whole concept of what death actually is remains mysterious to many. Periodically it flares up again (loss of institutional memory) and, sadly, is fuelled by misguided, though heartfelt attempts to prolong life in hopeless cases (futility medicine). A reset is needed. Again. Then again it is vital not to assume that an unconscious or unresponsive patient cannot hear or see. I was asked to give an opinion on a young man who had been in a coma for several weeks and the medical team thought he was in a persistent vegetative state. He was in a side room. One of the nurses was filling me in with the story of his horrific road accident and subsequent progress, or rather lack of it. We were talking across him as she told me he was completely unresponsive. I suddenly noticed a flicker in an eye. So I turned towards him and said "Do you understand what we have been talking about?"

Nothing. But a tear trickled down his cheek.

I said "Can you hear us? Blink twice for yes."

He blinked twice.

The poor lad was quite desperate thinking someone was going to terminate his treatment, and all the while was gazing at a blank ceiling, with no stimulation, hour after hour, day after day. Not even acoustic tile holes to count. So he was not in a vegetative state, but had locked-in syndrome. Read "The Diving Bell and the Butterfly" for an account of this awful condition, or read "Dumas' "The Count of Monte Cristo" and think about M. Noirtier.[143] Changing the diagnosis changed the management. He was sent off to a specialist hospital and sadly I don't know what happened thereafter.

---

[143] Jean-Dominique Bauby, *The Diving Bell and the* Butterfly, Fourth Estate, 1998. Dumas' tale of revenge was first published in 1844 – containing probably the first description of locked-in syndrome

Teaching about dying

During my first ever job (not having got the endocrinology job at the Middlesex Hospital with the eminent, brilliant but fearsome Dr Nabarro I was on the Professorial Medical Unit, traditionally reserved for the final year top two) we were given the opportunity to switch from taught to teacher, with a weekly session for the students on the firm. While I was at the Central Middlesex on a medical firm one of the middle-grades taught me a valuable lesson. A patient had died and he was going to see the relatives to break the news. He asked if I would like to come along. I sat in the corner and watched as he explained what had happened. It was very uncomfortable. After we had left he said "No-one will teach you that. You may not have agreed with how I did it, but at least you have seen how it might be done and decide how you might play it."

The Professorial firm covered respiratory medicine and some specialised endocrinology; the third consultant, Jeffrey O'Riordan, was an expert on calcium metabolism and most of his patients had parathyroid gland problems (the parathyroids control blood calcium levels, put crudely). Best to leave the clever things to the top people, I thought, not least because the arcane biochemistry of hypophosphatemic osteodystrophy was beyond me, and teach my little flock the things they won't get taught. So my sessions covered explaining test results, breaking bad news and death. With the last I worked out a role play, and got them to tell me, the imaginary husband, that his wife had died. They managed quite well between them.

At the end of the firm a couple of months later I asked if they had found my sessions useful. There was an uncomfortable pause as they all looked at the floor and shuffled about. Then their spokesman said "Well, we were expecting you to teach us about calcium metabolism."

I made some feeble excuse about esoterica being best left to esotericists, but what I should have said was "In your professional career you will see dozens, if not hundreds, of people who die, and their relatives. You might see one or two people with abnormal calcium metabolism. So should you learn about the rare, or the common?". But one's best responses always hit the mind half an hour too late.

Retrospection may not be great

The one certainty of life is death but there are various paths to it. Sometimes serendipity takes a hand, while on occasion things proceed in an orderly or planned manner. However it can be a mistake to return to your past and expect to find that everything is as it was. It may be your hope, even your expectation, but it will not be your reality.

Things change, and people change. Go back to the workplace you left a year ago and your erstwhile colleagues will have learned to get on with your replacement. Go back in five years and those you meet will have no idea who you are. Also (and this certainly applies if you have retired) they are probably too busy working to spare you much time. It is easy to feel hurt at the transient nature of your influence and power, but the truth is that once you have left a place it will have moved on without you, and not necessarily in the direction you might think was right. But it isn't your problem any more, and if you try to tell people what to do they will give you odd looks as if to say "What's it to do with you? You don't work here." So get used to it.

That said, the places themselves have a resonance which, when they are destroyed, can be quite painful. Some years after I left the country branch of the Brompton Hospital at Frimley, where I had spent a happy three months dealing with convalescent cardiac patients and the odd alcoholic TB sufferer, I returned for trip down memory lane after lecturing at a neighbouring hospital (curiously the person who invited me had mixed me up with someone else but I hope the talk he asked me to do passed muster). Reminds me of when the British Society of Rheumatology invited the Chief Medical Officer, Donald Acheson, to give a keynote lecture. Unfortunately someone invited his brother Ronald, who was a Cambridge statistician and rather dry).

More like amnesia lane. The first problem was that I couldn't find the old Brompton country branch because there had been so much development around it that all the roads had changed. When I finally did find it, the grounds around which I and my colleague had gone running each morning, on the old graduated walks for the TB convalescents, had vanished under a sea of new houses. The hospital itself was now turned over to administration and no-one was really interested in showing me around. It was a salutary lesson.

Just recently I visited a restorer in London's Cleveland Street with my wife, taking a couple of pictures that needed attention. I checked the exact location on Google Maps and phoned to arrange a time, commenting that I knew the spot as it was opposite the Middlesex Hospital's Medical School building that I had first entered as an undergraduate 45 years before.

"No it's not!" I was told. "That's just a large hole."

And so it was. Like its parent hospital, which might have been converted to elegant apartments on its closure but had been razed immediately planning permission for development was granted (although the money had then run out, so nothing happened initially), it had simply vanished from the map.[144]

There is something rather upsetting about finding that your alma mater, seat of so many happy memories, is no longer there. The hospital itself is now a fancy development of shops, apartments and offices. The listed chapel survives incongruously in its centre, as do the paintings from the front hall by Frederick Cayley Robinson depicting acts of mercy, which were rescued by the Wellcome Trust.[145] I know that progress means such things are inevitable but it was, frankly, horrid. The Middlesex has been subsumed into University College, London, but in my day there was a healthy rivalry between UCH and the Middlesex, and I had never been comfortable with being told, suddenly, that I was now a proud graduate of a college I had never been at and even perhaps looked down on a little. But now it was if the Middlesex had never been.

Occasionally it's nice to go back, but in my experience the past is often best left alone. But one should not forget it. Retrospectoscopes, institutional memory…

****

---

[144] It has been replaced by the new Sainsbury Wellcome Centre, University College's neuroscience research building. Very smart, although the ground floor lecture theatres are open to public view from the street, which I would find distracting.

[145] See Baron JH, *Frederick Cayley Robinson's Acts of Mercy murals at the Middlesex Hospital, London.* BMJ 1994; 309:1723-4

Clinical vignettes

My next series of essays and notes is mostly directed at doctors. However the lay person may learn quite a lot about medical practice and thinking from it, so don't think that just because it says "clinical" it's only for clinicians. I have discussed many of the opinions here with my patients and friends. One of them said they wished their GP had some common sense. None of it is other than that, really.

Is psychiatry dead?

For decades or longer we have colluded in the belief that the brain and the mind are in some way separate – that the mind somehow sits like a halo or cloud over and around the brain rather than being seen as the sum or differential of the chemical processes in the brain. Thus neurology and psychiatry have taken different paths and the artificial distinction has led to problems for all of us in managing conditions that might reasonably be considered to have a chemical basis. From a patient perspective the split has reinforced a belief in the essentially unpalatable concept of things being "all in the mind" – which, as it is separate from the brain, means to the layperson that the problem is imagined and thus not real.

Now, after nearly 40 years in clinical medicine, from student to retired senior physician, I have come to the conclusion that psychiatry as a specialty should be dismantled. I am not the first[146]. You might question why a rheumatologist feels able to make such a sweeping statement. Well, I ran a neuro-rehabilitation unit for most of my consultant career. I have, through custody of my hospital's archives, developed an interest in shellshock (or whatever you care to call it). I have treated patients with severe brain injuries and even had a member of staff with one. I treated patients with chronic pain (or whatever you care to call it). As an avid reader I have devoured the works of Oliver Sacks, who has delineated the tricks played on the mind by damage to the brain[147]. As a small-time investor I have embraced the concepts of Nicholas Taleb – in particular that of the "Black Swan",[148]

---

[146] M Baker, M Menken, *Time to abandon the term mental illness*. BMJ 2001 322: 937.
[147] Start with *The Man who Mistook his Wife for a Hat*, Summit Books, 1985
[148] Taleb NN. *The Black Swan. The Impact of the Highly Improbable*. Allen Lane, 2007

though I am by no means the first in medicine[149] – and so have become a healthcare epistemocrat, or one who holds his own knowledge in greatest suspicion. It is perhaps the Black Swan that is the most important principle; it brings together all the individual hypotheses with which I have analysed various problems by reminding me that, simply because one has not found a cause for something does not mean that that cause does not exist. In neurology and psychiatry there are still many unknowns, but I consider that there are enough Black Swan moments to justify a merger of the disciplines that look into the nervous system – neurology, psychiatry and pain management – and call them something else. Jay Goldstein's suggestion of neurosomatic medicine is not all-embracing enough, at least as he imagines it.[150] Neurocraniology (or neurocerebrology) are awkward but accurate. My friend and fellow retired rheumatologist Adrian Crisp suggests neurochemical medicine. I like it.

There is one unassailable benefit from such an approach. People with mental illness are stigmatised and that has largely been on the basis that their complaint has no demonstrable cause and is thus not only dangerous but mysterious. Abolishing the label will abolish the stigma. And as we can increasingly show that disorders of the mind are simply disorders of the brain, be these structural or functional, I think we can justify such iconoclasm.

Back in history most neurological diseases were a mystery, except for the crude analyses conducted on the brain post-mortem, perhaps – after the 16th century – with a microscope. But no-one today would argue that there is anything other than a clear cause for the problems. We might not quite understand the last detail, but we can find things that in such conditions are different. Thus more modern investigative techniques have allowed us to learn that stroke is not a single entity (crudely, they are clots or bleeds): muscular dystrophies appear to have a genetic basis; multiple sclerosis has an immune one; epilepsy results from disordered activity usually related to damage; personality changes after traumatic brain injury appear to be a function of frontal lobe problems. We have hypothesised that chronic pain is the result of a feedback problem, partially mediated through alternative nerve pathways and proved this by using drugs that block specific neurochemicals. CT and MRI have reduced and in some cases abolished the need to take a fully detailed history and examination. So the neurological

---

[149] See http://www.medrants.com/archives/3537 and CM Nezerue et al, *Black swan in the kidney": Renal involvement in the antiphospholipid antibody* syndrome. Kidney International (2002) **62**, 733–744; doi:10.1046/j.1523-1755.2002.00500.x)
[150] J Goldstein, *Tuning the Brain: Principles and Practice of Neurosomatic Medicine.* Taylor Francis 2004

Black Swans of the early 20th century have been laid to rest and we must move on to the next unknowns – those of psychiatry.

Depression has a neurochemical basis. I first learned this while assisting in experiments on the biochemistry of schizophrenia.[151] One control subject (they were all medical students) had serum tryptophan levels that appeared significantly abnormal – so much so that we broke the code, finding that the subject already had a known history of severe depressive illness (indeed they sadly committed suicide a few years later). We now understand that schizophrenia itself has a chemical/genetic background (to do with glutamate and/or gamma-aminobutyric acid or GABA for short) and that environmental factors may trigger it. Is there any difference in genesis between the hallucinations of schizophrenia and those induced by LSD? If overuse of banned substances can cause the disease and reproduce its symptoms then it becomes difficult to argue that it is not due to some fundamental anomaly, however induced, of brain chemistry. There remains debate about whether cannabis use can precipitate schizophrenia or psychosis, while my father propounded this theory for decades following his time in Bombay at university in the 1930s. Recent experience of "Spice" use (or rather abuse) in prisons shows he was not far off the mark; the zombie-like behaviour of users, and the development of paranoid psychosis and other clear-cut disorders mirror his descriptions of addicts on the Bombay streets. Autism has been linked with abnormalities of serotonin metabolism; again, profound psychiatric signs and symptoms do not come from some ethereal "mind" but from damaged neurochemistry or neuro-anatomy.

Years ago we did not understand why dementia occurred; it was thought to be a "degeneration" of the brain. Pathological examination advanced from simple realisation of loss of tissue and ventricular expansion to an understanding of microscopic pathology (the neurofibrillary tangle), through imaging (demonstrating the vascular component) to supermicroscopic pathology (where we see the prion and wonder about the role of amyloid). We knew that muscular dystrophy was genetically determined but as time has passed we now recognise numerous specific defects resulting in subtly different clinical patterns with differing patterns of inheritance depending on which gene on which chromosome is altered.[152] Parkinson's disease was known from pathological studies to be a problem of the basal ganglia, but it

---

[151] DA Bender, A Bamji, *Serum Tryptophan binding in chlorpromazine treated chronic schizophrenics*. J.Neurochem 1974, 22, 805-9

[152] Type "genetics of muscular dystrophy" into Google Scholar and over 42,000 references come up

took many years to discover that dopamine metabolism was key to the signs and that these could be modified by administering it.[153]

We know that traumatic brain injury results in a combination of changes – relating to standard cortical function (sensorimotor change), memory, cognition and behaviour. The pattern of disability and balance of these elements varies according to the site of the injury and to some extent one can predict, from that site, what the balance may be. Now – is there any fundamental difference between a disturbed patient with a known brain injury and one without (such as a murderer, rapist, football hooligan or personality disordered individual)? If so, on what basis? If we cannot determine why a violent criminal is violent, is it because we haven't looked in the right place using the right test? I suspect so.

For those bored with neurological parallels look at diabetes. In 1920 its cause was unknown. In 1922 it was known to be due to insulin deficiency. In 2002 it is back in the "not clear" file, as we have unravelled the fundamental differences between insulin lack and insulin resistance, appreciated the role of glucagon and only just begun to assess the influence of autoimmunity, and leptin. Understanding of rheumatoid arthritis has led to specific markers for disease but most importantly that RA confers a substantial increased risk of cardiovascular disease, independent of smoking (although smoking is also a risk factor). Each finding is a Black Swan moment, before which it could not be, and was not envisaged that causes and consequences would ever be known.

These observations return us to the belief of Hunter and Macalpine[154] that psychiatric illness should not be labelled as "functional" until some "organic" cause has been excluded – but on the Black Swan principle, and with these examples, it becomes easier to think that those illnesses for which no cause can be demonstrated are not cause-less, but that we have not measured or examined the right things to point us at the cause. Henry Miller famously referred to psychiatry as "neurology without physical signs". There are some good examples from rheumatology. Repetitive strain injury became fashionable in the 1980s until "debunked" in an Australian court.[155] However

---

[153] Oddly enough my most cited paper is on this subject (not that I was anything other than the office boy); D Calne, PF Teychenne, PN Leigh, AN Bamji & JK Greenacre, *Treatment of Parkinsonism with Bromocriptine*. Lancet 1974, ii, 1355
[154] See R Hunter R & I Macalpine, *George III and the Mad Business* (New York: Pantheon Books, 1969) for a well-known example
[155] There is an interesting analysis (JL Quintner, *The Australian RSI debate: stereotyping and medicine*. Disabil Rehabil 1995; 17: 256-62) which points out that as well as stereotyping patients the debate also spied out stereotypes of doctors. Let him who is without sin…

many cases clearly have limb dystonia and careful history-taking will reveal this (Sacks' "Musicophilia"[156] contains an excellent analysis, but I see the same problem in computer users and indeed suffer from it mildly myself). Perhaps the best example is that of chronic widespread pain. Functional MRI scanning demonstrates that sufferers have persistent high activity in certain areas of the brain when these should be quiet – in particular in the cingulate gyrus. When one starts to deconstruct the concepts of "ME", fibromyalgia and chronic fatigue – conditions for which there are no known tests – one sees the significant overlaps with chronic widespread pain and even post-traumatic stress disorder. It is curiously apparent that some people develop these symptoms while others exposed to identical triggers do not. My own clinical experience suggests that the problem may run in families. Does this imply a genetic basis? Are our tests negative simply because we are doing the wrong ones? I believe so. Folk may argue that cognitive behavioural therapy's success devalues the concept of some purely neurochemical cause, but sensory re-education after physical injury, for example using mirrors in stroke patients or therapy techniques in brachial plexus and peripheral nerve injury confirms to me that midbrain centres are chemically modified by higher brain activity and directed cortical activity works by that mechanism. It is no different to the blocking-out of the noise of a pneumatic drill in the street.

What is interesting is that if one explains this to patients – and they understand the concept – their fear that you are labelling them as mad, and the negativity of half-believing that the problem must be "in the mind" evaporates. This is itself positive, even if thereafter one still cannot cure the problem (another Black Swan moment is needed).

On a more personal note as a sufferer from migraine and irritable bowel syndrome I am irritated by the assertion that these are psychosomatic or functional disorders. Both are assumed to be worse as a result of stress (interestingly in my case migraine attacks occur when the stress stops) but what of course we do not yet understand is what chemical cascades result from changes in stress levels although some research documents different neurochemical changes in different parts of the brain as a response to different stressors.[157] The etymology of "functional" is of course important; there are disturbances of function, but in common medical parlance the use of the qualifier adds an implication of non-organicity. It is abundantly clear that, whatever the triggers may be, the underlying pathophysiology of

---

[156] Oliver Sacks, *Musicophilia*. London, Picador, 2007
[157] F Petty, GL Kramer & AL Larrison, *Neurochemistry of stress: Regional brain levels of biogenic amines and metabolites with ten different stressors*. Biogenic amines 1996, 12: 377-394

migraine is a disorder of serotonin metabolism and platelet plugging,[158] while the symptoms of IBS point to an autonomic dysfunction which may be triggered by changed reactivity of the gut mucosa as a result of infection[159] or allergy[160] but which is, nevertheless, mediated through the nervous system. When one trawls the internet using search terms of IBS and allergy one of the top references looks at the link with anxiety and depression; trawling IBS and neurochemistry it is interesting to see that one is taken to sites relating to fibromyalgia – further evidence of the huge overlap between these so-called "functional" disorders. I consider that we should plant our stake in the ground now to anticipate the Black Swan moment when the neurochemistry of them all is revealed (and in my expectation the abnormalities will be common to all of them).

The fable of the blind men and the elephant should remind us that there is more than one way of looking at a problem and what we see may not be the whole answer.[161] There is no doubt that psychological assessment may identify the clinical issues and provide management clues (thus the head injured person may show specific deficits that are amenable to specific treatment – a diary for memory loss, for example) but that assessment does not look at the structural or indeed functional aspects that could be viewed with CT, MRI or PET scanning. Conversely the finding of specific defects on scans gives us no clue as to how to deal with the expressed consequences. So we need both. In relation to those conditions deemed "psychiatric" we should be further investigating the structural and chemical differences, the genetic background and the relation of environmental triggers. I have no doubt we will find them. When we do, then the conditions now deemed neurological will merge seamlessly into those labelled as psychiatric.

[158] E Hanington, RJ Jones, JA Amess, B Wachowicz, *Migraine: a platelet disorder.* Lancet 1981; 318: 720-723
[159] RC Spiller, *Role of infection in irritable bowel syndrome.* J Gastroenterol 2007; 42: 41-47
[160] E Isolauri, S Rautava, M Kalliomaki, *Food allergy in irritable bowel syndrome: new facts and old fallacies.* Gut 2004; 53: 1391-1393
[161] For those ignorant of the tale, seven blind men got hold of different bits of an elephant and came to different conclusions as to what it most resembled; John Godfrey Saxe's poem on the fable concludes "And so these men of Indostan, disputed loud and long, each in his own opinion, exceeding stiff and strong, Though each was partly in the right, and all were in the wrong!
So, oft in theologic wars, the disputants, I ween, tread on in utter ignorance, of what each other mean,and prate about the elephant, not one of them has seen!"

If a patient is on too many drugs that is only your opinion

Many patients come into hospital on polypharmacy. It may seem bad to you (not least if you find a whole cascade, each treating the side-effects of the one before) but if you stop everything and do your own thing one of two things may happen.

> 1.   the patient develops different side-effects
> 2.   the GP will observe the patient going off at home, ask why on earth the stability of a decade has been fiddled with, and put all the old drugs back again

Remember the advice of the old Roman, Seneca:

Nihil aeque sanitatem impedit quam remediorum crebra mutatio

Which, translated, means nothing prevents a cure better than a constant change in the medicines. Or, if it's not bust, don't fix it. On the other hand if it is bust, constant change won't necessarily fix it – as most of what I have written about the NHS proves.

Don't judge a book by its cover

There are all sorts of prejudices surrounding the old and infirm – which is what most of the old in hospital are. This is made worse by the behaviour of those with dementia, who shout all night (and sleep all day), wander, ask the same question over and over and leave messy trails along the floor on their way to the bathroom (or looking for their own room at home, as many don't actually know where they are). It is tempting to ignore them and joke about them. Don't. The old were once young.

I was alerted to this by several experiences and while I am happy to jest in the right circumstances and would not by and large consider myself the model of political correctness (see above), I am careful. I would no longer write LONOI in a case file (for those who are too young, it stands for Lights On No-One In).

First there was my mother whom I have described before. We had just returned from a visit to her when her care home phoned to say "You are not going to believe this…" She had fallen and broken her hip barely 12 hours since we had left. I took the train to Torquay, booked into a hotel near the hospital and found her rather dishevelled and not a little confused. While the nurses were nice they adopted a parent-to-child approach (and how I hate the disrespectful familiarity of first name address on a hospital ward). And they shouted. Which was fair enough, because Mother was pretty deaf, but the combination seemed somewhat degrading.

Most people I know have mothers or have had in the past. What did your mother do? If she went beyond filing her nails and reading The People's Friend then maybe she was something once. Reasonable enough? Worth a bit of respect? My mother had questioned the nurses about her medication and this was reported back to me as being awkward (being osteoporotic she had been written up for alendronate, but it gave her awful gut rot and constipation, so she refused to take it – a bit like me and the statins). Therefore she was "naughty". The unspoken sentiment was that I should do something; they knew I was a hospital consultant.

I smiled and said that as a retired GP she knew enough about risks and benefits and had tried it before and I was not going to intervene. It was enough. The attitude of the entire ward staff appeared to change as a result of the revelation. I suppose I could have iced the cake by telling them how she sold the Daily Worker on Charing Cross Road before the Second World War, how she had worked for Professor JBS Haldane during the war (and had fractured her spine while testing the Davis escape apparatus and being oxygen-deprived in a high pressure tank and having a convulsion under water), and how she had stood up to her own family and married a black man (well, OK, not that black, but certainly foreign) and then studied to become a doctor while still working full-time, and getting honours in medicine, and setting up a practice from scratch to pay my father's way through medical school, and coping with nearly 3000 patients on her own during a flu epidemic while father was ill. But transition from old confused lady to retired GP sufficed.

I returned to the hotel, slept badly and went down for breakfast. The menu board offered a "Special" alongside the Full English Breakfast. I enquired what the Special was.

"Grilled tomato, Sir."

(Apropos the alendronate, when she was admitted for the third time in four years, this time with a broken arm, it was written up again. She had also had quite a lot of pain in the hip and complained of it; the team investigated, and had decided that it could be fixed by re-operation and it took a bit of work to convince them that a deaf, blind old lady who had had several small strokes, a rectal prolapse and a chronic urinary infection resistant to all antibiotics, who had signed an advance directive and wanted now to die at the age of 94 should not be mucked about. I am pleased to see that the next generation of doctors has some common-sense folk in it.[162]). But I have been here already.

Then there was Arthur (not his real name) sliding happily into dementia. Pleasant, rather vacant old fellow. He had rheumatoid arthritis and I had been monitoring his treatment for years. He was retired from what appeared to have been a boring office job. One day I asked my usual "How are you" (it's odd how many patients get that in first) and he said his arthritis was fine but he had had a bit of bother at home. He told me his wife had got upset because (a) he refused to let her buy a duvet and (b) he would not go to barbecues. I switched into counselling mode and asked why. He told me he had been in the front line in Korea and one night the Chinese had attacked *en masse*; his platoon were firing flat out but one Chinese soldier got up to the trench, screaming like a banshee, and Arthur had bayoneted him as he came over the edge. He fell back with this man on top of him, now shrieking with pain, then gurgling and finally falling silent, dead. He was wearing a quilted jacket, and Arthur was covered with his blood. Every time he saw a duvet this nightmare vision recurred. As for the barbecue problem he could not go without getting a flashback to the tank that was hit by a shell just beside his position, and forever associated the smell of the cooking meat with the screams of the men in the tank. Then he burst into tears and told me he had never been able to tell anyone before. So don't think the chap with the odd phobia is odd. There may be something behind it. And be prepared for the clinic to overrun. The Arthurs of the clinic cannot be sorted by stopwatch (I arranged for him to be seen by Combat Stress, which helped, though rather late in the day).

Susan was one of those sharp-as-a-razor seventy-somethings with a lovely smile and a rather mundane problem – neck pain. There was not a lot to find. X-rays showed considerable wear and tear as they so often do in this age group. Before I had time for my diversion approach (it's your age, dear, you need to maintain the range of movement, have some physiotherapy to teach you the exercises you need to do) she asked if her old occupation could have had anything to do with it.

I don't always ask about occupation, certainly not of old ladies who are like as not long-term housewives and child-rearers (actually that's most unpleasant – I withdraw it), notwithstanding the example of mother given

---

[162] See Yasmin Akram, *When is "enough" enough?* BMJ Careers, 4th February 2012, p.3. In the same print issue Graham Mulley writes in similar vein (*Stop the medicalisation of old age*: BMJ 2012; 344: e803) while reviewing *Rethinking Aging: Growing Old and Living Well in an Over Treated Society* by Norton Hadler, University of North Carolina Press, 2011)

above. One of my colleagues always took a detailed social history, and was often diverted from the medical cause of admission, giving long descriptions of work, life and family to increasingly bored juniors – although it was through this that I had the opportunity to talk with one of the handful of survivors from the First World War. I should have followed her example. It transpired that Susan had been in the circus. She had done everything, from riding elephants and horses (her favourite memory was taking her elephant into the sea for a wash in Morecambe Bay) to doing the lions and tigers, the trapeze and the high wire, off which she had fallen more than once. I could suddenly see the old trouper under the wrinkles and makeup and realised that when I had gone to Chipperfield's circus as a child I must have seen her perform. She had been something then, while I, the high and mighty top doctor, had been nothing. And yes, her occupation was probably relevant.[163]

Sheila Rhodes reminds us that some care homes have twigged this principle, and have a memory board of old photos outside, or in the rooms.[164] This is a Good Idea.

Most people were something once. Maybe to many, maybe to a few, probably when you were a rebellious and rather nasty teenager; worthy of respect whatever. And one day – you will be old, too. And your teenage son might remind you that it will be he who chooses your nursing home.

Don't judge a book by its cover (2)

Sometimes people still are something.

Mr T came to see me, accompanied as always by his delightful wife, knee high to a grasshopper, the most inoffensive grey-haired lady. I knew them for 18 years and saw Mr T through two hips, two knees and an elbow replacement as well as innumerable disease-modifying drugs for his rheumatoid arthritis.

We discussed holidays. In the course of this it came out that their son was a martial arts practitioner at international level and Mrs T was SE England's assistant chief instructor for judo and a black belt 3rd Dan.

---

[163] One of my colleagues made a diagnosis of lead poisoning in a small group of patients. It transpired that the local company had won a contract to paint-strip Liverpool Street Station in London. Old lead paint, fumes, no masks…
[164] Sheila Rhodes, Letter, "The Times", 16th September 2010

I had another of these jolts recently. Following my summons for driving at 72mph on the M25 when the speed limit was set at 60 I chose to save money, not collect points on my licence and go on a motorway speed awareness course. It was more interesting than I expected (for example, variable speed limits are set for accidents and breakdowns, but can also be set if the air pollution readings are high). One of my co-attendees was a petite grey-haired lady in, I estimated, her 70s. She was noticeable because she asked lots of questions. When the course was over we all dispersed to the car park. I got in my car and suddenly beside me appeared the small grey lady, wearing full leathers; she donned an expensive full-head helmet, climbed aboard the most enormous Honda (or Kawasaki) superbike and vanished in a puff of exhaust. I could swear she was doing 60 before she got to the car park exit.

> *Moral*: Even after 18 years you don't know people as well as you think you do. Also beware of inoffensive small elderly grey-haired ladies. They could be a lot more dangerous than they look.

Don't judge a book by its cover (3)

Many doctors (even students) will have been taught about, and encountered, "heartsink" patients. These are the ones for whom nothing goes right, and all goes wrong. They turn up, time after time, limping in on their stick (they are only in their 30s or 40s), with miserable faces, bother you with every small detail of about five system problems, complain about their benefits, and your thought is "I could cope with that; why can't you?".

Beware. I saw Mrs J. She was exactly as described above and sent with a rather despairing referral letter. Her foot had hurt ever since an operation on her great toe, she was walking awkwardly on the outside of the foot and this had set off the "osteoarthritis" in her hip.

Well, I said brightly, let's look at the foot. (It's always a good idea to examine the relevant part but you would be amazed, even horrified, to find how many patients turn up in my clinics unexamined by their GP). She couldn't get her sock off and the nurse had to help, while she exhibited the Cantona syndrome.[165] And her foot was rather red, and puffy, and exquisitely tender. Her X-rays did not reveal the osteoporosis I expected but I remained sure that she had reflex sympathetic dystrophy, which had gone undiagnosed for some years. And RSD is very, very painful. Surgery can

---

[165] A popular terrace chant when the footballer Eric Cantona was at Manchester United was "Oooh, Aaah, Cantona"

precipitate it. I was once involved with the care of an RSD patient who was completely mad, and asked for her foot to be amputated, which we did (after making sure it was anaesthetised long enough first so she didn't get phantom pain) and she became completely normal. Pain can drive you crazy.

Mrs J's hip X-ray showed no osteoarthritis.

Treatment of her foot (and her very stiff back) began and was quite successful. The moral is – don't take someone else's word on the heartsink issue but examine the patient and make up your own mind.

Don't judge a book by its cover (4)

When a patient appears with a story of joint pain and swelling, but there is nothing to see, the cover is misleading you. Just because you cannot see it doesn't mean it isn't there. The intermittent form of inflammatory arthritis we call palindromic rheumatism results in joints going up and down like yo-yos. Whether it's actually there when they finally get their appointment is a matter of chance.

So if the cover is blank, how do you come to a diagnosis? First, the history is important. A typical story is that they get a swollen wrist, or ankle, say, which lasts for 24 hours and then after an interval of days to months pops up again somewhere else. Second, there is often an odd rash around the swollen joint, as here. There is ill-defined redness around the base of the toe. In black and white it's difficult to see but take my word for it.

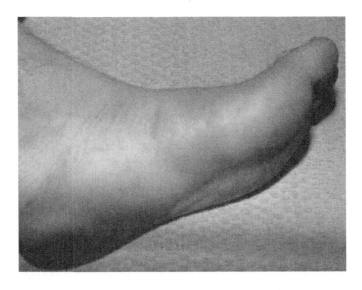

I took this photograph myself because I kept a camera in the clinic; nowadays a phone camera will produce perfectly acceptable pictures – better than in the 19th century when a country doctor would send a watercolour of a rash to his specialist colleague up in town. There are two strategies to capture the moment:

1. Get the patient to take a selfie of the affected bit when it's affected. You would be surprised how many diagnoses can be made this way.
2. Ask the patient to turn up unannounced at the clinic to be seen at once (of course warn your dragon receptionist that this may happen, or the patient will get a fiery earful).

Result: a patient happy they have a diagnosis and no delay in starting treatment.

Furthermore you may be able to capture some good pictures for teaching – classic examples, rarities and oddities. Using the same stock pictures of a pair of hands becomes boring and there is often some subtle difference that makes a new image interesting.

As an example, here is a picture I took back in the 1970s. As you can see, there are numerous little dark lesions over the right foot. Now there is a condition called purpura, which looks just like this. It's caused by little bleeding points under the skin and can suggest a disorder of blood clotting.

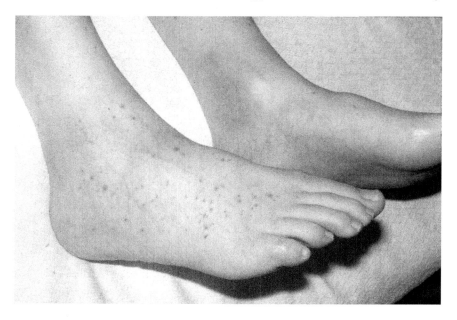

I used to put this in the hospital Christmas Quiz now and then and ask what the cause could be. Most people would give a list of causes of purpura. But actually the patient had severe numbness in the first sacral root distribution, which is over the lateral aspect of the foot, and the cause here was over-enthusiastic testing of sensation by a medical student with a pin.

I was asked to see an elderly lady with a painful shoulder, and when she had removed her blouse I was puzzled by the deep scars on her back and I asked how she had come by them.

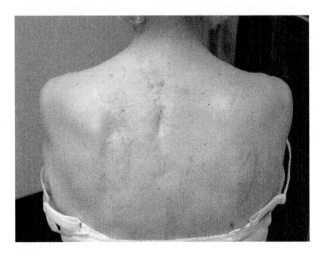

She fished in her handbag and brought out a photograph.

"This is me with my parents and sister" she said. She was top left. She went on to explain how their house had been hit by a V2 rocket towards the end of the Second World War and she was the only survivor from their house. I confess I was a little dubious and asked her address at that time.

"Bagshot Street off the Old Kent Road."

The bomb damage map of London (I have a facsimile of which was produced in 2005 by the London Topographical Society, to which I belong) proved the story. This V2, which destroyed the R White's bottling factory, and most of Bagshot Street, exploded on December 17th, 1944. Altogether 17 were killed and 50 injured.[166]

Sometimes a boring clinical case develops a fascinating twist but there is a message for doctors: if something doesn't fit, or is odd, ask about it. I encountered a delightful chap who had lost half his left ear. It looked odd, so I asked about it notwithstanding his problem was with a knee. He explained that the lower half had been removed for cancer which his surgeon had told him was down to sun exposure. He saw my still puzzled look.

"I was a Desert Rat" he said.

Of course! How do you wear an army beret? Pulled down over the right ear, which remains in shadow while the left is exposed to the full glare of the Egyptian sun at Alamein and beyond.

Don't judge a book by its cover (5)

A Very Important Rheumatologist was going to an event at the Hilton Hotel on Hyde Park – the "Hospital Doctor" awards, for which she had been a judge. Knowing she would be working late at University College Hospital she took her glad rags to work, changed when she had finished and in all her finery walked the few yards to Tottenham Court Road to hail a cab.

What she had not realised was that she had taken up position outside a notorious club called "Spearmint Rhino". A cab stopped, she got in and ordered it to proceed to the Hilton. The cab driver looked round and smirked. "You on the game, then, darling?" he asked.

---

[166] Southwark News, May 5th 2016. https://www.southwarknews.co.uk/history/9255-2/ (accessed 3rd September 2018)

186

The VIR tells this tale against herself so I have no compunction in repeating it (with her permission).

The lady concerned seems to have a penchant for attracting attention. Inhabitants of London (and other cities around the world – for I have seen them in Granada and elsewhere) will know of the mime artists who white themselves up, don fancy dress and stand motionless for hours, occasionally breaking their pose to terrify passers-by who think they are installations, which I suppose in a way they are. She told me recently that, while all dolled up in her academic robes for a degree ceremony at the Royal Festival Hall on the South Bank, she overheated and went outside to cool off a bit on the breezy Embankment. There, she was mistaken for a performer and joined by the Grim Reaper.

What the folk at home in Tokyo will make of the numerous photographs taken and sent home by Japanese tourists I know not.

I am pretty sure that I feature in some of these holiday snaps, for our house looks down Mermaid Street in Rye, which is one of the most photographed streets in the world; if the tourists are not being regaled by tales of Rye ghosts by their guide, sitting on our doorstep or photographing the street they are photographing themselves and their friends in front of the house. So to any readers of this in Japan who have seen a ghostly figure in the window, it's me. Hello!

I have a select following in Japan. The book which I helped edit, "Clinical Rheumatology" (Gower Medical Publishing, 1983), was produced in a Japanese edition. There is a photograph of toes which stick up in the air. Our traditional description defied the translator.

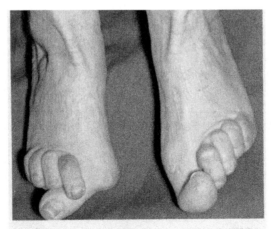

図 4・48 Cock-up 変形．MTP 関節が亜脱臼し，PIP の二次的な屈曲変形がみられる．皮膚の変化や潰瘍化が靴からうける圧力のためにみられる．

Apropos this, if something goes wrong the probability that this is due to a conspiracy is a fraction of the probability of it being a cock-up.

Don't judge a book by its cover (6)

Sometimes you need to look at the dust jacket as well as the cover.

A diabetic patient came in and showed me an ulcer on their foot. Having a diabetic neuropathy they could not feel anything below the ankles and only realised there was a problem when they noticed some bleeding. There was a curiously placed red mark on the instep on examination of the foot, and on examination of the surgical shoe (made to measure) the cause was apparent.

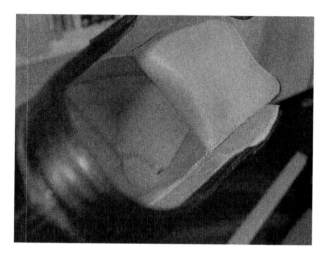

I peeled back the inner sole. Can you see the nail poking up?

Understanding your place in the nature of things

Jodie had learning difficulties, spent her schooldays in special schools and was now at college. She never complained about her arthritis despite obvious pain; often she turned up in a wheelchair. I longed for her to get worse so I could give her a biologic agent; her Disease Activity Score remained resolutely below the cut-off point. She needed and expected frequent joint injections. Meanwhile I tried to keep up her spirits, although she surprised me with her perceptiveness; she was the only patient who noticed when I had my hair cut and she clocked a change of spectacles. At her last appointment (left elbow) she accused me of forgetting my lines: "Dr Bamji, you haven't said it; what *are* we going to do with you, Jodie!" So as I began and she flinched and prepared herself I suggested we needed to sing the Earwig song

188

– earwig-O! earwig-O! earwig-O! – and she nearly shook the needle out
"Don't make me laugh!"

When I was finished she said I should do a concert. I told her I don't sing
much these days but I am probably the only rheumatologist who has sung in
La Scala (Highgate School Boys Choir, Britten's War Requiem, 1963) and
showed her a picture. In the thumbnails on the computer screen she spotted a
costume photograph, so I blew it up to reveal her consultant's hand being
kissed by the Director of the Princess of Wales Memorial Fund (Cesario)
while a famous novelist and columnist (Sir Andrew Aguecheek) looked
lasciviously on, for I was in "Twelfth Night", playing Olivia in a huge wig
and slightly short frock, peering rather short-sightedly across the stage, sans
spectacles (at least I would have been peering, if I had my eyes open).

Just in case you are curious, here it is (Andrew Purkis on the left, Nigel
Williams on the right. I don't know what became of John Bergman who
played Sir Toby Belch).

Jodie's mother decided she wanted a copy (signed, of course). I printed one
off. She then told me it would possibly go in the hall, next to another
precious signed photograph she had – of the Kray twins. When I suggested
that the juxtaposition might be awkward she relented and said it would go in
the lounge next to her signed Elvis photograph. I felt better.

Sending patients away with a smile makes them feel better. But I am not
certain that I want to be shown off to my patients' friends as a teenager in
drag, even if I am on a pedestal between the King Rats and the King of Rock
'n Roll.

How to educate pharmacy assistants

Pharmacists have to some extent become the Thought Police in hospitals and prowl about looking for prescription errors and so forth. While this can be very irritating, particularly if the subsequent approach is somewhat aggressive, it is probably a Good Thing, as it keeps doctors on their toes and has indeed picked up some terrible mistakes both with doses and forgotten or unappreciated interactions.

However it has spread into the retail trade, where it can be unnerving. I was queuing for my regular box of aspirin behind a poor chap who asked very quietly if he could have a tube of Canesten, an antifungal agent used in the treatment of thrush, so one could not be sure whether it was for him or his wife (or perhaps both). Or maybe he had athlete's foot. I didn't hear him ask, as he was so quiet, but the pharmacy assistant produced a box and, waving it for all to see, shouted "WHAT SIZE?" He agreed that the one proffered would do, whereupon she yelled "HAVE YOU USED THIS BEFORE? YOU MUST APPLY IT TWICE DAILY TO THE AFFECTED PART BUT NOT IF THE SKIN IS BROKEN!"

By this time everyone was trying to look the other way. Hopefully not everyone understood the minutiae, but it was certainly most embarrassing for him.

My turn came, and the assistant took a deep breath but before she could scream "HAVE YOU USED THIS BEFORE" at me I smiled sweetly, and said, "Don't worry – I am a hospital consultant" and she started – and then yelled "HAVE YOU USED THIS BEFORE?"

Maybe you can't educate pharmacy assistants and must accept your place in life as just another human being.

Mind you, one can be brought down to size. I was on the concourse of King's Cross Station when a middle-aged man collapsed in front of me. I could not find a pulse and started cardiopulmonary resuscitation. Someone had already called for an ambulance and as it happened on of the very first ambulances staffed by paramedics was driving by and was diverted (we are talking the late 1970s). One took over CPR while the other opened a kitbag from which a cascade of instruments clattered across the floor, including a laryngoscope and a collection of endotracheal tubes of varying sizes. I said I was a doctor and asked if he would like me to intubate. He looked at me askance. "Doctor," he said, "I think I've probably done more of these than you have."

Did I look that young? Or that old, for that matter. Of course he was right. Probably.

What patients understand (or don't); anatomy

I first met Mr Rajah in October 1990. A retired greengrocer, he was enormously overweight with bilateral knee pain from osteoarthritis. It responded so well initially to injection that ever since he begged for his knees to be re-done whenever they were the least bit painful and along the way we injected his shoulder and dealt with various minor problems. He even lent me a video of his own performance in "Twelfth Night" in India; things, had they taken a different turn, would have resulted in a Bollywood mogul rather than a suburban shopkeeper. He told me in great detail about some of the alternative treatments that he had taken to make things better.

The first of these was water treatment (four glasses of water taken every morning which he claimed improved his knees considerably). He felt that they were being lubricated better following this intake and who was I to disagree.

Mr R would keep turning up, sometimes without an appointment, when things were going badly and I used to see him occasionally around the hospital because he was also under the care of the diabetic department. If he couldn't get me, he would bother my secretary. She would occasionally leave me messages about him, one of which ran as follows:

> "I did explain the situation of the clinics and that he would most likely have to wait for a cancellation appointment but he seemed not to hear me and burbled on about what a great chap you were and how you ALWAYS fit him in and help him!!! Well??? Has he licked your boots enough to warrant an earlier appointment or does he have to wait his turn like everyone else?!"

I fitted him in.

A little later, she wrote:

> "This chap remembered that he hasn't bothered us for a while and had noticed that his back had gone with a little lump having formed up."

We dealt with this problem, which was of no major significance, being a little bit of gluteal muscle spasm.

One summer Mr R informed me that he was getting married. He had, of course, been married before, and had grown up children but life had become very lonely and it was quite clear that he missed the physical side of a relationship as well. His bride-to-be was a "Russian voman" some twenty years younger than himself and he informed me with great relish (even though my clinic nurse was in attendance) that the sex was wonderful. He wanted his knee and back sorted out to make things better still. He had a lot of fluid on one knee so I dealt with it and hoped that I would put him off from repeated visits by simply giving him a one-year appointment. This seemed to work but I saw him in the corridor when he was up for another clinic. "Ah, Dr Bamji!" he beamed. "I am very sad."

"Why is that?"

"You remember I told you about my wife? Russian voman".

"Yes indeed."

"Well. She died."

It turned out she had succumbed to a massive heart attack. He was rueful. Life had been good to him for the year that they had been together and now once again he was on his own and was already beginning to feel very lonely. "Ah well," he said, "I will have to get another wife."

A few weeks later it was his turn to come to my clinic and he told me the sad story of how his Russian bride had lived a life of relative poverty and had indulged herself to excess with the rich food available in this country. Four eggs, four boxes of cottage cheese and half a chicken a day (cooked in chicken fat) were, he felt contributory factors to her demise. Mind you, from his weight he was matching her egg for egg, chicken for chicken, though I am not certain which came first. We, as always, expressed our commiserations. We briefly discussed his knees and then suddenly he said:

"Doctor, I wonder if I can ask you something of a personal nature?" He glanced at my nurse and added that he didn't mind her staying while he asked me. "How many times doctor can one have sex a week? I ask this because I have been told that one should not have sex more than three times a week as it is bad for the knees." I was somewhat taken aback by this change of tack and suggested that it might be bad for the knees but only if one was adopting sexual positions that would put strain upon them. He looked greatly relieved at this. "Oh no, doctor," he said, "I do not put strain on my knees, after all ladies nowadays do all the work for you!"

My clinic nurse at this stage was beginning to have some difficulty in controlling herself. When I said that Mr R was, as far as I was concerned, welcome to have sex as often as he wanted and more than once a day if necessary, he looked very pleased with himself and then said:

"You see, doctor, my wife told me that if one had sex more than three times a week then the marrow jelly in the bones would work its way out."

My clinic nurse lost it and left the room. It had occurred to her, just as it occurred to me that his youthful Russian bride may well have sustained her coronary as the result of some excess quite separate from the pots of cottage cheese, the eggs and the chicken fat. I believe the euphemism is "she was found dead in bed".

Mr R left with a gleam in his eye and a six month review appointment. I did not do anything for his knees. Indeed, I was not sure that I would ever need to do anything more with them, but I wanted to hear the next episode of the saga.

I waited in vain. No new wife materialised.

What patients understand (or don't); Physiology: how to breathe (or not)

You can explain something until you are blue in the face, but the knowledge base from which doctors work is, medically speaking, light years from the general public.

I learned this when as a medical registrar I admitted a lady with a massive pleural effusion secondary to advanced ovarian cancer. Fluid around the lung (a pleural effusion) makes you very breathless because it collapses the lung. The fluid kept re-accumulating and once the trainees had all had a go, and she was getting weary of the repeated painful fluid aspirations, my boss decided that she needed a pleurodesis. She was alarmed by all the fuss. So I explained how the procedure was designed to stop the fluid coming back; by putting an irritant into the space between the two pleural layers these would be encouraged to stick together. Fluid would not then form, and her lung would not collapse.

My explanation was exemplary, precise and clear. To me. The following morning I was accosted on the ward by an angry husband.

"You aren't doin' that to my woife", he said. "She'll die. If you'se sticking both 'er lungs together then 'ow the 'ell is she goin' to breathe?"

If you make a diagnosis and administer the treatment, and the treatment fails to work, it's the diagnosis that's wrong.

I once had a 17-year old patient with low back pain referred after the GP had become exasperated by his failure to improve – oh, and by the way, his ESR is 57. For lay people the erythrocyte sedimentation rate – how fast red cells in a tube of blood settle to the bottom – is a crude measure of inflammation, infection or possible a marker for malignant disease. In a young man with a sore and stiff back – and his was very stiff – being a rheumatologist the first thing I thought of is ankylosing spondylitis, not least because his SI joints looked fuzzy on the X-ray. In A.S. a high ESR is common.

After two trials of different non-steroidal anti-inflammatory drugs for a month each I put him on phenylbutazone – a highly potent drug with potentially serious side-effects, and so reserved for A.S. This didn't work either. It now became apparent that his pain was quite localised to the region of the second lumbar vertebra – which was just off the top of his original pelvic X-ray – and further investigation confirmed that he had osteomyelitis in L2 and L3 presumably from the discitis between. Common? No. Certainly not in an otherwise fit 17-year old.

> *Moral: if a physical sign doesn't fit the diagnosis, reconsider the diagnosis.*

An Indian gentleman in his 70s presented with typical symptoms of polymyalgia (pain and early morning stiffness across the neck and shoulders) and a high ESR. His son said he had just returned from India and had been investigated for an intermittent fever, but his malaria tests had proved negative.

I gave him some steroids (prednisolone-EC 10mg daily) for a fortnight. He did not improve at all. I assumed I had not started him on a high enough dose and doubled it for another fortnight. Nothing.

So I followed the corollary and wondered whether this was some sort of malignancy (myeloma and prostate cancer can both masquerade as PMR) and did some further tests – bloods and a bone scan. Cancer was my bet, when a message came round from A&E that he had been admitted with a paraparesis; he had lost power and sensation in both legs.

Have you remembered the fever?

The liver tests were right up the Swanee and the scan showed a hot spot in the 3rd thoracic vertebra. Osteomyelitis (probably tuberculosis) was the diagnosis on biopsy at the neurosurgical centre.

Patients with polymyalgia respond dramatically to steroids and the ESR comes shooting down; if this does not happen, then either we have some other unrelated pathology (as above) or we are dealing with some other sort of inflammatory joint disease. Medicine is like buses, not trams. You need to be able to make detours when things are not right, not just grind to a halt.

Hercule Poirot makes the same basic point in Sophie Hannah's novel "The Monogram Murders". Every fact has its place and you must make the theory fit the facts, not the other way about. I have said this before…

Decide whether a test result really means anything before trying to treat it

Many is the time I have had a patient referred because of concerns about a high or low test which is "abnormal". Many is the time the test result is so close to the normal range that it doesn't matter. You have to get a proper perspective on how abnormal it has to be to be really significant.

At a meeting recently a case of SLE (lupus, a serious connective tissue disease) was presented with various management problems. One aspect was that the patient had a persistently low white blood cell count. Repeated tests confirmed this, although there did not seem to be any relation with the activity or otherwise of the underlying disease. Many clever and expensive tests were suggested to try and get to the bottom of it.

I asked "Why worry?" Did it matter? Clinically – no, it didn't. It might have been relevant if the patient was getting repeated infections, but they weren't.

As a corollary to this the patient had not responded well, lupus-wise, to standard treatment and so a powerful anti-lymphocyte agent, rituximab (which knocks off a set of white cells called B-lymphocytes) was suggested. However not only was the overall white cell count low, but the B-cells were so infrequent as to be almost undetectable. The rituximab was given anyway. The patient improved. This raises several questions:

1.   Why give a drug that kills something that isn't there?
2.   Why did the patient improve?

I don't have an answer to the first, but there are two possibilities for the second – either the improvement was a coincidence or rituximab has some other action on cells other than B-lymphocytes (which currently appears to be the right answer but doesn't justify the treatment in an empirical sense).

You cannot make a diagnosis of exclusion without actually doing the exclusion

In other words, do not make a diagnosis of fibromyalgia without first doing all the tests for polymyalgia, lupus, rheumatoid arthritis and so forth. If then we *know* what it isn't, we might then *presume* what it is. I had one such patient who had lupus, having lived with an incorrect diagnosis of fibromyalgia for over four years.

See one, do one, teach one? Maybe – but make sure you see one before you do, and always do your first under supervision

This may seem very obvious, and if you are a patient you would be rightly appalled by such a cavalier attitude, but this was medicine in the raw in the 1970s and before. One must never ever assume that a procedure is easy.

A patient was scheduled for an intercostal block – an injection between the ribs to anaesthetise an irritable intercostal nerve. I had never done one; a colleague had and agreed to supervise me. At the last minute she was called away. The theory is clear; you insert the needle under the appropriate rib, where the intercostal nerve hides, and infiltrate. The pleura (lung lining) is nearby, so penetrating this and creating a pneumothorax, where air gets out of the lung into the pleural space, so the lung begins to collapse, is a possibility. I proceeded.

Guess what happened with my block.

It was a long time ago, before the consent form became obligatory for this sort of thing, but I never did another intercostal block.

Honesty is best; Learn to say sorry

A patient with lupus was not doing well, and it was decided to start her on antimalarials. I was away. My locum commenced chloroquine, which I never used because of the risk of ocular toxicity. I failed to notice this and when the GP (who was issuing prescriptions) queried what monitoring was necessary I said none (which is true for hydroxychloroquine, which is the only antimalarial I used).[167]

So perhaps it was no surprise that she developed retinal damage. I heard from the eye doctors and arranged to see her urgently. There was no doubting the diagnosis.

"What do I do?" she asked.

I suggested that as harm had been caused, for which we were all very sorry, she should consult a solicitor.

"Are you saying that I should sue?" she said.

I replied that if her legal advice was to that effect, then she should consider doing so.

She paused for a moment, then said "If I sue, will you still go on seeing me?"

There's trust for you. I said I would (and I did until I retired). She sued, the lawyers briefly discussed whether the GP was to blame (for prescribing without monitoring) or I was to blame (for giving wrong advice about monitoring to the GP). In the end it was me that was considered at fault and she had a compensation award in six figures.

What if I had blustered and denied all? I expect we would have been on the front page of some red-top. I have so many times witnessed attempts to cover up the truth. It isn't worth it. Apologise and explain. Chris Huhne would not have gone to prison if he had followed this advice.[168] And how different things would have been, in the terrible aftermath of the loss of

---

[167] Even the ophthalmologists have abandoned monitoring of hydroxychloroquine
[168] A Liberal Democrat politician of some skill, he persuaded his wife to take the rap for a speeding offence so he didn't lose his licence, and was found out with the ruin of his family and career (the marriage had already broken down, and the scorned wife couldn't keep her mouth shut). He also got another speeding ticket so it was all in vain anyway.

Flight MH17 over the Ukraine, if those responsible had held their hands up and apologised. Of course it would not have brought back the 298 lost souls. But to acknowledge such a frightful error rather than hash up a series of increasingly bizarre and contradictory confabulations would have nipped the recriminations and bitterness in the bud.

Patients respect honesty. I have seen many a complaint that would never have come in had the staff concerned given a full explanation and said "Sorry".

"It's nothing short of a medical miracle. She came here mildly arthritic, and walked away the winner of a multi-million dollar malpractice judgement."

Be nice to your elders and betters

Many has been the time that I have been quietly approached by a GP who has had a telephone confrontation with one of the hospital trainee doctors, whom they perceived as being aggressive, defensive, rude and difficult. Usually this was to try and stop a referral into hospital.

As a result, when I was Clinical Tutor and responsible for trainees' induction I would belabour the point and suggest that, while the occasional GP was lazy and useless the overwhelming majority were extremely clued up and highly experienced, knowing far more than they, the trainees did and often more than I did. I would then follow up by telling them that my wife was a local GP but did not practise under her married name and I wasn't going to tell them who she was.

We had a notable downturn in complaints at the start of a six-month posting. There is no place for cocky arrogance against the knowledgeable. A GP knows their patient. Also, even if a referral seems absurd it is happening because the GP is out of their depth, whether the pool of their knowledge is two inches or nine feet deep. And it's the patient that matters.

I put this in (1) because it's true and (2) because what I have written previously about general practice may have caused offence to any who did not note the light irony. I was a specialist who knew a lot about a little; GPs have to know a lot about everything. With two GP parents and a GP wife I should know.

NHS tourism: you won't stop it

I have seen a lot of this in various guises, beginning with a patient with Munchausen syndrome who pitched up when I was a houseman at the Middlesex Hospital, and reappeared a year or so later at the Hammersmith. He stayed long enough for me to take a full set of photographs – a symptom perhaps of his acceptance that his life would be forever peripatetic (although in the end he died under expert psychiatric care, and our growing understanding of the background to these sad cases has led to a marked decline in incidence).

We wrote the case up and had the distinction of having the correspondence columns of the British Medical Journal closed twice.[169] More of him later.

Two overseas patients pitched up in my rheumatology clinic. One had already been diagnosed in Turkey with a complex connective tissue disorder, but it became apparent that her stay in England was simply so she could get access to free drugs that were not available at home. The second was a gentleman from Somalia, although perhaps to call him gentle is an

---

[169] CA Pallis, AN Bamji, *McIlroy was here. Or was he?* BMJ 1979, i, 973-5. This was picked up by the national and international press and I gave an interview to the Canadian Broadcasting Company one evening during supper with my mother, much to my wife's irritation. We later discovered it had gone out live, all 20 minutes of it. The paper was a source of great anger, however; it was submitted, and the proofs came back, with me as the principal author, but appeared in print with the author order reversed. I do not to this day know who changed it but have my suspicions; ever after I have been scrupulous in advancing the interests of my trainees by putting their name first where appropriate.

oxymoron, because he knew exactly what he wanted (sick notes) and got aggressive when these were not forthcoming. I could find nothing wrong with him, but on the basis that by seeing him irregularly I kept him out of other people's hair I continued to review him until I retired.

The last example was an extraordinary story. Dr S turned up to do an unpaid clinical attachment when I was a medical registrar in Bath, years before cardiac investigations included ultrasound. He came from the Indian subcontinent and was a polite chap in his late twenties or early thirties – but he knew no medicine at all, offering a choice of therapy for every condition of either digoxin or antibiotics apparently chosen at random. I got rather tired of trying to teach the unteachable and palmed him off on my immediate junior – not really fair, but Richard said he would have a go with him.

Richard confronted me a few days later and started to tell me about the comatose patient with an intracerebral bleed that he had taken our friend to see. He could barely contain his laughter. He had asked Dr S to examine the patient. Our chap lifted one arm, and then the other, then letting go of each and watching them fall back to the bed. He turned to Richard and said "Oh. He has weakness". Richard suggested he should determine the level of consciousness. Dr S slapped the patient, pinched a leg (nothing happened) and said "Oh. The patient appears not to be responding". Richard enquired what he thought might be the matter, but it was clear he didn't know, so he was asked to look at the pupils, one of which was dilated and the other very small (indicating raised intracranial pressure on one side). He correctly identified the discrepancy. Richard asked what he thought this might be due to.

There was a long pause. Then Dr S said "Oh. (He always prefixed every remark with this) Sir, if both the pupils are very large and do not react to the light, then the patient – is dead!"

However the grilling was obviously too stressful for Dr S, as he took to his bed and sent a message that he was too unwell to attend the following day – indeed, he now had some chest pains, and asked if I would come and see him in his room. I attended. He was lying in bed in a brand-new pair of pyjamas, looking very miserable indeed. Dr S informed me that he thought he had angina. Noting the large number of textbooks, as brand-new as his nightwear, of every specialism on the shelf, and thinking that perhaps he knew something after all, I asked what led him to that conclusion. "Oh. You see, Doctor Bamji, angina often occurs in patients with coarctation of the aorta. I am having coarctation".[170]

Oh, yeah. Pull the other one. It's as rare as hen's teeth. But wearily I asked him to take his pyjama top off so I could listen to his chest and disabuse him of this foolish notion.

Bugger me. He had the classical signs of coarctation with a typical murmur. Furthermore his chest X-ray showed the characteristic rib notching seen in coarctation when blood diverts through the intercostal arteries.

We sent him to the cardiac surgeons in Southampton, who decided it did not require surgery, but it transpired that Dr S had come to the UK via the States, where his brother was apparently a doctor, and we assumed therefore that he had come over because the surgical option there was unaffordable, and he reckoned he could get operated upon here for nothing. However once it had been decided that nothing was to be done he left, and I have no idea what happened to him, but I doubt very much that he is working as a doctor. I hope not.

Doctors: listen; patients: be patient

Many a time my clinic nurse has come in to report unrest in the waiting room because I am running late. The patients rarely complain to your face (which upsets the nurses, who have taken all the muttering and backchat and are cross when the patient is all sweetness and light). I always apologise for the delay, and the patients always say "That's all right" not least because they know that once they are in they will get what time they need – thus, of course, contributing to the backlog. Actually once a patient didn't, and muttered at me, so I told her straight that the last patient had needed to have both her knees aspirated (there had been about 150ml in each which is eight large syringefuls so it took forever) and the one before had come up for her appointment despite the fact that her husband of 55 years had dropped dead two days before, and I was sure she would agree that that was not something that could be dismissed in thirty seconds, not least as she had spent the first two minutes weeping. Chastened, she did. She then produced a four-page symptom list. I listened. It's better to have a reputation as a doctor who

---

[170] Aortic coarctation is a severe narrowing of the body's main artery, the aorta, in the arch. Patients show signs of impaired blood flow particularly to the lower part of the body, and the left ventricle, fighting to squeeze blood through a narrow outlet, gets enlarged and tired.

listens (and therefore cares) than one who cuts people off short because they are clock-watching. This is why I think the growing habit of GPs of saying patients can only produce one complaint per appointment is stupid, uncaring and non-holistic. Talking makes people feel better – and it isn't just about their complaint today, it's about their family, hobbies, holidays (and, of course, yours), because patients go away thinking you are really interested in them. Which, of course, you are.

A man's best friend can have a man's worst diseases

A patient came to see me with back problems. There were some minor root claudication symptoms,[171] with sensory changes, and a feeling of weakness after prolonged walking, and I was explaining how we thought these occurred and what we might do when she said "Well! Our dog will need surgery, then." She explained that she owned a Labrador which demonstrated its affection by enthusiastic tail-wagging, but as it had aged it had begun to develop weakness of its hind legs, so after much wagging it was unable to stand, and dragged its legs along. If it rested it recovered in a few minutes. I wonder if this was the first time a dog was diagnosed in a rheumatology clinic.

Apropos dogs, my mother once made a diagnosis of mange in a patient (rather brilliantly, because she didn't know the patient had a dog). But she was rather a brilliant lady – and apropos that, my general practitioner wife, another such, made a diagnosis of diphtheria in one of her patients which was rather pooh-poohed by the microbiologist until the culture result came back. You see what I mean about GPs knowing a lot about everything. Hats off.

Self-help is cheap…

I have two examples of this.

A patient was sent up with severe cervical root irritation – pins and needles, numbness and weakness in the C6/7 distribution. She arrived rather

---

[171] For the lay reader, claudication results from a limited blood supply; in this instance the nerve root's supply is compromised by compression of the blood vessel, and the nerve lets you know by gradually failing to work. So you get pins and needles, then numbness, then loss of power. It comes on with walking and goes off when you stop; because of the anatomy it goes off quicker if you sit or bend forwards.

shamefaced and said she thought she was wasting my time, as three days previously she had fallen over and banged her head. To her amazement the arm symptoms had immediately vanished.

A second patient had low back pain – from her description a problem of the lumbar facet joints – and was sent to see me. Her pain had gone by the time of the appointment. It had disappeared instantly when, going through the patio doors to the garden, she had stepped on a slug and whoops! Over she had gone. I wrote a poem about this and sent it to her; she was delighted. [172]

I myself had low back pain that I attributed to irritation of a facet joint, which responded to manipulation, but I cannot explain in print exactly what this involved…

> *Moral:* Try falling over when you have cervicalgia or backache. Self-manipulation is cheaper than private physiotherapy or osteopathy.

…No help is cheaper

It is a truth universally acknowledged[173] that about 90% of patients with mechanical back pain, without "red flag" signs, will get better within 6 weeks. That's why our local triage service excluded patients that early on in the game. However, many patients will creep through the barrier and consult sooner, often telling you that their osteopathy or chiropractic has made things much better. I sometimes suggest that it has worked by lightening their wallet, and so reducing the inequality of weight in handbag or back pocket, but this does not always go down well, especially if you discover the practitioner is a relative or they suddenly realise they should have come to see me before going down the alternative route. But the natural history makes it very clear that improvement happens, whether there has been intervention or not.

Sometimes patients enquire whether such things might help, not having had them. I quote the case of a patient who came to see me with severe neck pain who had been manipulated under anaesthetic by a charlatan physiotherapist (I don't know which GP gave the anaesthetic, but I know the names of a couple who were involved). There were red flag signs, not least that the pain was exceedingly bad, and worse at night. An X-ray revealed that the fourth

---

[172] Now you want the poem, I suppose. It's at the very end. Read on!
[173] Jane Austen, *Pride and Prejudice*, opening sentence

cervical vertebra had been replaced by metastatic tumour from primary cancer in the lung. He was lucky the manipulation did not render him instantly quadriplegic, not that the poor soul survived for long.

What was worse was that he had had an x-ray and been told there was a displacement that required manipulating to get it straight. Another victim of the same scam told me quite explicitly that the X-ray he had been shown bore no relation to the one I had done. We suspected the same X-ray was being used for everyone (not least because the therapist always refused to let the patients have a copy). Eventually an end was put to the whole business, but not before his X-ray machine had been tested and shown to be leaking more rays round the back than passed through the tube.

I was telling this to another patient. He grinned and told me that his father had made this same therapist a piece of "diagnostic" equipment which had lots of flashing lights and dials on the outside and nothing but some connecting wires within.

Some tests test the imagination. Mr Fanshawe told me that he had been found to be allergic to tomatoes, and that his arthritis had got much better after avoiding them. The allergy test involved holding two thick wires for 10 minutes or so, and then a printout of all the allergens tested for was given to him. Had the list been sensible I suppose I might have been less sceptical, but it included a long list of parasites that could only have been culled from a textbook, including several flukes, hookworms and, best of all, *Diphyllobothrium Latum*, the fish tapeworm.[174] Now one does not exactly get an allergy to one of these, and it's not terribly likely you will have acquired one unless you have been eating lots of raw fish in Siberia. Actually that's not entirely fair, because it is also found in Scandinavia and Northwest America, but still. But think about it; if you were truly allergic to it, how can it live happily and undetected in your gut for years?

I have no idea why tomato avoidance helped Mr Fanshawe. All I do know is that if you take every exclusion diet recommended in rheumatoid arthritis and stick them together, you can eat little more than rice, fish and chicken and will probably develop beri-beri or scurvy. Or both.

---

[174] E.g. G Lepage, *Animals Parasitic in Man*, Dover Publications, 1963, a copy of which I required for 1st MB in 1967, and still possess.

Nothing is the best treatment

I was often approached by people with painful backs, necks, shoulders, elbows and other joints and asked for my recommended treatment. This could be awkward. They were not always patients of mine, and many had already sought advice from their own doctor or another specialist, though often they had not got that far and it seemed reasonable of me to diminish the load on the overstretched NHS by offering advice.[175] However this had its risks; first and foremost, it may be quite difficult to conduct an examination in the supermarket or on the street. To suggest treatment when you have not made a diagnosis is not really right. However, one can diagnose without an examination, or with a very cursory one. Making a diagnosis of tennis elbow requires no more than pressure from the thumb applied in the right place. My wife tells me I am viciously heavy-handed in my medical examinations but there we are. I am pictured opposite.

The downside is when you learn that your opinion has been repeated to the person's real GP and/or specialist, and has been ignored.

"That hurts, does it ?"

I would often be asked by these folk whether they needed physiotherapy, osteopathy (though quite a number had already been down that route

---

[175] Not any more. Having relinquished my licence to practice I may still offer advice but with the warning that I haven't a licence and may be well out of date – not that I am really.

already) or some other specialism, conventional or not. I would ask how long they have had the problem. It started three days ago, they say. So I would tell them what I would do if it was me – at least, I said "What would I do if it was me?" and paused. They looked expectantly. I said "Nothing".

Mostly their faces fell, or they looked confused. But very many musculoskeletal problems get better on their own. The process may take days, weeks or even longer; after I was knocked down by a car in front of which I had darted into the road, looking only the other way, my shoulder and neck pain took over six months to resolve, but resolve they did. Most back pain, assuming there are no red flag symptoms and signs, will resolve within six weeks. My acute lumbar disc prolapse, which confined me to a stick and left me taking half an hour to get down a flight of stairs, switched off within a minute some three weeks after onset. In anthropomorphising my disc I imagine the bit that was sticking out and pressing on nerves decided to drop off. So if you have any sort of treatment up to that time there is no way whatever of knowing whether the treatment has had an effect, or whether the problem got better because it was going to anyway. Probability is the latter. You have only to look at trials of tennis elbow treatments to find that most of them don't do anything.

So nothing can be a treatment. People don't like that. A treatment should surely be something. Nothing can be dressed up as "watchful waiting" – I used to write WWS in the notes for watch, wait and see – and it has the enormous advantage of being absolutely free.

"You've got a rare condition called 'good health'. Frankly, we're not sure how to treat it."

What would I do if it was me?

This really is a Very Useful Question.

Aspirin prevents my migraine attacks. Aspirin can cause significant bleeding in the gastro-intestinal tract. So – if I take aspirin, my risk of gradual brain atrophy may diminish, and I don't suffer from weekly visual disturbances. The risks of G-I bleeding pale into insignificance compared to the blessed relief of knowing I am not going to get migraine. So I take aspirin.

A patient with chronic widespread pain found that her symptoms were completely cured by taking hormone replacement therapy. Her GP, however, bang up to date with the risks of prolonged HRT, frightened her by telling her she was at very high risk of developing breast cancer, and she should stop at once. She asked my advice. I said that if I thought the symptom relief outweighed the (small-ish) risk of cancer then I would consider continuing.[176] She broke down in tears of relief and said that if she had been forced to stop she would have contemplated suicide. Her GP agreed to continue when confronted with the stark risk-benefit equation.

I saw a lot of people with severe arthritis of the knees who enquired about the possibility of knee replacement surgery. There are lots of things that might be significant; the level of pain, shortened walking distance, instability of the joint, fixed deformity (often arthritic knees, and elbows, lose full extension, and if a knee cannot straighten fully it is effectively short, putting strain on the other knee and hip. So – what would I do if it was me?

I might well recommend a surgical opinion. I could choose between two excellent surgeons, one who would operate at the drop of a hat and the other who would set out the risks of surgery graphically. "My knee replacements work in nine out of ten patients, who will be very satisfied" he would say "but that means that one out of ten are not happy. Also there is a one in one hundred and fifty chance that you will die under the anaesthetic."[177] Whether I thought the knee was ready for surgery or not would determine which surgeon got the patient. I would always warn those I sent to the latter what he would say (and it was remarkable how many came back to report, incredulously, that I was spot on). But I would pre-empt a referral with another Really Useful Question. I would ask the patient to ask themselves "Given the benefit and risks, can I go on like this?" – and if they showed any

---

[176] In 2019 research suggested the risk was double what had been previously thought.
[177] Peter Savage notes that this risk quote is obsolete; the 30-day knee surgery mortality rate is now one in four hundred. Things are getting better.

hesitation they were not ready. I would send them off with the enjoinder that once they had decided they could not go on like this, then it was time to act.

Such an approach reduces surgical workloads by changing from convenience to necessity.

If you can remember it's called Alzheimer's, you probably haven't got it.

I can't remember why I put this in.

Oh yes, I have. It was this nice little quote (I forget from where):

> Grant me the senility to forget the people I never liked anyway,
> the good fortune to run into the ones I do,
> and the eyesight to tell the difference.

As a corollary to this, remember that questions designed to test senility may not always add up correctly. I had a patient in who had been the victim of a frightening temporary loss of memory, transient global amnesia. She told me she had been asked for her age and couldn't remember it. Suddenly her date of birth popped into her head, and she delightedly revealed it. The doctor then gently asked whether her maths wasn't good enough for her to calculate how old she was.

"Oh yes" she replied, "but that's quite difficult when you don't know what year it is now!"

However there are occasions when you think you may be losing the plot. I went to a memorial service for a colleague and thought I should wear a suit. My usual one (bespoke, c.1986) was traditional and extremely heavy – not the sort of thing to wear on a hot summer's day, not least because a tiny moth hole had appeared in one sleeve. So I shuffled along the rail to find my other, lighter weight suit (c.1994, worn inside pocket, hole in one trouser pocket). It wasn't there, but a brand new made to measure pinstripe was. I could not recall buying it. I put it on anyway and attributed its snug modern fit to a change of personal shape (in other words I had got fat). On my way out I attempted to put my keys into the jacket pockets to find they were still sewn shut. Now I am wearing a suit that just fits, but is tight, that I don't recall buying, is so new the pockets are as sold, but is in my wardrobe.

I texted my son Nick. He was slimmer than me. He doesn't live at home and hasn't done for some years. Have you mislaid a suit? I asked. The reply came back "Erm, no. But if it's going begging…"

I wore the suit all day and was complimented on my trim appearance. When I got home I checked the sizes. Chest 39 inches (I am a 41). Waist 34 (I am 36). Inside leg 33 (I am 31). It was not my suit. Neither was I losing it. Nicholas had bought it for a job interview and had had no need to wear it since; he had forgotten it and it had escaped his moving-out of clothes and ended up with mine when we had moved. So I felt better.

I am still 41-36-31 but Nick found the suit – a tad snug. Dear boy, he has put on a few pounds. I bought two new suits and my tailor-made heavy number went to the charity shop, moth-hole and all.

A while after I wrote this a dear friend and colleague developed Alzheimers. I went to see him; he was his usual charming and urbane self, but conversation went in rapid and ever-decreasing circles. However he was obviously anxious to confide in me about his diagnosis, having previously assured me that he had mild cognitive impairment.

"It begins with M, I think" he said. He struggled to remember and called out to his wife.

"What is it they said I had" he asked.

"Alzheimers" she replied.

So the title of my little anecdote is not really funny at all.

Beware analogies. They can confuse

I suggested this analogy to a patient whose failure to improve as we tried serial disease-modifying drugs was distressing her; I was trying to explain that although we do the impossible at once, miracles take a little longer. Life is one long experiment, and drugs are a part of the experiment, I said.

Her husband, who had been a policeman in deepest south London, said that the junkie residents of "Cardboard City" at the Elephant & Castle used to say the same thing.

Perhaps another analogy would be wise. Help.

However – in this context it's important to remember that not only may you be testing the drug against the patient, but you may be using it as a test in itself. Thus a patient with polyarthralgia can be tested with steroids to make sure that it is not inflammatory; if it is, the patient will improve significantly (though usually not as dramatically as in PMR). If not, and interestingly in this event patients usually complain of odd side-effects, then you may presume ME, fibromyalgia, chronic pain syndrome or whatever name you care for. This is part of the diagnostic exclusion process (see above).

Look at the original material; do not base your decisions on second-hand work

I was once sent a short paper to review; four cases of an unusual problem, reflex sympathetic dystrophy (see above for its sometimes awful effects), had followed an attack of shingles.[178] The report stated that this was the first report in the English scientific literature.

RSD seems to be set off by many things. It was first described by a German called Sudek, so I set off to trawl the continental literature. I found a monumental review paper with hundreds of references, from which I uncovered the original paper written by Sudek – in German. Guess what. He had already described his syndrome post-shingles. The moral of this was that the Royal Colleges, in their exams, were perhaps over-hasty in removing French and German from their Membership examinations. Now, of course, almost all the literature is in English, and Google Scholar makes easy work of searching (in the old days we had to plough through huge volumes of "Index Medicus" in the library) and Google Translate will render any foreign text into English, or vice-versa. So maybe today's researchers will be more diligent, although one could nit-pick and say that strictly they were right because the paper was not in English. But it is easy to quote references that were quoted by someone else, without checking the original, and mistakes will occur as a result.

There is a postscript to this. I have been reading Anne Somerset's book "Unnatural Murder: Poison at the Court of James I (Weidenfeld & Nicolson, 1997). It had been sitting on my bookshelf unread since I bought it, thinking it looked a ripping yarn, but it has taken me 18 years to get round to it. Sir Edmund Coke, the Lord Chief Justice, was in charge of investigating the murder of Sir Thomas Overbury. He was by all accounts a fearsome man. Somerset writes "He had won his very first case – a libel suit – by catching

---

[178] A secondary reactivation of *Herpes Zoster*. If you haven't had chicken pox you can't get shingles.

out the lawyer on the opposing side who had quoted from a faulty English translation of the relevant statute, rather than consulting the original text in Latin. Though at times 'so fulsomely pedantic that a schoolboy would nauseate it', Coke had gone on to win great renown as a lecturer at one of the Inns of Court, characteristically enjoining his students 'always to read to the statutes at large and not to trust to the abridgements'. We are talking about the beginning of the seventeenth century. *Plus ça change…*

And a personal PPS… a short article appeared in a plastic surgery journal referencing the early history of phalloplasty (reconstruction of the penis) and quoting a review which suggested that the first such operation had been done in 1936 by a Russian surgeon, Nikolai Bogoraz (notable because he continued working despite having both legs amputated after he was run over by a tram). Now as a proselytiser for the British plastic surgeon, Harold Gillies, and having discovered the notes of his (and the world's) first female-to-male transformation I was interested to note a reference to his own paper on penile surgery from 1947. I obtained a copy.

Well. One of his cases referred to an eleven year follow-up. 1947 minus 11 equals 1936… so was Bogoraz the first? I worked out that Gillies had performed his surgery at St Bartholomew's Hospital, London, and went there to consult the archives. I was presented with an admissions book and theatre book covering that year. Sure enough, there were the entries. First operation? 1935.[179]

The customer is always right

If a patient won't take pills you prescribe it is not for you to get cross. A patient once complained to his GP that the new pills were different from the old ones. When asked in what way, he said that when he put them down the toilet they floated, which the previous lot had not. If a patient won't, he won't, short of you going home with him and forcing them down his throat each day (and staying there until you are sure he has swallowed them and not kept them in his cheek and spat them out).

You may however wish to take precautions if a psychiatric patient is off their drugs, especially if they have delusions. While I understand in a way the drive to provide care in the community it has led to some awful catastrophes. Maybe the answer is in this next cartoon…

---

[179] Andrew N. Bamji, Peter J. Taub, *Phalloplasty and the tube pedicle: a chronological re-evaluation.* Eur J Plast Surg 2019; https://doi.org/10.1007/s00238-019-01539-5

I worked briefly in an ice cream parlour when I was a medical student (serving knickerbocker glories as well as the bewildering variety of flavours and specialities (note: medical subdivisions are specialties. My banana splits were matchless). I also did some of the backroom stuff, making up cartons and delivering frozen basins to the cassata chef (who called me Dottore Banditto). On the door between the factory and the shop was a notice with the header of this vignette. It's just as true in medicine.

I lived in fear for a decade after breaking the rule. The parlour (Marine Ices in Haverstock Hill, London – some of you will know it or of it) was opposite the Roundhouse, which in the sixties was becoming the place for weirdos, pop stars and political activists. A West Indian group turned up and I served them their cornets (chocolate and rum butter was a common combination). One of the group handed the cornet on to another, who looked disapproving, muttered something and handed it back, and it was held out to me.

"It's too small" he said", "put more on". I told him it was a full measure, and no. The recipient gave me a look but walked away. I later learned he was a notorious local gangster by the name of Michael X (also known as Michael de Freitas and Abdul Malik, he set up a Black Power group in North

London). Violence was part of his stock-in-trade. I had been clocked. Would he return for revenge?

Thankfully not. Skipping bail on an extortion charge he escaped to Trinidad, set up a commune, was convicted of the murder of two of its members and hanged in 1975. But that ice cream haunts me…

There is another way the customer may be right. As a student I was taught that in ankylosing spondylitis the first movement to be lost in the spine is lateral flexion. It's one of those curious facts one simply accepts. I never thought why, but merely repeated it to iterations of medical students and trainees. One day I was so pontificating in front of a patient (incidentally it's worth noting that patients notice pontification and will say in their feedback that they prefer you to address your remarks to them rather than to the students). The patient asked why. I said it was merely an interesting observation. He said "No it's not. There's a very good reason why it goes first". He smiled as he said "When do you ever do it? You said yourself that if you don't exercise you get stiff."

Think about it. The only time I laterally flex my cervical spine is in a bookshop to read the titles on the spines (you flex the opposite way on the continent, a bit like driving). So ever since I have incorporated this astute comment from a bricklayer by asking the students why, and triumphantly revealing the answer in my pompous twaddle.

The third way (nothing to do with Tony Blair) is illustrated by this tale. We were seeing a girl of 26 with cerebral palsy in the multidisciplinary rehabilitation clinic. A little while before, her father had written me a note, to which I had replied. The consultation went quite reasonably; we sorted out changes to her care plan and, as there were nursing students and a new trainee doctor in addition to the six permanent staff, I did my "I am a listening doctor" act and asked "Have you any questions?"

Tracey smiled and said "Yes."

I sat back with a patronising smile.

"I am 26 years old" she said, "so why did you write a letter to my dad and not to me?"

Nowhere to go, nowhere to hide. I, a consultant for 26 years, was horribly and rightly humiliated in front of an audience.

Patients can have good ideas

This is another of those "Why did I not think of that?" moments. How do you get children to take tablets three times a day? They always forget the lunchtime dose, either because they forget to take it, or forget to take it (to school, that is). One mother had a simple and probably very sensible answer – before school, after school and before bed, which was probably a better 24 hour spread anyway. However indicating to patients that they must have a four times a day (qds to old-fashioned docs) regime can cause problems, as I discovered when one patient told me how tired the course of treatment had made him. He was setting his alarm clock for 2am to get the fourth dose timed correctly and then couldn't get back to sleep.

"So you think there's nothing wrong with me, then"

This is a common response to a negative consultation in which the patient remains unhappy, or unclear, about what you are thinking. It is never a question, always a statement. It is usually down to my (our) inability to decide on a clear diagnosis because all the tests are negative.

There are a variety of correct answers to the challenge:

1. If there was nothing wrong, then you wouldn't be here
2. Something is very obviously wrong, but I cannot yet decide exactly what
3. I wish I could give you a clear diagnosis as much as you want one – but I can't do so yet
4. No. I want to get to the bottom of this as much as you do

Failure to recommence dialogue with these, or similar phrases, will reinforce the patient's feeling of rejection, and they will set off, disgruntled, to bother someone else.

Being a null-hypothesist may influence people, but it can lose you friends

Much research is based on the null hypothesis; in outline, this requires that when you set out to prove something, you have only got to find one small thing that irrefutably refutes it (*sic*) to know that it cannot be. As I have noted, such a Small Thing is often known as a Black Swan on the basis that all swans were white – until someone got to Australia and proved they weren't. When you are faced by bright-eyed, keen managers purveying a new approach to something it may be easy to be swept along by their enthusiasm. But what you should do is analyse what they are trying to sell and find one reason why their solution will not work. Just one. This may not be difficult. It may not need to be precise. For example, if you are shown a system that works from the USA, you may stall everything by asking why, if the solution is so brilliant, hospitals X, Y and Z in Idaho, Illinois and Iowa have abandoned it. Or you might ask why, if the concept is so good, no-one except the single speaker hawking it round every management conference has implemented it. You will not be popular – everyone hates a killjoy – but you may save time, money and stress. You may also save a PR disaster. I was invited to learn about one of these new initiatives by visiting the United States together with a number of my fellow clinical directors at the hospital – I suspect on the basis that we "opinion leaders" would become cheerleaders. I managed to scotch this one by pointing out that it would look bad going on an American junket when we were cutting staff.

If cleaning is a problem, ask the cleaner for the solution, not the Chief Executive

Don't even ask the management consultants. They came in to reorganise our outpatients because there was an ongoing problem of notes getting lost. They analysed procedures including the file tracking system, which they reckoned was the problem, and decided on a solution. Unfortunately they failed to ask anyone who actually worked in outpatients what they thought, and their ideas were rubbished (but implemented – the manager trying to sell the concept to the staff refused to listen).

Guess what.

After about 6 weeks the plan failed and normal service was resumed. I did actually suggest that if notes were failing to be tracked out of outpatients then perhaps they shouldn't be tracked in – but tracked to the consultant whose clinic was there that day – but expensive investment was made in trolleys and all sorts, the staff were furious and patient confidentiality was compromised (this was an unforeseen consequence of leaving notes in the trolleys but forgetting that the nurses looking after them were also, as part of the new system, scurrying round trying to find missing results and leaving the trolleys unattended). Curiously one of the faults pointed out by a visit of the much-derided Care Quality Commission was exactly this problem.

*Moral: If you make a plan (or write an article) get someone else to
look for the flaws (PS please tell me of any in this book)*

I designed a lovely invitation for my 60th birthday party which started "Your
are invited…". My son spotted it as soon as he received it. My wife and I
had both missed it, being too busy cooing over the picture of me as a baby
(and nobody else invited commented, so perhaps they missed it too, or
perhaps were too polite to raise senility issues or were too struck by how
little I had changed). Did you spot it? Look again.

Actually we had a little problem over cleaning. A circular came round on the
global email noting that staff were bringing their own cleaning materials and
air fresheners into the hospitals, and as these would by definition not have
been checked for safety by the cleaning company (or PFI Partner, as it was
called) any such materials would be confiscated.

Someone was paid good money to come up with this little piece of Stasi-
dom. Three questions come to mind (1) why do staff feel it is necessary to
bring in their own cleaning stuff (rhetorical, really) (2) is it really likely that
the Cif bought in Tesco (or my Crabtree & Evelyn air-freshener) would be
sold if they were unsafe and (3) could any removal of said personally
purchased products amount to theft?

If driving is a problem, beans must be spilled

Most people know that if they develop certain medical conditions then limits
may be put on their driving. These include recent heart attacks, cardiac
arrythmias, epilepsy and ataxia (which is unsteadiness and incoordination
due to various neurological diseases, such as multiple sclerosis. Most people
also know that they should not drive if they cannot see. Most people do not
know that (a) there are people who continue to drive when they should not
and (b) if their doctor knows they are doing this, in the UK they can shop
them to the Driver and Vehicle Licensing Agency, DVLA for short.
(individual confidentiality is outweighed by the common good).

I have seen a number of such cases and indeed with my then colleague John
Winfield wrote up several of them in a report published in the Journal of
Traffic Medicine, which I doubt you have heard of (we hadn't).[180]

You tell me if you would tell on the following.

---

[180] J Winfield, A Bamji, *Medical fitness to drive: some practical problems*. J Traffic
Med 1980; 8: 54-56

Mr Peters had had a stroke, as a result of which he had a left hemianopia, or in English the stroke had damaged the right visual cortex, and he had lost the entire left side of his vision (the optic nerves cross over on their way to the brain). Such loss is sometimes not realised by the sufferer, a phenomenon known as sensory inattention. Although he also had one-sided weakness he could just about manage to steer and change gear. The problem was that the rehabilitation centre where he was being seen as an outpatient was on a small lane off a dual carriageway. To go home he had to turn right. That was fine, as he could see traffic approaching – until he got to the central reservation when it came from left field, which he did not have. After two near misses and a scrape we suggested he should stop driving, but he didn't.

Mr Andrews had multiple sclerosis which was gradually worsening. He had a right sided intention tremor; when he started an action, particularly with his leg, the opposing muscle groups no longer worked smoothly against each other and the leg juddered uncontrollably. He had been a bus driver but stopped when he had to brake suddenly near Marble Arch, his leg did the juddery thing and the bus bunny-hopped into the car in front. So far, so good, but he had become a driving instructor, and to stop his feet from jumping off the pedals in his own automatic car he had made a set of wooden blocks which he could strap to the pedals and then to his feet.

Miss Fletcher had had an accident in her sports car, sustaining a serious head injury and various limb injuries. We saw her two years later. She was emotionally very labile, and was markedly ataxic, but lacked insight into the extent of her disabilities. She wished to buy a new sports car and expected us to confirm she was fit to drive.

Mr Johnson came for rehabilitation with a diagnosis of multiple sclerosis. He came in a wheelchair, having driven himself to my unit. His muscle spasm was so severe that we thought he was as serious risk to himself as well as everyone else on the road but he ignored our advice not to drive and said he had notified his disability and that the DVLA had said he could drive.

You shopped the lot? Well done. So did we. However Mr Johnson turned out to be a little bit more complicated. When I checked with the DVLA to be sure he had been cleared to drive not only had he not notified them, but his record showed he had been disqualified for drink-driving and was banned. Thereafter his whole story unravelled; our neurologists confirmed that he was faking all his symptoms and there was nothing wrong with him at all. When his wife was confronted with this web of deceit she was aghast and left him.

Good material can be destroyed by bad presentation

I was well-known for taking my afternoon nap on a Friday afternoon in the medical meeting.

I cannot be alone in dropping off when the lights go down and the Powerpoint goes up. It no longer seemed to matter what time of day it is outside, and as I did not switch time zones for conferences I could not blame jet lag. During a particularly boring session at an international meeting I came up with the following reasons (excuses).

1. Ambience (a). It is dark
2. Ambience (b). My neighbour has gone to sleep already
3. Content (a). The talk is stupefyingly boring
4. Content (b). Also I have heard it all before
5. Auditory input (a). The speaker drones in a hypnotic monotone, without modulation…
6. Auditory input (b). …and possibly with an impenetrable accent
7. Presentation. The performance has no drama. Some brilliant researchers are very poor communicators (which shouldn't encourage lecturers to leap about like scalded baboons) and some patronise us old fogeys
8. Imagination failure. All the data is on the slides, and the presenter reads it all
9. Overload (a). All the data is on the slides in such quantity that it becomes an incomprehensible blur
10. Overload (b). It is all too difficult to grasp (I was getting better at immunology, but not a lot)

I have nodded off in committee (reasons 2, 5 and 6 above) and been perilously close even in conference sessions I have chaired. One thing that did keep me awake was when a presenter decided to use every Powerpoint transition at random – but you get so wound up trying to predict the next one that you forget the message. Another was in those (now thankfully rare) multilingual conferences when I could not decide whether to try and listen to the native French or try and match the slides (done with double projection and out of sync) with the simultaneous translation (which was usually not simultaneous at all). And the last pick-me-up was the illiterate presenter in whose slides it became obligatory to spot the spelling mistakes.

However there were two redeeming features of my somnolence.

1. I did not snore. I recall one poor elderly chap awakening the whole hall, but not himself, during a particularly tedious talk in which

interminable gene sequences, and their amino-acid variations, were presented, as he had a dramatic nightmare and began to mumble in a growing crescendo

2. Somehow I remained able to hold the thread; waking one afternoon I realised I was being asked a question and, to my surprise (never mind that of the audience), gave a lucid and relevant response.

My son told me that I should keep a can of "Red Bull" in the car in case of travel fatigue. Maybe I should also have kept one in my conference bag, or drunk coffee between sessions instead of tea (except too much coffee upsets the gut, and Red Bull is quite disgusting and I cannot think of anything worse). Or stand up. But this can be disconcerting to those behind you. Perhaps lecturers could take note and think how they might engage the continuing attention of their audience.

My Hammersmith boss, neurologist Chris Pallis, was utterly fanatical about presentations. In those days one used cards put on an epidiascope. You would create the presentation, his secretary would type it onto the cards and he would then go through it with us, revising every card (which the poor secretary would have to type out again) until it was perfect. It was then fit for presentation at the Grand Round in front of the professor of medicine, Sir Christopher Booth (with whom my Chris did not get on and longed to score points off) and assorted worldwide dignitaries, who would take ages to be introduced.

I presented the patient with Munchausen syndrome mentioned in a previous essay who had used (or abused) the Hammersmith a few times, with photos and all. At the end of the case the Prof lumbered to his feet. "Well" he said "the diagnosis is so obvious only a fool would miss it. Which team was he admitted under?"

"Yours, Professor" I said.

The howl of laughter that greeted this was not good for my career prospects but the glee on my boss's face was matchless. And everyone was very awake.

Presenting abroad

Now that you can translate stuff online you can have a jolly good stab at presenting in a foreign language assuming you have the rudiments. My French accent is reasonable and I thought it would be polite to try and address a conference of the Union des Blessés de la Face (the Gueules

Cassées) in Paris in French, half-expecting that the participants' English would be poor and that some of my message would get lost in translation. I converted my script using Google translate, ran it past a couple of bilingual friends to tidy it up, and read it. Slightly to my surprise some of the French presenters read theirs too. They all thought I was totally fluent, which was a problem at question time and slightly awkward during the rest of the conference, because my comprehension is not reasonable. A useful phrase was, I found "Un peu plus lentement, s'il vous plaît".

Interviews and how to get there

It may not be as easy now because of the prescriptive (and in my view idiotic) way in which a CV has to be submitted for a job application, but there are some things I told trainees to bear in mind when they applied, and were interviewed, for a job.

1. If your CV is crap or boring, you won't get to the interview. There are lots of people with reasonable or even good CVs and yours has to stand out above them.
2. Make sure you have not mis-spelt anything (such as the name of the hospital you are applying to or currently working at, the name of the consultant you hope to join or the name(s) of referees. I have seen all of these; they suggest laziness. I confess that when trying to read a list of past jobs it drives me mad when they are presented in reverse order – but this not appears to be custom and practice. Think about it.
3. Add something of interest to your otherwise bald and unconvincing narrative. It may strike a chord. As an example I offer the clinical attachment doctor from overseas who came to see me because he had applied for zillions of jobs and not got an interview. His CV was bland and unenticing. Under "Interests" he had put down "Swimming". When I explored this he told me, diffidently, that he had been a member of his country's Olympic swimming team. So on his next application he added this information, was short listed, got the job and the rest was history.
4. Treat every job application as if this post is the only thing you want in the whole world. If you cannot, don't apply.
5. Be yourself when you go for the pre-interview visit (it may be worth asking, even if there appears to be no visit suggested, as it shows keenness). People can tell when you are hamming it up.
6. My father-in-law was Personnel Director for a large company and taught me many of the tricks used to flush out the unsuitable. These

included inviting candidates to lunch and plying them with drink to see whether they would refuse (or could hold it) and observing their table manners and conversation in an informal setting; in those days such politically incorrect things went on. In medicine we had sherry parties at which wives were sometimes invited also. Dearie me. I went to one place, met the team and went to lunch with two of the consultants in the department. They took two courses; so did I. Have you ever tried to eat tinned grapefruit segments out of a metal ice-cream bowl with only a plastic teaspoon? Well don't.

7. Be yourself in the interview. I went to one interview and was told by informal feedback that I had been too cocksure (it still took them over 40 minutes to deliberate on what I understood was a shoo-in for the other main candidate, though perhaps they were having tea). At my next interview I intimated I would do anything I was asked. As you can guess the message I got back on that was that I seemed rather supine.

8. They are interviewing you, not the other way around. That bit was in the pre-interview visit. If you start telling people that the job they have carefully constructed needs major revision to fit you, then unless you have a remarkable case you will be politely (or otherwise) shown the door. I experienced this once with a candidate who read a prepared statement before the interview even began. As far as the clinicians were concerned they were toast. Strangely a non-exec director from the business world was rather impressed.

Having made the point about having an interesting CV, when I was being interviewed for my very first job by Dr John Nabarro at the Middlesex Hospital, a man of formidable intellect and strong, even terrifying personality as I mentioned earlier, he smiled at me.

"You have an interesting and broad CV" he said and proceeded to list the various extracurricular activities I had put down to make myself look desirable. I started off displaying my enthusiasm over some of them.

He paused.

"So, with all these things… when are you going to have time to do my job properly?"

One can over-egg the pudding. I didn't get the job.

Exam experiences

I was examining for Membership of the Royal College of Physicians with Professor Parveen Kumar at a London hospital. The restructured PACES exam for what used to be known as Part 2 was quite new, as was the use of actors to role-play in the section designed to test the softer parts of medicine. The scenario was complex - a father had been summoned to hospital where his teenage son had been taken after a sudden collapse playing football; he was alone, as his wife could not be contacted, and was, it suddenly turned out, of the orthodox Jewish faith. The salient points were thus the difficulty of breaking bad news to one parent alone, followed by the need to reconcile the requirement for a coroner's post-mortem with the family's need because of their religious belief for a funeral the next day.

The actor, whom we met for the first time some five minutes before the start, was charming and "resting"; he gave us some interesting insights into his work as a surrogate patient. The candidate started well, but when the second part of the scenario began to unroll things got rather tense. Playing his role exactly, our actor began to lose it. He became argumentative, angry and upset; not expecting quite such vehemence we sat, increasingly uneasy, as the temperature rose, and then – the candidate said fairly bluntly that any decision on post-mortem, burial etc was not something he could discuss further as the law was the law.

Oh dear. Our actor banged the table, screamed (with expletives deleted) "Are you telling me that I cannot even bury my son according to our traditions? Do you even understand them, and what you are saying? You have no idea!" and then burst into tears.

It was the most realistic simulation I have ever seen. It was absolutely, totally, spot-on, brilliant. Why the man was "resting" when his method acting was of such quality I have no idea. We were however more than uneasy. Gobsmacked? Appalled? The right phrase eludes me. The candidate was now pale and almost as upset as the actor was feigning. The bell sounded.

As a result of our experience I understand that new instructions were issued to the actor cohort that they should not over-egg the pudding. Our candidate passed.[181] I bet he won't forget his experience in a hurry.

---

[181] Curiously the scoring system for MRCP under the PACES regime gave a total of 42, which is of course the ultimate answer (see Douglas Adams' *The Hitch Hiker's Guide to the Galaxy*). After this event it was reduced to 41 although Dame Parveen assures me our experience had nothing to do with it.

The clinical part of the exam sends candidates round a series of "stations", one for each major specialty and one for a mishmash of minor things. At each station there are several volunteer patients, many of whom have been exam subjects before, and each candidate gets one. A one-line history is given, and the candidate invited to examine the patient. Briefly, concisely, accurately, confidently, sensibly. At least, that's how it should be. But often isn't. There are some things in the exam setting that irritated me intensely.

1. Examination of the shoulder. This takes place at the cardiac station. The arm is held by the wrist and firmly yanked high in the air, sometimes occasioning a yelp from the unsuspecting patient. This manoeuvre is supposed to show that the candidate knows how to find a collapsing pulse. I never have. A sphygmomanometer to measure the blood pressure seems more useful.

2. Common sense failure. This is a neurology station phenomenon. The card over the bed says "This patient has difficulty walking. Examine their legs". It seems to me that the best way of seeing why a patient has difficulty walking is to ask them to walk. Most candidates spend all their time examining and re-examining sensation, reflexes, lifting and dropping the legs and occasionally trying the heel-shin test, all on the bed.[182] They then get the diagnosis wrong.

3. Heavy-handedness. Best seen at the abdo station. The candidate locks both hands together and makes a karate chop movement, fingertips first, under the right sided ribs ("I am feeling for the liver, Sir!") or over the top of the pelvis. I once watched this done on a patient with a renal transplant and had to hang behind afterwards to make sure the transplanted kidney hadn't been ruptured.

4. Ignorance - the mother of invention. A respiratory station one; the candidate has no idea what s/he is hearing and makes up a plethora of amazing signs. Come on guys! There are only a few things it can be!

5. Ignorance per se - on the examiner's part, as the candidate launches into a long discussion of the various deletions, duplications, snips and other arcane genetic bases of ataxia etc which the examiner

---

[182] In the heel-shin test the patient is asked to put one heel onto the other knee, and then run the heel up and down the shin. This tests weakness and ataxia, where action and counteraction of opposing muscles is not smooth and the heel wobbles uncontrollably.

knows nothing about but has to give a high mark even if it's all bullshit because it's impressive bullshit but may actually be right.

6. The two mark difference. Usually occurs when the case is in one examiner's specialty, and they mark more viciously than the ignorant other. A rheumatology example is in discussion of the acute hot joint, where administration of antibiotics before aspiration will provoke a bad fail from me but not often from a gastro or neuro colleague. It always provokes a local enquiry, which is uncomfortable.

7. Eye, eye! As a high myope with masses of floaters I could not see the retina through an ophthalmoscope unless I was very patient, or desperate. Retinal photos are now so quick and good they should replace face-to-face contact - a consideration during a flu epidemic.

8. 'Allo, 'Allo! Why are candidates taught to waste their first half-minute saying "Hello Mr Anyone! My name is Dr Someone - is it all right if I examine you?" Yeah, like, the patient wouldn't be there if it wasn't. I have been tempted to prime a patient to say no and see what happens.

9. ABC. Who teaches these things? If I hear it one more time I will scream. It is usually clear which candidates have been on which course.[183]

10. Repetition; you, the examiner suddenly realises they have a candidate they have seen before. Perhaps you should withdraw; the look of horror on their little faces when they see you is pitiful, and it makes one feel terribly guilty to fail them again (I should know).

Actually, not quite lastly. I present you with a question. You are asked to examine the abdomen of a patient, and as you have been unnerved by your experience with the last three cases you have seriously overheated in the hot ward (no windows open, air conditioning off because of the legionella) and a bead, or beads, of sweat have formed upon your stressed brow. As you bend over to examine your patient, the beads coalesce, run down the side of your nose and drip onto the patient.

Do you

---

[183] Stands for Airway, Breathing, Circulation

1. Ignore it and hope no-one noticed
2. Apologise profusely, and extract a ragged tissue in which you have already blown your nose, and blot your brow
3. Apologise profusely, and extract a ragged tissue in which you have already blown your nose, and blot the patient
4. Apologise profusely, and ask the examiner for a clean handkerchief, paper towel or swab to blot the patient
5. Burst into tears and run

This happened in my MRCP Part 2. One of the examiners was the Professor of Medicine at the distinguished hospital where the exam was being held, the other was the Chairman of the General Medical Council. I chose option 1 and passed.

When the consultant goes away the service continues; when the secretary is away everything collapses

No comment necessary. Just wait.[184] Or ask your patients.

Learn the difference between absolute and relative risk

Read the statins section for more information, or return to Goldacre's "Bad Science" or listen to Wolfgang Gaissmeier from the Harding Center for Risk Literacy in Berlin, whom I have mentioned previously.[185] Or all three.

> *Corollary: if everyone tells you that you are wrong, it may be true but not always*

It can be quite a labour of love telling people you are right, but it becomes frustrating, as Galileo and Cassandra discovered, when no-one believes you. Actually I decided to call myself Cassandra in some of my writings, but was berated by Professor Allyson Pollock, a noted critic of privatisation in the NHS, who said she had prior claim. The evidence suggested she was right. So I have decided on Casilles, an amalgam of the prophetess with Achilles,

---

[184] A letter in "The Times" (August 10th 2010) makes an identical point
[185] Or read G Gigerenzer *et al, Helping doctors and patients make sense of health statistics*. Psychological Science in the Public Interest November 2007 vol. 8 no. 2 53-96

who went off to sulk in his tent during the siege of Troy. I could be Galileo, I suppose. It's a bit more classy.

Most counter-intuitive plans are flawed

If something looks as if it won't work, then it probably won't. So spend a lot of time trying to work out why it won't. You only need the one good reason (this is a variation of the null hypothesis theory; Black Swans again).

Be prepared for the flip patient

There is something about cardiac patients. Maybe perioperative oxygen starvation does something weird to their sense of humour. Years ago I had a convalescent patient post aortic valve replacement (in the 1970s we gave them two weeks at the country branch of the Brompton Hospital to recover). Almost before I had finished clerking him he had quadrupled my selection of Jewish jokes (he was of course of that persuasion – they seem the only group ready to diss themselves – and the late Michael Winner ran a lovely series of Hymie jokes in his "Sunday Times" column) but told me how he had upset his surgeon. Way ahead of his time this nice chap had gone through all the possible complications and risks before allowing his – and now my – patient to consider the operation and in serious manner listed every possible complication.

He was also one of those rare surgeons who encourage dialogue and asked if there were any questions.

"Yes, just one", said Joe Cohen. "After the operation will I be able to swim?"

Obviously the surgeon was relieved to have such a simple question.

"Of course!" he replied.

"Excellent," said Mr C, "because I can't swim now!"

I pre-empt this when patients ask if they can drive after a shoulder/wrist/elbow injection along the same lines. Sometimes it breaks the tension.

226

Sometimes not. A joke is not always seen. I fondly recall my classmate at Medical School, Brian Heng, who would get the joke a good ten minutes after everyone else and then puzzle us all with an outburst of mirth. But the po-faced husband of a lady with a trochanteric bursitis sticks in my mind. She groaned and whined as I examined her, and then again as I marked the spot (a fingernail indent is a good trick; for a more professional approach use a retracted ballpoint. Try them). I remarked to my clinic aide that she was obviously sensitive and would perhaps benefit from the wooden spoon to bite on. She replied with a quiver in her voice that it had gone AWOL, and we giggled.

Two weeks later the complaint letter arrived from Po-face.

"He hurt her again and again although she had told him already where it hurt (me, identifying the most tender spot, which is the best to inject). Then he said she would need the wooden spoon to bite on BUT IT COULD NOT BE FOUND!"

Moral: Watch who you jest with

Watch what you put in a letter; someone might read it

I was asked to see a patient with neck pain. She had fallen over in a supermarket (usual thing – slipped on a spillage). When she came in, with a relative, she was completely spaced out. Indeed she fell asleep while I was attempting to take the history.

It turned out that her husband had dropped dead only a week before. Naturally she was devastated and her GP had put her on sleeping pills and antidepressants which were clearly in her system.

I arranged physiotherapy, wrote back to the GP that she was difficult to examine because she was drugged up to the eyeballs and thought no more about it.

About two years later a solicitor's letter turned up. Damages were not only being claimed from the supermarket for her pain and distress, but an apology was now required from me because she had been distressed and angry to read my letter to the GP with the eyeballs bit.

This was before patients could by right read all medical notes and had I known she would read it I would perhaps have rephrased what I said. However, the tone of the solicitor got to me. I wrote back (expressing sincere regret at his client's distress) explaining the circumstances and ending "Therefore I consider the phrase 'drugged up to the eyeballs' was an exact description of her clinical state which I am prepared to justify in court".

I heard no more.

Read your letters before letting them out

I knew a medical secretary once who got so fed up with her boss not reading his letters, but just signing them, that she typed a polemic to a GP accusing him of incompetence, stupidity and questionable parentage. He signed it. She showed him what he had done, and he never did it again.

This was the same secretary who invented verbal constipation by typing "He takes laxatives for his vowels". Easy slip – look at your keyboard.

Also watch out for the missing "not", which when the letter says "I have told her firmly that she has got cancer" can be quite important, and check drug doses. Your regular secretary may know that methotrexate is given weekly, and thus correct your dictated letter saying daily, but the temp might not; nor will the outsource slave in Mumbai.[186]

A nice more recent one was a new protein belonging to a chap called Benjamin Stone. Ben Stone's protein. Geddit?[187] There are also two quite pretty girls you can find on Google Images called Gillian Barry, though interestingly if you type this name into main Google the first thing that pops up is Guillain-Barré syndrome. Work that one out.

---

[186] Some hospitals decided to save money by arranging for electronically dictated letters to be sent to Bangalore for typing by an army of clerks. They thought they could get rid of the secretaries this way. Tests of the service were conducted with excellent results. However, no-one realised that the best clerks were used on the pilots, and once the contract had been signed then lesser beings took over, and the quality plummeted. So the old secretaries had to be retained to check and correct the returned letters. Saving? None.

[187] Fair's fair; a lay person will not have heard of Bence-Jones protein, a finding in multiple myeloma

Always believe what a patient tells you

If the patient tells you they have pain in the right leg and you are sure they don't have directional confusion, then they have pain in the right leg.[188] If the MRI scan shows a disc prolapse on the left, it is irrelevant.

This is an example both of the useless investigation (in fact, in most cases, the pain is referred pain from the facets and is not root pain, so an MRI is not an appropriate investigation, which you should have worked out from a proper history and my table earlier) and of the need to take a proper history. If something in it doesn't quite fit, explore further. Are all the symptoms part of one thing, or could more than one thing be going on?

Don't always believe what a patient tells you

They may confabulate because their brain is rotted by alcohol or worse, or they may be after something. When writing reports never be definite; always hedge what you say with "She told me that…" or "he described how the accident happened by saying…". After all, you weren't there yourself.

I had a policeman patient with back pain who was recovering slowly with physiotherapy; I reviewed him now and then to check on things (you can tell this was a long while ago – back patients are one-stop now).

I had a call asking if I could speak to his superiors about his prospects for returning to work. I suppose I should have been suspicious when the two officers who came to see me had enough scrambled egg on shoulders and hats for a family full English breakfast. They talked me through the history and I confirmed that recovery was slow but would in my estimation be complete in another couple of months.

They exchanged a glance.

Then one said "Dr Bamji, given your knowledge of his condition, would it surprise you to know that last week he was observed climbing a ladder to the roof of his house with a roll of roofing felt over his shoulder?"

Er, yes.

---

[188] Directional confusion: Left-right confusion and a tendency to become disoriented or lost. May be related to difficulty remembering sequences and short-term memory deficits.

Another patient had come with severe back pain, barely able to move and sweating at every attempt at examination. His referral letter was of the "This is a heartsink" variety. He too went to physiotherapy (and the Pain Clinic). A short while later I was contacted by the local council to ask my opinion on his disability. He was applying for a grant to adapt his home for downstairs living as he was on the point of becoming dependent on a wheelchair. The council wanted me to cast my eye over something they had been sent.

It turned out to be a videotape shot by a disgruntled neighbour who was fed up with this chap repairing cars on his drive and in the cul-de-sac they lived in; access was often impossible because of the various vehicles parked everywhere. The neighbour had set the camera up in his upstairs from bedroom and the tape covered three seasons, with commentary. My disabled patient was seen taking car batteries out, carrying them to his garage and in the *pièce de résistance* climbing a very tall stepladder and trimming a huge Leylandii hedge with a pair of shears. I was more "disabled" than he was.

My report was not exactly helpful to his plan to upgrade the house and I had an extremely abusive phone call asking what the hell I was about. I told him I didn't like liars and that the council had shown me something that proved he was a liar. "Goodbye!" I said cheerfully, though not feeling it. I wondered if he might ever turn up for a fight (and no, I didn't tell him what the evidence actually was, or he might have torched the neighbour's house).

I asked another patient, whose cough was fruitily horrible and who I knew had been a lifelong smoker, whether it might be wise to give up the fags. With a happy smile she said that she had. Whereupon her sister, who had accompanied her to clinic, grabbed her handbag and grim-faced, without a word, emptied the contents onto my desk. Here they are.

There were three inhalers, a hairbrush, two scrumpled tissues and a packet of Polos – and a cigarette lighter and packet of 20, half empty.

You cannot confiscate patients' possessions, on the whole. But Mrs Rose's sister tore each fag in half and tipped them, and the packet, into my waste paper basket.

Apropos that, if one sees a patient with weight loss, looking awful, who you think might have lung cancer, you ask if they smoke. The exchange that follows that question is diagnostic.

"No, Doctor, I've given them up."

"When did you give up?"

"Last week."

Sometimes believe what a patient tells you

Many patients complain of hip pain, and then indicate the outer part of the thigh. Pain from the hip *joint* is perceived in the groin. In other words, you can believe the patient's *localisation* of the pain, but disregard their words of *interpretation*. By the same token, watch as the extent of the pain is described. A broad sweep of the hand indicates much more diffuse pain than a pointing finger and you can distinguish between a trapped nerve in the wrist (carpal tunnel syndrome) and a trapped nerve in the neck by watching where the patient indicates the numbness actually is. It makes life easier. It's difficult to tie a tie from verbal instruction with your eyes shut.

Be sure to record everything a patient tells you

If you are rigorous, it can prove useful if a patient says you weren't.

A patient came up with odd mechanical back pain and I took my usual proforma history, noted no red flag signs and sent him for physiotherapy. I heard no more until I suddenly, and some months later, had a letter from him telling me he was reporting me to the General Medical Council (GMC) for negligence, as he had been found to have a chordoma (extremely rare tumour) which had required a very lengthy operation which had failed to remove it all. The basis of his complaint was that I had ignored his symptom of severe rectal pain, known to us medics as proctalgia.

Now I don't suppose that in 30 years I have ever had a patient with low back pain who has mentioned severe proctalgia, which is a red flag symptom. I had certainly not recorded it, so could only presume that he had told someone else about it, but not me. I never heard from the GMC so hope that he was happy with my expression of deep regret but denial.

If you keep written notes, put lots of detail into any correspondence. Another patient referred me to the General Medical Council for what I suppose you could call neglect, judging by the letter I had (from the GMC itself, telling me it had investigated her allegation and found no substance in it, though this was the first I had heard of her complaint). In fact she had written me a letter after what she thought was a dismissive consultation, to which I had replied in considerable detail over three pages. I did ask the GMC what business it had investigating a complaint without informing the subject but got no satisfactory reply.

I referred a colleague to the GMC once. I was told my concerns would be investigated, but despite three further letters asking what their judgement was I heard nothing. It may make you wonder how any cases of medical misconduct are ever pursued...

Use scientific rationale in acting on what a patient tells you

I arranged a review appointment for a young patient and said, "Let's make it 3 months" and on noting that the date fell over the Christmas period added "Unless you are going to be holidaying in the Bahamas".

I have no idea why I chose the Bahamas, but her mother blanched and said "Why, that *is* where we are going! If you can know such things you should buy a ticket for the Euro Lottery; there's a double rollover jackpot this week!"

So, casting odds analysis to the winds, I did. Of course I got nothing, except an ear-wigging from my wife for wasting money (and quite right too). But if I hadn't, I would never have known, would I?

Some gifts from patients are less unacceptable than others

Whatever a doctor may be told or ordered by managers in the receiving gifts line, I think they should take it with a pinch of salt. Hospital policies that ape political practice (refuse the gift, or pay for it) are stupid. A well-chosen gift brings pleasure to both donor and recipient and to turn gifts away can cause great offence. I don't really believe that accepting a gift places any particular obligation on a doctor (maybe managers don't like the process because they never get any). However some gifts, or attempted gifts, may be beyond the pale, but in 30 years I have never been left a car, or a house. Ever. Now I am retired it will not happen. Pity.

I was once offered a parrot in a will. Now parrots can be possessive creatures, and a bit of gentle enquiry revealed that this parrot, an African grey, was quite old and very cantankerous (the owner was only the former). Nevertheless I had to write a polite note to decline the kind offer, which was made twice.[189] My wife on the other hand was given a budgerigar one Christmas; its donor ran a small souvenir shop in one of London's rail termini, and this budgie is wooden. It is very realistic. We have put it on the kitchen window sash, and innumerable tourists have done a double take (we hear them first – "Gorblimey Jade, look at that budgie! Is it real?" And after several seconds "'s not movin' innit!") while the Japanese, who seem to have mastered the art of walking on cobbles holding an iPad in front of them at arm's length, take a snap. Mermaid Street in Rye is supposedly one of the ten most photographed streets in the world. I suspect our budgie is one of the world's most photographed budgies.

One patient, many years ago, had learned through my secretary that I was partial to a nip of whisky now and then. Rather than produce a bottle of said beverage (for which I was always most grateful, of course and of which I had a fairly regular supply) she presented me with a cut-glass tumbler on a wooden stand labelled "Dr Bamji's special whisky glass". I have it still and use it for my nip (or rather my triple nip). For heaven's sake, it had my name on the stand; how could I possibly refuse it?

Legacies can get you into trouble, although for an account of how John Bodkin Adams was unfairly vilified (and how a microscopic search for

---

[189] A previous owner of our house did possess a parrot, which had its cage by the high window in our kitchen adjacent to the side alleyway, the window being usually open. It drove the neighbours crazy by singing "Yellow Submarine", to the extent that they devised a tool that would pull our window shut.

evidence got him off) you should read Percy Hoskins' book.[190] So too can offers of personal help. One of my patients, whom I was telling of a difficult experience with a patient's husband who had threatened to kill me, said, as he was leaving "Any time you ever have a problem like that, Andrew, just give me a bell". I was being offered the services of a hit-man. Temptation has been rare, and lasts but a nanosecond…

Should we ignore the nanny state?

We rheumatologists use a lot of methotrexate and have perhaps become a little blasé about it. However, after a patient had an accidental overdose and died (one patient, mind, and there were several stages at which a problem should have been picked up) the National Patient Safety Agency went berserk and issued strict guidelines for prescribing and monitoring (forgetting to consult us specialists, which did not go down well at all). The guidance included not prescribing more than a month at a time and not prescribing the stronger 10mg tablets and only using 2.5mg ones; for patients on a standard dose of 20mg weekly this means 8 pills at once, which is far easier to get wrong than two, and one of my patients got confused as to whether she should split the dose through the week. It's also much easier to accidentally knock eight tablets on the floor. Furthermore, the blood monitoring suggested by the NPSA was excessive, and the booklet all patients were recommended to have was both unnecessary and confusing. The leaflets some practices have issued, explaining their stance, were likewise baffling.

All in all it's a bit like the bag of cashews that says "Warning! This product may contain nuts". I like to treat my patients with the respect and common sense they deserve, so resent stupid nanny attitudes (and diktats that cost patients money – monthly scripts are more expensive than 6-monthly ones).

And then I discovered after all this fuss that Methotrexate can be bought over the counter in Spain! A patient told me this having run out. They cost €3.30 for 11 (why 11?). Clearly EU harmonisation has a way to go, not that we need, post-Brexit, to care any more.

---

[190] P Hoskins, *Two Men Were Acquitted: The trial and acquittal of Doctor John Bodkin Adams*, Secker & Warburg, 1984. Hoskins was chief crime reporter for the "Daily Express" and was convinced of Adams' innocence in the face of almost universal belief in his guilt; the jury took only 40 minutes to reach its verdict.

There is another good reason not to have large quantities of small tablets to take. One of my patients put out her heap of methotrexate on the kitchen counter, next to some sweeties for her grandson, only to turn around and find the dog had had them (pills and sweets). She reported that the dog's limp disappeared after two days and did not return for some months… but I am grateful it was the dog that got them and not the grandson.

It may take time but sort the notes out. It will save time and trouble in the long run.

When I was a Senior House Officer at the Hammersmith Hospital years ago the pathology request forms were A4 sheets. For my sins I looked after the geriatric ward (female only) where the inmates (who were there often for years) got repeated urinary tract infections, or UTIs for short.

So you filled in a request form for a midstream urine specimen (MSU), and a while later a photocopy came back with the cell count and growth, if any, and after a little while longer back came another copy to which had been added the antibiotic sensitivities. Then along came a cumulative sheet on which all the info for that test had been transcribed into a single line (25 lines per form, so room for lots of UTIs).

When I started, some of the notes files were enormous and in total disorder. I began to weed them.

You can see where I am going. For every 25 MSU requests there were 75 sheets of paper in the notes, and three of these had all the information on the other 72. The waste bins were full for weeks. The notes became manageable, and usable.

Cuts in medical records staffing at Sidcup led to a rise in missing notes, and thus a rise in the number of temporary files. If the main file turned up later then the staff never bothered to sort the temporary file into the right sections and file the pages chronologically, so the notes become a random and disconnected mess. One was not helped by enthusiastic medical records staff who, after you had carefully tidied up the notes, dismantled them and stapled each separate admission into separate sections, thus destroying the order.

If you sort them yourself you will be surprised by how often the chronology suddenly becomes clear (also by the number of times you find important results which have been overlooked; my last example was when I got involved with a patient with Lupus, whose positive bloods had been done 6 months previously and never been seen, so she had had another three emergency admissions).

Another example; we had a serious complaint about a patient who died. Having been on a medical ward, she was returned to the rehab unit (she had multiple sclerosis and was well known to us) and then shuttled back to a medical ward when she deteriorated. There was fortunately no serious criticism of the Unit, but there was concern that while she had been acutely unwell there was a gap of 2 days in the monitoring of her vital signs. I thought I should go through the notes before the meeting with the relatives.

To say they were a shambles was an understatement. Our unit receptionist kindly volunteered to sort them; it took her a couple of hours. When I went off to the meeting they were a shining example of well-organised practice. We got to the part about the missing observations. Sure enough, there was a gap in the nursing records. While everyone was talking about how this could happen I leafed through the file and to my surprise found that the two missing days had in fact been recorded, but in the *medical* notes. They had been missed because (a) the notes were in such a mess and (b) because whoever had made the entries had used the American date notation – so 4th January came out as 1/4/09, and not as we might expect in the UK as 4/1/09 (actually as she had died in the February someone should have spotted the fault). All was clear; there had been no missing entries at all. The relatives then got upset at having been told there were missing entries, which goes to show that you cannot please everyone all of the time.

> *Moral: if dealing with a complaint, or worse, examine the data in microscopic detail – and don't use American date format*

I was sued by a private patient who claimed I had missed and misdiagnosed the problem in her shoulder. It is the only time I have been sued personally.[191] Her claim ran to several pages. The expert she had consulted claimed my management was "cavalier in the extreme" (it was a thoroughly unpleasant, even unprofessional report from a retired orthopaedic surgeon, but he's now dead) and she had required, as the result of her problem, a waterbed, an automatic car and various other expensive items.

I was, naturally, mortified. Unlike the chloroquine retinopathy case I considered that I was in no way to blame, not least because the patient had missed numerous appointments and had distracted me by developing what

---

[191] The patient whose eyesight was damaged by chloroquine was an NHS patient and the claim was dealt with through the NHS Litigation Authority

appeared to be a generalised inflammatory arthritis. So I started to build my defence.

This seemed strong enough to me from my own notes (the expert heaped criticism on my written notes, but each entry was backed up by a detailed letter to the GP), but I got the GP notes as well. They were old style notes on cards in a folder, known as Lloyd George notes, as the format was introduced by said politician in 1911 as part of his national insurance scheme.

It was a killer blow. Buried in the cards was a barely legible entry which I reproduce below. There was no mention of the shoulder.

My expert, who at first thought the case was only just defensible, agreed that if you have a shoulder that is so painful that you cannot drive then it would certainly be too painful for you to put on a wetsuit and aqualung and go scuba diving. And there was more; she had claimed also that she had had to pay for her surgery herself, which she could not afford, because as a result of the delay her private insurance had run out. But just after that time was another entry:

★ This column has been provided for doctors to enter A,V or C at their discretion.

ROS is shorthand for removal of sutures). So while the shoulder surgery was not affordable, liposuction was…

My solicitors at this point asked for full receipts for the surgery, bed, car and all. Two days later, and two days before we were due in court, the case was withdrawn.

This tale of course indicates the terrible risk to medicine from loss of the throwaway written comment, which will disappear for ever when all notes are computerised and additions are made in shorthand. Vital background information will not be passed on and so justice will not be done.

My late friend and colleague, gynaecologist Julian Woolfson, saved our hospital literally millions on a "damaged baby" case when he was able to show that the blank in the recording of the foetal heartbeat was not a blank at all, but appeared when the paper roll was changed and the clock on the machine wrongly reset.

It pays to examine the most minute details. Of course, if there is even then no defence, "sorry" is a useful, even essential word, as my previous story of the hydroxychloroquine story indicates.

I have another example. I wrote some acid comment about the paucity of the referral letter on Mr R. in my reply to the GP and had the following handwritten reply from another partner in the practice.

> "I have recently been reviewing this chap's notes, in particular your letter of 17.4.1990. I think I should explain the background. Dr J retired just over a year ago, and he and Mr R used to "sink a few jars" in the Conservative Club, and Peter J would promise him a letter of referral – he (Mr R) would ring the surgery about the letter, which Peter would say he'd done and so on!
>
> Unfortunately Mr R as you know has become more immobilised, and Dr J sank a jar or two too many and was disqualified from driving. Hence neither of them could get to the other.
>
> This is a good example of the fact that consultations should not take place in the pub, Sainsbury's etc etc.
>
> I have written this from my home address to explain matters."

Doctors and lawyers

Doctors can get sued and it's not nice. I believe that if a suit is brought maliciously then the appellant should be named and shamed; while I have no truck with rape, recent cases where the complainant has made a palpably false accusation should lose their right to anonymity. After all, the alleged rapist may have had his career and reputation ruined, without recourse. [192] The suit might never have been brought if the appellant knew they would have their reputation trashed when they were found out. The accused's name is dragged through the courts for months. I had a friend who was exonerated but was never the same again.

That said I have had some interesting experiences in court as a witness in fact and as an expert witness. The very first lesson I learned was that one should not take the patient at face value (see above). I was asked to appear on behalf of Mrs O'Flaherty, who had chronic neck pain after her car was sideswiped by a council truck. She could no longer work, walk the dog or carry heavy shopping. She was depressed, too, during my consultations and I wrote a report summarising these problems and turned up in court to hear her repeat her story in the witness box. Under oath.

I thought the questioning was rather pointed, asking very specific questions about what she couldn't lift, managing steps, need to be accompanied everywhere, and all became clear when the defence barrister waved a VHS tape and suggested I might like to look at it. Our barrister agreed this would be sensible; she also smelt a rat. So the trial was adjourned and I took the tape home.

Oh dear. The defence had arranged an examination by their medical expert in Harley Street and she had been followed there and back. Having told the court she had arrived in a taxi and had been accompanied by her daughter the tape watched her on and off the train both ways. The private eye with a camera hidden in a sports bag had also done some local surveillance, as a result of which the tape showed my disabled patient walking the dog, picking large heavy frozen food items out of the chest freezer in the supermarket and doing all the things she said she couldn't. The *pièce de résistance* was a hurried shot of her taking the steps at London Bridge Station two at a time when there was a sudden announcement of a platform alteration for her train home; rather artistically it finished with her walking home uphill from the station, silhouetted by the setting sun..

---

[192] Most recently this has proved the case for those smeared by a series of appalling lies by Carl Beech, who defamed the dead, made the living suffer, almost certainly hastened the end of one relative and lost one innocent his job and home.

My report was therefore complete rubbish. I wrote another that evening and presented it in court the next day – end of trial. Our barrister was apoplectic, not least when the silly woman insisted that she wanted to go on with her suit. "You have lied to me, to Dr Bamji AND TO THE COURT UNDER OATH!" she thundered. There was no way back.

However my patient found another angle. In the bad old days it was allowable for evidence such as this tape to be revealed dramatically in court. The law had just been changed. So she appealed on the basis that the videotape should have been disclosed before. But the Appeal Court judge, while agreeing that what had happened was a breach of regulations, nevertheless concluded that justice had clearly been done. My colleague who was appearing for the other side and gave me some useful tips afterwards. "Andrew" he said "ALWAYS preface anything you get told be some qualifying phrase. 'She told me that'; 'it was alleged that' – something that shows you are not stating your facts but someone else's. What you are told is hearsay unless you were there, which you never are. Then if it's rubbish it's quite clear that it's not you doing the misleading."

Some six months later my Chief Executive forwarded a letter that he had received from Mrs O'Flaherty. It was a complaint, asking for me to be disciplined for encouraging her to take legal action.

There was a sad ending to the story, however, because a couple of years later she suffered a serious stroke and was left genuinely disabled. Despite the fact that she had run rings round me, and made me look a fool, I did feel sorry for her.

I had one notable success. Mrs Peters had been injured by a filing cabinet that almost broke her wrist. The office in which she worked had several very old filing cabinets that were both crappy and fire-damaged. The drawer runners didn't run and the handles had been replaced by loops of string. When you pulled a drawer out, being full of files, it dropped. To stop this you put your other hand underneath the front end to support it. As Mrs Peters was heaving a drawer open the string handle snapped, she caught her hand underneath and got a severe blow, with a large cut, across her wrist. This was dealt with in A&E but she was sent to me with residual numbness in the hand and quite a significant loss of power. So she sued her employer for forcing her to work with unsafe equipment. I had examined her and diagnosed an injury to the superficial branch of the radial nerve. There was no other possible explanation for her symptoms and no other putative cause.

In court I was somewhat distracted by the defence barrister, who had suffered from facial cancer and had a significant facial disfigurement. I was fascinated in a professional sense. He called his expert, who I will call Mr Foster, who was a long-retired orthopaedic surgeon and ponderously stated that the so-called injury she had sustained was anatomically impossible, he had never seen one and it had never been reported.

Sadly for him I had done my homework and found a description of injury to the superficial branch of the radial nerve producing exactly the same symptoms with a very similar cause. It was in a respected textbook. The defence barrister was poleaxed by this and by my revelation that, despite the old duffer claiming there was no evidence of nerve damage, the numbness and weakness had been clearly documented in the A&E notes. That Foster was actually in an alcoholic haze did not help. It was only mid-morning. The judge caught my eye and smirked; I had great difficulty in keeping a straight face.

Apropos that I had another experience of surgical expert witnesses when I was a very junior trainee. Mr Anderson was a long-retired orthopaedic surgeon, still engaged in medico-legal work. He had come into hospital with aplastic anaemia (bone marrow shut-down) and was being nursed in a side room because without white blood cells he was at risk of infection.

Various tests were needed so he had to stay a few days, and then have a transfusion or several. He had brought in the paperwork for his current legal case. On day five he went berserk. Completely and utterly. Shouting, screaming, lashing out at the nurses and doctors. It was almost as if he was suffering from acute hard drug withdrawal – cold turkey, if you like. He was sedated, heavily. A couple of days later his wife came in with a suitcase.

"I found these in his wardrobe" she said, opening it to reveal several dozen empty bottles of Dr John Collis Browne's "Chlorodyne".

Chlorodyne was a splendid mixture invented as a cholera treatment which back then still had its original formula. Hale-White and Douthwaite's Materia Medica, 21st edition (1932) gave a recipe thus:

Mix chloroform 75, tincture of capsicum 25, tincture of Indian hemp 100, oil of peppermint 2 and glycerin 250 with alcohol (20 per cent) 450. Dissolve morphine hydrochloride 10 in the mixture. Add to it diluted hydrocyanic acid 50 and enough alcohol (90 per cent) to make 1000. Strength. 1 millilitre contains chloroform 7.5 centimils; morphine hydrochloride 1 centigram; acidum hydrocyanicum dilutum 5 centimils.

Advertisement for Chorodyne, "The most wonderful and valuable remedy ever discovered"

So basically it was a mix of chloroform, cannabis and morphine. 1ml contained 10mg of morphine. Mr Anderson was a morphine addict. He had indeed gone cold turkey. The case he was working on was reallocated to another expert; word got round, and although he lived a few years more he was no longer called upon.

However, being an expert is extremely arduous. Sometimes you realise there is a difference between truth and justice, and sometimes if another expert bamboozles the jury with fake science (in one case of a motor accident my opposing expert confused speed and acceleration, and there was no opportunity to come back at him and correct the error). My overall record was won four, lost five, drawn three.

The lessons of these tales are

- It's bloody hard work
- It's pretty stressful
- It's great when you win
- It's frustrating when you don't
- You can be humiliated
- But it pays well

242

It helps that nowadays experts for each side are encouraged to agree before going to court, so that the adversarial element is reduced, but you have to take care not to try and rewrite the law in court the way you think it should be.

"I'm not surprised his hands were shaking with five solicitors and a doctor specialising in medico-legal reports in the gallery."

Comparable wages

The Doctors' and Dentists' Review Body used to make recommendations each year for pay levels based on comparisons with other professions. Then the government would reject the report and do what it liked (which meant, as a rule, a smaller rise).

I was at lunch one day (in those heady days when we did lunch in the consultants' dining room) and some of us were discussing what we charged for legal reports. The fees varied, but were, we agreed, quite reasonable, at around £30 per offering (a further clue to how long ago this was).

A wise old neurologist who did reams of medicolegal work (he was the one who had acted for the defendants in Mrs O'Flaherty's case, as it happened) arrived for the tail end of the discussion. He looked around and said, in his usual slow and deliberate way:

"You chaps have no idea. If a lawyer is going to charge the client £100 to read a report, then you need to charge at least that to write the bloody thing!"

If a doctor, try to be cheerful, whatever.

Your colleagues and patients will appreciate it (and making people laugh causes endorphin release). I reckon I am a Tigger type. One of my colleagues was not (this is the glass half full half empty debate although my son insists that the glass has been wrongly designed – he's an engineer). I was in a bookshop (flexing my cervical spine to the left[193]) and found among the little books full of wise sayings a compilation of A.A. Milne's Winnie the Pooh extracts called "The Little Book of Tigger". Remember that Tigger bounced a lot. Next to it was another volume entitled "The Little Book of Eeyore".

Now Eeyore was not just gloomy; he was a philosopher. Exactly like my colleague. I bought a copy, wrapped it up nicely and gave it to him one lunchtime. As he opened it his face fell.

"Someone's already given me this", he said.

I had a nice patient with really bad rheumatoid arthritis whom I had been seeing for years. His joints were never good and he had tried most disease-modifying drugs; by the time methotrexate came on the scene it was really too late for it to work.

He fell ill with pneumonia, was admitted to intensive care, had a horrendous time, was transferred eventually to an ordinary ward where everything went wrong and he died. He was not under my care, but I had heard of the circumstances and expected a complaint to come in, which it duly did.

A few months later I received a letter from his widow, recounting the sad chronicle of his last admission. Her anger was palpable. Slowly, as I read on, my failure to cure his arthritis got mixed into her diatribe. "You saw him for years" it said, "and yet you never made his arthritis any better and I often wondered why he wasted his time coming to see you".

I turned the page.

---

[193] As noted in a previous essay, in a French bookshop you have to flex to the left, as titles are printed bottom to top. It's a bit like driving on the other side of the road: "The rule of the road is a Paradox quite, for if you're on the left you're sure to be right"

"But when he came home from your clinic" it continued "he always seemed much better and told me that you had made him laugh and I thank you for that. With best wishes…"

I shared stories with patients; we exchanged poems and discussed holidays, photographs etc (one of my RA patients took up photography at my suggestion and became very accomplished, rapidly gaining her LRPS and a great deal of lost self-esteem).[194] Medicine is not just about treating the disease; it's the whole person who matters and there are more ways than drugs of making them feel better. You may tire of the old ladies who bore you with giant symptom lists but bear in mind that their visit to you may actually be the only time they have left the house since the last visit. It's holistic medicine. I (and many others of a similar way of thinking) invented it long before it came into print. Indeed one of my heroes, Sir Harold Gillies, the plastic surgeon, had a holistic approach way back 100 years ago.

Not everyone holds this view. Back in the days of WW1 and the development of the Queen's Hospital Sidcup as a facial injury centre, a Captain Rhind of the New Zealand Section commented adversely on the habit of Gillies of joking with his patients, which he felt was unprofessional. Judging by the accounts of patients, Gillies was probably the most revered of all the Sidcup surgeons, and I believe that the joshing had a lot to do with it. It put patients at their ease, and it puts them on a level with you. There is no need to adopt a regional accent (as Tony Blair did when Prime Minister) for that is patronising – having said which I find it terribly difficult myself not to slide into imitation, especially of Welsh and South African accents…

The corollary of this is that patients can also try and make their doctor laugh. It's good for the doctor-patient relationship. Many of my best short jokes were told to me by patients, though I did have to ask one politely whether he would desist as they were too crude even for me.

After I retired one of my clinic staff sent me an email. Part of it read "The majority of [the patients] left so much happier than when they arrived because you treated them not only with respect but with humour as well. I'll always remember you singing 'yes we have no bananas ' with an elderly man who left the clinic with tears of mirth in his eyes, no wonder I used to ask sister to put me in your clinic as often as she could, for me it was the happiest clinic in the department and although I am happy in my retirement I do miss those days."

---

[194] Licentiate of the Royal Photographic Society. She has progressed and is now an Associate, and an RPS judge to boot.

It can go horribly wrong. See "Be prepared for the flip patient"

Clinic nurses are most necessary

Doctors need to be sensitive about examining patients without a chaperone (as my hospital failed to supply nurse cover for one of my clinics I did sometimes have to manage without one. This can be a problem if the patient whose knee you are injecting has a full-blown epileptic seizure halfway through). In these days of false accusations, it is essential. However if there are male nurses in the department you may need to ask for a female nurse if you are a chap – and the same might apply for gay men patients. This can get time-consuming, so at worst you should ask if the patient would like a chaperone and record this in the notes.

Occasionally you have provocation – or attempted temptation. When I was a young and eligible house physician I went to see a new admission, a pretty girl in her early 20s, who had been admitted with chest pain. I indicated that I would need to examine her chest; something about her rang a warning bell and after pulling the curtains round the bed I excused myself briefly without explanation and went to find someone to chaperone me.

On my return I pulled apart the curtains and walked in to find the girl lying on top of the bedcovers, absolutely starkers and stroking herself suggestively. Her expression changed when my chaperone, a stout African staff nurse with a face like thunder, followed me in.

It reminds me of another tale. At a hospital show smoking concert – the old Middlesex ran a highly professional Christmas show which I was not good enough to get into, but suspect I got an invite as a failed auditionee – there was a Treasure Hunt. The players and guests were divided into teams, and given a list of crazy items to collect, each item having a different points value. The obstetrics Senior Registrar was on the list (50 points I think, certainly fairly high value, and I knew her quite well and had no hopes for acquiring a Thompson sub-machine gun, though I did get a photocopy of Hospital Property loo paper). I bagged her. Another Hunt item was a Soho stripper to do her act (many points). Our team did not get one; others, I learned, had clubbed together to pay, and there were eight altogether. My obs and gynae friend stayed on for the extra performance.

They were all, with one exception who could make her impressive tasselled boobs twirl in opposite directions at once, perfectly awful. Number four appeared and gyrated out of time to the music, and most un-erotically. The SR, sitting next to me, gave a start.

"Christ!" she said. "I know her. She's been in the gynae clinic with PID.[195] She's had more clap than you get at a Prom in the Albert Hall."

A Bamji theory; why does arthritis go away on holidays in the sun?

Joints tell you where they are by virtue of the proprioceptors around them. These are the nerve endings that tell you where your body is. You know where your hand is even if your eyes are shut by virtue of this, and proprioceptors are sensitive to changes in pressure.

Damage a joint and the receptors become more sensitive. I dislocated my shoulder years ago and could tell the weather by it – because sensitive, or sensitised proprioceptors can detect changes in the atmospheric pressure. When in Greece, the Canaries and so on the weather is settled; joints don't hurt when the atmospheric pressure is not changing, but they will detect change and so tell you when a weather front is approaching. It doesn't matter whether the pressure goes up or down – it's the change. So you become your own barometer.

This effect dims over time, and now I only get shoulder pain with a precipitate weather change, so I am good in the hurricane season.

Yes, it's only a theory, but do you have a better one? Of course all the research says that weather does not affect arthritis, but that's because they are not measuring the right variable, the barometric pressure and its rate of change, but are concentrating on temperature…

Needles and common sense

In my career I have done lots of joint and soft tissue injections – thousands if not tens of thousands. Various myths have been dispatched along the way.

Myth 1

You need to anaesthetise the skin before proceeding. Now – does anyone do this for blood tests? Does skin local anaesthesia somehow permeate to

---

[195] Pelvic Inflammatory Disease

deeper structures? Do you really need to use two needles, one for the anaesthetic and another for the procedure? The answer is no in all cases. So do the whole thing with one needle. It's kinder and quicker. The exceptions are children and the seriously needle phobic adult. Both may require a general anaesthetic, so I used to tag my occasional cases onto the operating list of an orthopaedic colleague and do them in the anaesthetic room. I was not always popular; lists were delayed if I had a problem, and on one memorable occasion the child escaped the loving hands of mother, two operating department assistants, the anaesthetist and me and disappeared through the theatre suite to hide in a cupboard.

Myth 2

You should prep the skin with a cleaner, preferably iodine, with the area fully draped and using gloves. Unless there are obvious local septic spots the risk of introducing infection is pretty well zero, and you certainly don't want to wipe bugs off a boil across your injection site. Draping simply obscures all the necessary anatomical landmarks.

Myth 3

Patients should look away as you do it. Well – it's their choice, but there is now good evidence from functional MRI scans that looking as it's done reduces the perception of pain, as the anticipation appears (usually) to convert the perceived sensation into pressure. So...

If in doubt, stick a needle in it...

One thing I am sure of – more people have suffered from *not* having a needle stuck in a joint than suffered from having this procedure.

In my whole rheumatology career of more than thirty years I have seen just one patient who got an infected joint from a doctor who was a staphylococcus carrier. I have seen many who were thought to have infected joints but actually had an acute reaction to the steroid injection – what one might call steroid gout. I proved this is one case (funnily enough the same patient who wanted to help me with a hit man) by finding the odd shaped crystals and comparing them (at the suggestion of the pathologist, Gopi Menon) with steroid straight out of the bottle.

Miss an infection and you can lose a joint – or limb.

248

Take the following scenario. A patient came in with a hot swollen knee and was very unwell. They were started on antibiotics. I was sent for, to discover the orthopaedic team had already been and advised the medics not to aspirate the joint (which happened to be a prosthetic one) in case they introduced an infection. *But it was already there!* In this case the antibiotics had successfully suppressed any bug growth; as a result, despite the signs in the blood count that something serious was going on and my suggestion that I would review in 2 days, the patient was discharged "better". On his return, now even more ill, the other knee (also prosthetic) had come up and this time I was in time to get fluid out before any idiot started antibiotics on spec.

You cannot make a firm diagnosis of gout without finding crystals in the joint. You cannot do this without aspirating the joint. And as it could be infection, pseudogout, steroid gout or an acute flare of inflammatory joint disease you cannot proceed.[196] You only need a squirt from the needle onto a slide. So send the syringe down to the lab with needle attached, and get them to blow the drip back out (or take it down, if you have a friendly lab that lets you use the polarising microscope, and do it yourself).[197] I made a diagnosis of gas gangrene from a blind suck from the thigh soft tissues and have even got the fabulously rare cholesterol crystals from the acutely swollen wrist joint of a diabetic patient, saving an unnecessary course of antibiotics or gout medication.

That said I injected a thumb carpo-metacarpal joint (the thumb base) with my usual mixture of steroid and local anaesthetic only to see the patient's hand go white and dead. Some of the injection had leaked and surrounded the radial artery, which went into acute spasm. Likewise I injected a tennis elbow; the radial nerve ran an aberrant course, it would appear, because the patient developed an acute wrist drop. The first time such a thing happens you wet yourself. The next time you say gaily "Oh, some of the anaesthetic has leaked a little; quite common, should recover in an hour or two, like going to the dentist!" And then you hold your breath hoping there isn't a phone call three hours later saying "Dr Bamji, it's still not right…"

[196] In gout the crystals are of uric acid. In pseudogout they are pyrophosphate. You can tell them apart by the way they colourise under polarised light – and the shapes are different

[197] If you don't have a lab, get a cheap microscope and a couple of bits of polarising plastic sheet; put one over the top of the microscope slide, and one over the light source, and rotate the second. For many years I kept my mother's old microscope, c.1947, but sold it when I retired.

...but make sure the patient is safe...

Patients may think they are tough, but you would be surprised. One Greek lad came to see me with a painful shoulder which, after examination, I thought should be injected. I explained everything carefully. "Does that mean a needle?" he asked. When I replied that it did, he went white and passed out. I hadn't even touched him.

...and don't forget everyone else, either

A girl aged 18 or so with a hugely swollen knee needed an injection and confessed that she hated needles, so I laid her flat to do it and her mother came over to the side of the couch to hold her hand.[198] I was concentrating on extracting the quite substantial volume of fluid when there was a tremendous crash. Mother had fainted, fallen onto my equipment trolley and was almost inextricable from the narrow space between the examination couch and my desk. We got her out eventually and mopped up the blood from her head wound where she had caught it on the trolley frame. Then we called a porter and shipped her round to the minor injuries unit.

No sooner had we done so when daughter, who had been fine (and was still lying flat), suddenly said "I feel sick". She had gone a whiter shade of pale, tinged with green. My clinic nurse tossed the cotton wool swabs which we kept in a large instrument bowl onto my desk and passed the bowl to the young lady, who fainted before she was sick. What a mercy (the patient who had a fit was incontinent during it, and we had to get the carpet steam cleaned). So we got the porter back and sent her round on another trolley to join her mother.[199]

Doctors are not immune to this, though usually for different triggers. In my case it was heat and standing still. While a student on the ear, nose and throat firm I was asked to assist at a private operation – a trans-sphenoidal hypophysectomy, or in ordinary language removal of a pituitary tumour from the base of the brain through a small incision in the side of the nose. In the cramped private wing theatre, mid-summer, wrapped in theatre gear, with mask making my glasses steam up, my job was to hold a small retractor very still. The next thing I remember is waking up on the floor surrounded

---

[198] We are taught it is physiologically impossible to faint while lying flat.
[199] You can faint while lying flat

by concerned staff, who de-sterilised themselves to assist me and had to re-scrub while the surgeon waited patiently. I was not asked again.

Don't rely on one odd test result; check the past, and consider the future

I was telephoned by a GP who wanted me to know that he had stopped a patient's methotrexate therapy on the basis of an abnormal liver function test.

The guidelines recommended cessation if the level of one liver enzyme (AST) rises further than twice the upper limit of normal. I checked the lab database and found not only that it had not reached this critical level (though it was not far off) but also that the AST had been raised throughout treatment – but was unchanged from pre-treatment levels up to five years previously.

Context is important. If a result is unexpected, repeat it. Very occasionally samples get mislabelled, but all sorts of things can cause transient blips in results and often the second sample is normal.

The problem is compounded by a rigid interpretation of normality. Patients are often given copies of their blood results, and it is not uncommon in rheumatology practice for patients to ring up in a fluster because they have noted the red flag marked against a value, but if the upper limit is, say, 10 and the result is 10.2 then it doesn't actually matter much. Likewise I saw many patients investigated for "anaemia" whose haemoglobin was only a weeny bit below the lower end of normal – which in rheumatoid arthritis is often seen anyway as a result of the inflammatory process suppressing the bone marrow. Keep calm and carry on!

What's in a name?

A patient recently told me that she suffered from Palymygena. Some years ago I wrote a letter to the BMJ commenting on a storyline in "The Archers" in which Peggy had developed polymyalgia, and noting the remarkable and unrealistic ability of all the other characters to pronounce it perfectly.[200] Curiously "The Guardian" picked this up and ran a small piece on it.

We should not expect patients to get spellings etc right. One of mine told me she had been prescribed Pregglezones for her polly-thingy. Another said that he took champagne anti-sickness pills. I don't suppose domperidone was

---

[200] AN Bamji, *Medicine and the Media*. Br Med J 1987; 295: 1055

quite as enjoyable as Dom Perignon. And there was the patient whose overindulgence of carbohydrate-heavy Cornish style pies led him to need an angiopasty.

Apropos which, when asked for my views on glucosamine (now a discredited supplement) I always used to say that it would relieve back pain because it lightened the wallet, but that I would prefer to spend my money on a case of decent Côtes du Rhône from the Wine Society.

It's not what you do but the way that you do it.

A patient with uncontrolled polymyalgia was on large doses of steroids, and got stuck there, all the while getting more and more breathless on exertion. She came into the clinic with her worried husband. I thought she was quite wheezy, but she had test results suggesting obstructive airways disease. Her husband asked if she should ease up on things, and so I enquired how. "Well," he said "she is always dashing about doing things and can't sit still. She's knackered after hoovering just one room. It's a heavy Hoover – it even tires me out".

He was sitting just behind her, out of eye line (useful tip, this, as disagreement with what the patient is saying can be communicated without them seeing) and smiled happily when I agreed that she shouldn't overtire herself. "Just do a couple of rooms" I said "and then take a break".

She looked crestfallen. "But I like my house to look clean"

A thought occurred to me. "How often do you hoover?" I asked.

She perked up. "Why, doctor, I do the whole house every day!"

No wonder the poor woman is wheezing; no sooner have the poor dust mites crept back into the carpets than she's beaten them out again. My diagnosis of her breathing changed from COPD with a bit of asthma to the reverse, perhaps with a bit of heart failure from the steroids, and I eagerly awaited the result of my treatment (which would indubitably be enforced by her husband) – vacuum once a week only!

Sjogren's syndrome and the science of acupuncture

These are not terms you would normally associate (science and acupuncture, that is). However… a patient came in to clinic and told me that her Sjogren's symptoms (mainly dry mouth rather than eyes) had been significantly improved by acupuncture. She told me it had been administered "scientifically".

I was about to open my mouth and treat this sceptically when she told me the acupuncture needles had been applied to her ear.

A lost memory surfaced of some lecturer reminding me that you can stimulate the vagus nerve by wiggling a finger in your ear and thus aid digestion. So maybe the needles do something similar. I see an experiment looming.

Popeye and spinach

While rummaging through my mother's files after her death I found a report from "Time" Magazine in 1953, commenting on a letter she and my father had written to the British Medical Journal pointing out that spinach was not all it was cracked up to be. [201] The oxalic acid content was so high it would chelate any iron, and so Popeye would not have benefited at all from the cans he ate (even if he ate the cans as well as the spinach, which careful viewing of many cartoons proves he didn't).

Their letter generated other national and international comment. It was the only exposure they ever got in the press, unlike me, with over 70 letters in "The Times" (except for another later piece about allergic reactions to biological washing powders which was picked up by Radio 4). [202]

In fact they were right and wrong. There is another reason that the high iron content of spinach is no use. It isn't, actually, high. When the original calculations were made (not by them, I hasten to add) the decimal point was put in the wrong place.

Moral: When debunking myths it helps if you get your facts straight (and complete). And watch those decimal points, and percentages. Murder

---

[201] JE Bamji, NS Bamji, *Spinach*. Br Med J 1953; 1:674

[202] E Bamji, N Bamji, *Severe dermatitis and "biological" detergents*. Br Med J 1970; 1:629

convictions have been overturned for getting them in the wrong place and thus misleading juries. Whether they should have been is a different matter.

Memory is like the seaside

Before you think I have gone mad writing about mad things, think of the number of times you get asked why short-term memory seems to be lost first (I am not sure why myself). Then think of an analogy. I use the beach. Everyone has seen one.

When you were little did you take a stick and scratch your initials in the sand one side of a heart, and those of your sweetheart the other? And did you see how they were washed away without trace when the tide came in? The deeper you made your marks, the longer they stayed, but they were always totally erased, without hope of recovery, eventually. You could make them last longer by redrawing them after each sweep of the incoming waves – or by making them further back up the beach, where the tide would not reach. Or longer still by scratching them on a cliff.

Think of short-term memory as the drawing in the sand. As you age, your mind is drawing too many things in the sand, and none of them are deep enough.

The explanation for time going faster is clearer. If you repeat something, it is not all new, so your brain can skip concentrating as it knows what's coming. That's why the second time you make a journey it seems to take a fraction of the first.

****

Coming to the end

Choosing a specialty

Apropos this tale it is worth noting an important maxim which my wife lives by:

If it's meant to be, it's meant to be.

I was always going to be a hospital doctor. My parents were both GPs and, OK, things are very different now but it was not the life for me. Hospital medicine is also different; maybe if I was starting out now, when hospital consultants have little say in how they run their hospitals (or even their own departments), I would take a different view. Also trainees find, thanks to the new career structure, that they are on tramlines and cannot easily switch specialties.

When I went for my first post-registration post it was at the Hammersmith and you applied for all the medical jobs *en bloc* and were interviewed by all the consultants. They were a daunting row of gods. I pitched to do gastroenterology. At medical school neurology was my weak spot, so that's what I got.[203] But six months with Chris Pallis and Donald Calne convinced me it was what I always wanted to do. So I planned my next moves with that in mind; writing off the option of medicine of the thorax was not a problem, following my ghastly experience of chest medicine outlined above, and I did two years of general medicine in Bath, which was wonderful, and led to aforementioned marriage as well. But by the end of my time there I was not only newly wed, but in need of a job near London, as my father was terminally ill. So I headed back to talk to Chris, who had been very supportive of my plans.

---

[203] In the armed forces it is a common belief that you get allocated at random, or in deliberate contradiction to your suitability. When I was a lad our next-door neighbour was Eric Fenby, the distinguished musician who had been Delius's amanuensis, and had taken down from dictation much of the composer's later work after he went blind. When WW2 began he offered his services and was posted to the searchlights. It was only later he discovered that the recruiting officer had noted his occupation not as composer, but compositor. Fenby ever after harboured a deep resentment of the conscientious objector composers whose reputations had flourished in the war.

However it was clear when we met that something was wrong. I don't know what, or why, but he seemed quite lukewarm about my future in neurology and when he sent me to Queen Square to talk to the Dean there I got the same bad vibes.

However, I had a problem. My spell at the Brompton Hospital had ended with me having a major falling-out with the Prof, who was in my view over-demanding of their trainees, and who I am sure engineered the withdrawal of a locum SHO post in cardiology I had been offered as a fill-in before going to Bath. So both those specialties were off limits. Having pinned my colours to the neurology mast while in Bath I had turned down the opportunity to learn gastroscopy. So gastroenterology was also out.

So – what to do? I thought for a while and decided that the least bad option (note this – it's not the same as the best) was to try rheumatology. I had turned down the offer of a years' rheumatology research in Bath, which was not a good start. But I had to be back in London and applied for a registrar post at my training hospital, the Middlesex.

Things didn't turn out too badly in the end, although that's a long story. However quite by accident, while trying to find some stuff for a research patient in a filing cabinet, I discovered my old application in which my last Bath boss had written "He has made a sudden decision to go into rheumatology, and I am not convinced of his long-term commitment to the specialty". I derived some pleasure, nearly 30 years later, by writing to him to suggest that by being elected President of the British Society for Rheumatology I had perhaps proved him wrong.

The moral of this tale is that, if a door shuts you should push another open but, once committed, stay there. There will always be something special that comes out of it; I certainly would never have thought that going to a small, just-out-of-London district hospital, I would end up as an expert on medicine and surgery of the First World War, appear on television with Michael Palin, Jeremy Paxman, Michael Portillo and Dan Snow among others and be elected an honorary member of the British Association of Plastic, Reconstructive and Aesthetic Surgeons.

Some things from the past that modern doctors will never see or know

These are all things that I have seen or done.

- Starting your own general practice from nothing by putting up a plate and waiting for patients to turn up
- Running general practice without an appointment system (these first two I lived with from an infant, as this is what my mother did)
- Going on GP visits as a child, with a parent
- Running a smallpox vaccination clinic (I did both of these as a schoolboy)
- Acting as a locum house physician while a medical student
- Doing a liver biopsy while a medical student
- Stitching children's wounds and removing foreign bodies from eyes in A&E while still a medical student
- Working a 104-hour week
- Working a continuous shift from Thursday morning to Monday evening (on-take day Thursday, then on take over the weekend and an operating list Monday afternoon)
- Living in a hospital room (not just on-call, but all the time)
- Dictating letters to a live secretary who took them down in shorthand in the clinic
- Dictating letters to a machine that recorded on plastic sheets wrapped around a cylinder, like an Edison phonograph
- Being summoned to a ward by a flashing light system
- Seeing patients in a large outpatient hall where six doctors are in the same room, separated only by moveable screens
- Practising hospital medicine without CT, MRI or ultrasound
- Interpreting an air encephalogram[204]
- Having no reliable chemotherapy for any kind of cancer
- Mixing renal peritoneal dialysis fluids by hand
- Shaking test tubes of blood with little glass balls in to stimulate the formation of LE cells (a primitive test for lupus)
- Sucking blood into graduated tubes, and watching them for an hour to determine the ESR (after washing your mouth out because you sucked a bit hard)

---

[204] This involved performing a lumbar puncture, introducing a quantity of air into the space normally filled with cerebrospinal fluid around the spinal cord and brain, and tilting the patient this way and that to make the air bubble go to where you want it. An X-ray then enables you to see the air shadow, and whether it is normal or is distorted by a tumour or similar. It's a very unpleasant procedure often resulting in a dreadful headache until the air had been resorbed.

- Seeing a case of tertiary syphilis
- Looking after an inpatient ward full of rheumatoid arthritis patients
- Watching four post-mortems in a week
- Living without a credit card
- Living without a computer
- Looking up references without the Internet
- Presenting case histories using an epidiascope and typed cards
- Sitting down to dinner in the doctors' mess with beer on the table (at the Brompton – the second-on-call dished up)
- Being served late night sandwiches in the mess by the kitchen staff
- Having a specially prepared roast lunch in the mess on a Sunday
- Living in (and decorating) your own hospital flat

Times have changed…

Doctor, look out for the future

There is nothing wrong with trying to see where medicine is going. Sometimes you may feel cross that others cannot see the future as clearly as you can, and sometimes you are badly wrong. But while historians have the benefit of hindsight (and we use the retrospectoscope) there is something intellectually stimulating about prophecy. And if you do turn out to be right, you can dine out for ever.[205]

Doctor, plan for your retirement

I have been lucky to retire on a final salary pension. I thought I paid a lot for it (8%) but for consultants the contribution rate is going up to a staggering 14.5% and it's going to be a career-average pension, so today's doctors are likely to get a bit more than half of what I am getting, allowing for inflation and all that. Especially as Clinical Excellence Awards will come and go; these are pensionable but maybe not for long. Once awarded, they can be removed at managers' discretion, which will be awful for whistleblowing dissidents like me, and more so when you are right and they are wrong. And

---

[205] I have had one such moment. I wrote in a letter (AN Bamji, *Combination therapy in rheumatoid arthritis*. Ann Rheum Dis 1985, **44**, 862) that the way forward in managing rheumatoid arthritis was to use early and large doses of serious drugs in combination, using the analogy of treating Hodgkin's disease and lymphoma. 25 years later we were well on the way as I never tired of pointing out… however, people come to dislike your smugness.

worse, the allowed "pension pot" has been almost halved, so if your pot now exceeds £1m (not that difficult for a lifetime in the NHS) any extra will be immediately taxed at 50%. It even appears that, although you are contractually obliged to contribute the 14.5%, if you are a high earner this will almost certainly result in you exceeding the newly introduced annual limit, so you are taxed on money you never got. I consider this to be theft. In fact the whole pensions saga breaks my first commandment, that when making a plan you should look to see what might go wrong with it before you trumpet its plus points (if any). Secondly it is my last example of oxymoronic medicine.

If a doctor is in his 50s, and earning well, then it will make sense to leave early. It will not pay to struggle on. Take the pension and run. So there could (will?) be an exodus of senior, experienced staff. At the other end there are even now not enough medical school places to fill demand. Every week there are news articles about the pressure on the NHS. A diminished and inexperienced workforce will not provide a top-class service. Add to that the possible restriction of medical immigration and there will be a crisis. While it is clear that there is jealousy in some circles over the generosity of final salary pensions enjoyed by the now retired baby-boomers, the envious forget how bloody hard we had to work – and in our early days saw the coming of a comfortable pension as reward for the long hours, the responsibility and the stress. Medicine is a life and death job; not for nothing was the first public demonstration of medical work on television entitled "Your Life in Their Hands". The government says it is concerned about understaffing, yet has proposed a pension scheme that will make things worse. The dreadful thing is that it did not see this. It took the doctors to point it out.

I confess I find it incredible that, in this age of the sanctity of human rights, the richer are no longer treated like everyone else, but are loaded with more taxes (income tax, capital transfer tax, pension contributions, potentially a mansion tax) than everyone else. I can see that if you earn more, you should pay more tax, but that's mathematics. I am all for a flat rate of tax, which would save zillions on collection because you wouldn't need an army of accountants in and out of HMRC to regulate it.

But it's not going to happen, is it?

Assuming some sort of cutback on pensions is inevitable, can it be mitigated? Young doctors start, of course, at a disadvantage, because of the student fees, which have to be paid back. Then they need a house, probably with a large mortgage unless the Bank of Mummy and Daddy is offering large interest-free loans or gifts. But if there is half a chance, they should salt money away in things where the tax rate is either low (antiques, works of art, jewellery etc) or non-existent (an Individual Savings Account, or ISA). The beauty of ISAs is that when you cash them in you pay either tax on the capital gain (which is half the income tax rate) or no tax at all. So, for example, if you were able to put the full allowance, currently £21,000 per annum, into an ISA for the next 20 years you could in all probability draw it back out again for the following 20, boosting your pension substantially and if it's a Stocks and Shares ISA, on past performance (yes I know that's no guarantee of future performance, but you have only to look at the Sunday papers to compare equities with other investments over the last 50 years to see that I have a point) it could be a lot more than that.

If it's works of art, you can enjoy them – even do a bit of buying and selling on the side (that's how my father saved for his pension – he was only earning for 17 years, so his NHS pension was pathetic – or would have been if he had lived to collect it; my mother got half of it but that was peanuts). Or buy a holiday cottage and enjoy that, or rent it to Dutch tourists, then sell it when you don't want it any more.

I once set up a seminar on retirement planning for a group of quite junior doctors, who were bemused by my insistence that it was important. But the more I watch the more convinced I am that I was right to make folk think about it. A pension of £15,000 a year sounds a lot, but with the price of coffee as it is it's about 10 cups a day. Of course, you don't smoke – but if you do, then there's another pot to raid and save with.

Doctor, Enjoy your work

If you don't, then move, or retire. I have done both. You may miss some of your colleagues and some of your patients, but you won't miss the mad NHS or oxymoronic medicine. You will have time to do things when you want. As long as there are things you want to do other than work. Like write books.

Saving the NHS

Much of what I have written exposes the madness of the NHS and its bureaucracy – its unresponsiveness to financial challenge, its fundamental bankruptcy, the pervasive culture of target-setting, intimidation and despair. It was ever thus. The NHS has never been financially viable, as costs have outrun available funds. Right at the beginning I reminded you that the old voluntary hospitals were bust, or would have gone bust, had they remained outside an NHS structure. During my career I have written (I think) to every Secretary of State for Health, and though at one stage our local MP in Sidcup was an ex-Prime Minister I have largely had dusty responses.[206] Those who have corresponded with ministers will know that there is a personalised top and tail (often spelling your name wrongly), a paragraph relating to the grouse and then two pages of government guff. Reorganisations have never achieved anything significant. Somehow the NHS has managed to battle on, with quite extraordinary results both clinical and research-wise. But it has been a battle, and now the screw is tightening it will get harder.

Oxymorons abound in this clash between clinical excellence and money. If you want excellence you need well-trained, motivated staff and lots of them. If you want financial balance you have to cut costs, and as the NHS staff bill represents some 75% of the total then it's the obvious place to start. There is a clear incompatibility. Cut staff and morale dives as people have to work harder, like hamsters on wheels, just to stay in the same place. People get tired and make mistakes. Rigid rota systems result in handovers so there is no continuity of care, and the mistakes simply happen. The merging of hospitals may cut costs, but then patients have to travel further and there may be delays in treatment. Cut bed numbers, and at peak times emergencies overflow (into routine beds, so elective work slows to a crawl) or patients even stack up in A&E departments, and in some cases outside them (there's no point jamming them full when you cannot move them on, and so threaten your 4 hour waiting time targets).

Basically if you have a bust system it makes no difference how good a management team you have – bust is bust. The only way to deal with a bust company is to close it or merge it. But why is it bust in the first place? Perhaps because the income it receives doesn't cover the costs. Contract prices for care in hospitals do not cover the costs. Is that the hospitals' fault? No. So if the system is bust as well, it needs fixing.

---

[206] Edward Heath gave you a maximum of ten minutes to make your pitch. However he was very good at turning up to open things.

My recipe is simple but painful – largely because folk have come to accept that the NHS is completely free at the point of delivery. So they won't like the idea of paying for something they previously got for nothing. But either they do that, or there won't be an NHS at all. Where is there fat to cut into without hitting lean meat?

1. We will stop practising futility medicine – which requires a sensible and non-hysterical debate about what we will no longer do. This should not just be about surgical procedures but should address the admittedly difficult subjects of end-of-life and dementia care. As I have said before, just because you can do something doesn't mean you should.

2. Hotel costs will be paid for in hospitals. The Cameron government came up with a plan to meet social care costs, but that plan excluded everything except direct care. So let there be a charge for food and services; after all, they would pay for these at home. It need not be a lot. Hospital food is very cheap – which is why it's often so bad.

3. Some medical costs must be paid for. Notional only, perhaps, but people value something more if they have had to pay for it, so levy a charge for surgery attendances and outpatient visits. If they then complain because they reckoned they didn't get value for money, standards will rise. And don't forget – patients pay for their prescriptions, so it's not exactly unprecedented.

4. System redundancies must go. Duplicated IT systems; layers of management that manage managers. Contracts… now, here's a thing. If we look at the cost of administering the purchaser-provider split it is immense. Abolish the split and the costs plummet, as we do away with all the interface accountants and administrators.

5. Renegotiate all the major cost pressures that have exposed the cost issues. In the bad old days hospitals ran over budget and somehow the shortfall got made up from somewhere, but PFI has made the whole thing explicit; it is unaffordable. In my old Trust, which was declared bankrupt, the administrator recommended writing off the old debt and making the ongoing cost interest-free. Let's do it.

6. Properly develop a list of things that won't be done any more.

7. Cut pay. Maybe that is a step too far. But where services have been contracted out, pay levels have often dropped.

8. Show more respect to staff. General practitioners are leaving medicine faster than they are coming in. It's time politicians realised that it's the intolerable pressure they are exerting, by putting good costs in front of good medicine and making the NHS hamsters run faster and faster to keep the wheel turning, that are causing the exodus and failure of morale.

I hope that others will think of others. But if we don't do something, the NHS cannot survive. Bleating about reform has gone on since 1948 but no reform to date has either solved the problems or stopped the bleating. I think this is where I came in…

Postscript to this piece. Since I wrote it five years or so ago things have (a) got worse and (b) many of my predictions have come to pass. Indeed I am really sorry for managers in the NHS. In September 2015 some 80% of Acute Trusts predicted an end-of-year deficit. At the end of 2016 all the hospitals in South-East England were in "Special Measures", i.e. failing. I cannot believe that 80% of hospital managers are incompetent. But they are on the horns of a dilemma. Hospitals "fail" on current criteria for two main reasons. They are financially "challenged" (which means in real terms they are bust) or clinically challenged. To meet a financial deficit requires cuts. This means staff as on the whole the staff budget is the only non-fixed cost. And then clinical services suffer, and the Care Quality Commission come down on the managers like a ton of bricks, and they all leave under a cloud. On the other hand, if the managers make maintenance of clinical services their priority, then the finances go haywire, the Care Quality Commission come down on the managers like a ton of bricks, and they all leave under a cloud. Would you do a job like that?

This may seem a very UK-centric view. That's because it is. I have alluded to the United States' system, which I find unpalatable, but what of other healthcare systems around the world? I once reviewed a book comparing the NHS with its state counterparts in Canada and Australia.[207] The clear message was that, while each system had its advantages, each also had its faults and it was impossible to adjudicate which was the least bad. Likewise a group of Sidcup doctors visited Sidcup's twin town in France. Evry is to Paris what Sidcup is to London; an almost separate entity to the capital's south-east. There we found some strange differences; it appeared that there were no resident doctors, but there were resident administrators. While some of the technology was impressive (for example, the delivery of food and supplies by robot carts, or "tortues" which followed tracks embedded in the floor, and could summon their own lifts) it seemed bizarre that the only way a patient in a single room could contact a nurse was through the hospital's switchboard. And most strange of all the Intensive Care facility, right next to the emergency ambulance entrance, contained a prison inmate with AIDS and a life-threatening pneumonia on a ventilator, unconscious. The only staff person in the room was an *agent*, in uniform, and with his gun on his belt. There were no nurses to be seen. Contrast this with a similar unit in the UK

---

[207] A Gillies, *What makes a good healthcare system?* Abingdon, Radcliffe Medical Press, 2003. Reviewed by me in *Rheumatology* (2004; 43; 814-815

and you would fall over nurses, and doctors. One of the administrators at Evry described how patients who could not pay their (moderate) bills were visited by the bailiffs, who would remove appropriately valued items such as furniture and televisions.

So perhaps medicine in our creaking NHS is not so bad after all.

And finally

You may have reached the end of this collection of essays thinking what a cynical and bitter old fool Bamji is. I'm not really like that. Mostly.

What else would I have done other than medicine? I wanted to do it from the age of eight, and apart from a brief hiccup when I was struggling with A-level physics and thought I might be better reading English at Uni, there is nothing else I would have done. Except, perhaps, become a fine art expert; I was offered a place at Sothebys just before I left school. But for all the frustrations and upsets, whether managerial or clinical, I have had enormous satisfaction being a doctor. It is fulfilling when a patient gets better and is grateful; if it happens like magic (for example when treating polymyalgia with steroids), it leaves you on a high. It is intellectually stimulating and not unrewarding financially. Not only has there been clinical medicine, but also research (not a lot), book editing, journalism, commentary, medical history – and, of course, the joy of meeting my lovely wife whom I encountered in Bath when she was the junior and I was the middle-grade of the gastroenterology and cardiac firm. So being a doctor in the NHS is often fun, and almost always rewarding. And watching medical science advance, with new technology, gene sequencing and such is amazingly exciting.

I received a message on LinkedIn which was as follows:

"Hi Dr Bamji. We [some of your ex patients] have never found another doctor as good as you. YOU are missed…Your name comes up most weeks as we sit having treatment."

This arrived seven years after I retired and gave me a golden glow. Say no more!

****

Endnote: The poems

Curing pain in the back

At eighty years one's bones are thin
So fractures are not rare;
A crumbling spine can cause great pain,
Pain oft too much to bear.

So when I saw our Kathleen, sent
With letter re her pain
I thought it was, as like as not,
A fracture once again.

Indeed her X-ray looked the part;
One vertebra was wedged
A crush it was, quite certainly,
The bets need not be hedged.

But Kathleen said "I'm right as rain;
There's no pain like before,
You see, I slid upon a slug
Outside the patio door.

"I fell, and crashed down on my back,
It was no graceful slip,
I thought that at the very least
I'd got a fractured hip,

"But when I scrambled to my feet
'twas not as I had feared,
My back pain had quite gone away
Completely disappeared!"

The treatment, then, for bad back pain?
You don't need any drug
You can manipulate your spine
By sliding on a slug![208]

---

[208] I have written an as yet unpublished anthology of medical and non-medical poems, some of which have won prizes...

Lament of an ageing Consultant (long version)

The tide of NHS reform sweeps to our hospital doors,
With plan on plan a-jostle for our delectation;
The credit culture deep ingrained it seems
As PFI becomes the means of renovation,
And contract, Payment by Results sets fees
That cannot be afforded by the local CCGs.

We struggle to maintain our patient care
For loyal secretaries have been snatched away;
While local GPs wish us to do less
Yet still our urgent patients must be seen today –
We know too well what tribulation we will see
If we don't straightway aspirate their swollen knee.

"Shift out the Care!" is now the clarion call
"Take all of it to the Community!"
For somehow it is now a crime
To work alongside others in one's specialty,
As if by some strange, slippery sleight of hand
Each hospital's become some odd and alien land.

Wither our training, and research? they surely will
As, isolated, we plough our lonely furrow;
Tucked in some dusty distant room, alone
Ill-tempered, raging, ageing Brock within his burrow,
Though fair, we might never need again to look
At all the horrors, hopelessness, of Choose and Book…

We strive to stay in touch with current jargon,
With all of management's doublespeak and lingo;
Essay efficiency; watch for the evidence base;
Strive for best practice as we play at bullshit bingo;
Work on through years and more, seeing again the ebb and flow,
As if by that tide washed up, as managers come, and go.

At least we can say this, we are safe grown old
Yet sadly bitter at those things we so detest
And that desire to move away, retire,
Might be the right reaction for the best,
Leaving the frustrated fear, despair and desolation,
To another, modern, quicker, fitter, generation.

But then we know that those who take our place
Are not trained justly in our ways and powers;
That, expertise, experience cannot come
If they no longer work our long, late hours,
And that it will be our sad, dismal fate
To be their subjects when they operate.

Bibliography

Abel-Smith B. The Beveridge report: Its origins and outcomes. International Social Security Review 1992: 45 (1–2): 5–16

Agarwal S et al. Risk of atypical femoral fracture with long-term use of alendronate (bisphosphonates): a systemic review of literature. Acta Orthopaedica Belgica 2010; 76 (5): 567-71

Akram Y. "When is "enough" enough? BMJ Careers, 4th February 2012, p.3. In the same print issue Graham

Anon, The Secret Barrister. Stories of the Law and How It's Broken. London. Macmillan, 2018

Anon. Care and compassion? Report of the Health Service Ombudsman on ten investigations into NHS care of older people. http://www.ombudsman.org.uk/care-and-compassion/home

Anon. Casualty (BBC1); series 24, episode 46, 2010

Austen J. Pride and Prejudice, 1813

Baker M, Menken M, Time to abandon the term mental illness. BMJ 2001 322: 937.

Bamji AN. An appalling "Panorama". BMJ 1980; 281: 1028

Bamji AN, Berry RJ, Windeyer B, The treatment of Ankylosing Spondylitis with radiotherapy: report of a long-term follow-up study. Brit Soc Radiol congress, April 1982; RSM Rheum Section 1983

Bamji AN. Combination therapy in rheumatoid arthritis. Ann Rheum Dis 1985, 44, 862

Bamji AN, Medicine and the Media. Br Med J 1987; 295: 1055

Bamji AN. How the NHS waiting list got its length. Hospital Doctor, 6/4/1989.

Bamji AN, Dieppe PA, Haslock I, Shipley ME., What do Rheumatologists do? A Pilot Audit Study. Br J Rheumatol 1990, 24, 295-8

Bamji AN, Erhardt CC, Price RP & Williams P. The Painful Shoulder. Can Consultants agree? Brit J. Rheumatol 1996; 35: 1172-74

Bamji AN. Brain injury rehabilitation: jaw-jaw not war-war, BMJ 1996; 312: 916-7

Bamji AN., Flying the flag. BMJ 2002; 325: 501

Bamji A. Tackling MRSA. Hospital Doctor, 22nd April 2004

Bamji AN, The Emperor's new business clothes. British Journal of Healthcare Management 2007; 13: 294-297

Bamji AN, Lane J. Impact of a community-based rheumatology clinic on a hospital department. BSR Annual Meeting 2010, Abstract 96

Bamji AN. Public finance indiscretion. BMJ 2010; 341: c4295

Bamji AN. The Times, 18th December 2010

Bamji AN. The Times, 18th January 2011

Bamji AN. We should scrap targets for outpatient follow-up ratios. BMJ 2011; 342: c7450.

Bamji AN New: follow-up ratios: Dogma or Design? BSR Annual Meeting 2011, Abstract 59

Bamji AN. Reduce repayment rates to 0.5%. BMJ 2012;345:e4789

Bamji AN. If facts do not fit theory, the theory is wrong. BMJ 2012;345:e6584

Bamji AN. The Times, 6th March 2013

Bamji AN. The Times, June 22nd, 2013

Bamji AN. Faces from the Front: Harold Gillies, The Queen's Hospital, Sidcup and the origins of modern plastic surgery (Helion Press, 2017)

Bamji AN. "The Times", 30th June 2018

Bamji AN, Taub PJ. Phalloplasty and the tube pedicle: a chronological re-evaluation. Eur J Plast Surg 2019; https://doi.org/10.1007/s00238-019-01539-5

Bamji JE, Bamji NS, Spinach. Br Med J 1953;1:674

Bamji JE, Bamji NS, Severe dermatitis and "biological" detergents. Br Med J 1970;1:629

Baron JH. Frederick Cayley Robinson's Acts of Mercy murals at the Middlesex Hospital, London. BMJ 1994;309:1723-4

Bender DA, Bamji A. Serum Tryptophan binding in chlorpromazine treated chronic schizophrenics J.Neurochem 1974, 22, 805-9

Bauby J-D. The Diving Bell and the Butterfly, Fourth Estate, 1998

Beveridge W. Social insurance and Allied services. HMSO 1942 Cmd 6404.

Binder F. Sown with Corn. Farthings Publishing, 2010)

Bochner F,.Hooper WD,.Tyrer JH, Eadie MJ., Factors involved in an outbreak of phenytoin intoxication. J Neurol Sci 1972; 4: 481-487.

Calne D, Teychenne PF, Leigh PN, Bamji AN, Greenacre JK, Treatment of Parkinsonism with Bromocriptine. Lancet 1974, ii, 1355

Carroll L. Alice in Wonderland.

Chin Kee On. Malaya Upside Down, Singapore, 1946

Cohen D. Out of Joint. BMJ 2011; 342:d2905)

Court-Brown WM, Doll R. Leukaemia and aplastic anaemia in patients irradiated for ankylosing spondylitis. HMSO, 1957, later published as a scientific paper (J Radiol Prot. 2007 Dec;27(4B):B15-B154)

Deer B. How the case against the MMR vaccine was fixed. BMJ 2011;342:c5347

Dieppe PA, Bacon PA, Bamji AN, Watt I. Atlas of Clinical Rheumatology. Gower Medical Publishing, 1986

Dumas A. The Count of Monte Cristo. First published 1844

Ernst E, Singh S. Trick or Treatment? Alternative medicine on trial, London, Bantam Press, 2008

Ernst E. SCAM: So-Called Alternative Medicine, Imprint Academic, 2018

Flanders M, Swann D. The Laws of Thermodynamics, In "At the Drop of a Hat", 1957

Gigerenzer G et al, Glaub keiner Statistik, die du nicht verstanden hast (Do not believe statistics that you do not understand). Gehirn & Geist 2009 (10), 34–39.

Gigerenzer G et al, Helping doctors and patients make sense of health statistics. Psychological Science in the Public Interest November 2007 vol. 8 no. 2 53-96

Gillies A, What makes a good healthcare system? Abingdon, Radcliffe Medical Press, 2003.

Goldacre B, Bad Science. London, Fourth Estate, 2008

Goldacre B. Bad Pharma. 4th Estate, 2012

Goldstein J, Tuning the Brain: Principles and Practice of Neurosomatic Medicine. Taylor Francis 2004

Hadler N. Rethinking Aging: Growing Old and Living Well in an Over Treated Society, University of North Carolina Press, 2011)

Hanington E, Jones RJ, Amess JA, Wachowicz B, Migraine: a platelet disorder. Lancet 1981; 318: 720-723

Hastings M. All Hell Let Loose: London, Harper Press, 2011, p.499.

Heath I. What do we want to die from? BMJ 2010;341:c3883

HM Government publications: Report of the Mid Staffordshire NHS Foundation Trust Public Inquiry. https://www.gov.uk/government/publications/report-of-the-mid-staffordshire-nhs-foundation-trust-public-inquiry (accessed 29th August 2018).

Hoskins P. Two Men Were Acquitted: The trial and acquittal of Doctor John Bodkin Adams, Secker & Warburg, 1984.

Hull L. Dying hospital patient phoned switchboard begging for a drink after nurses said 'No'. Daily Mail, 29th March 2010

https://en.wikipedia.org/wiki/Royal_Liverpool_University_Hospital

Hunter R, Macalpine I, George III and the Mad Business. New York: Pantheon Books, 1969

Huth E, Repetitive and Divided Publication, in Ethical Issues in Biomedical Publication, ed. A Hudson Jones & F McLellan, Johns Hopkins University Press, 2000

Isolauri E, Rautava S, Kalliomaki M, Food allergy in irritable bowel syndrome: new facts and old fallacies. Gut 2004; 53: 1391-1393

Kay A. This is going to hurt. Secret Diaries of a Junior Doctor. Pan Macmillan, 2017

Kendrick M. Doctoring Data , Columbus Publishing, 2014

Kendrick M. The Great Cholesterol Con. 2007;

Kirwan JR. Clinical Trials: Why not do them properly? Ann Rheum Dis 1982;41:551-552

Lamb C. Small Wars Permitting, HarperCollins, 2008

Lepage G. Animals Parasitic in Man, Dover Publications, 1963

Lindenbaum J. Bioavailability of digoxin tablets. Pharm Reviews 1973; 25: 229-237.

Litwic A, Bamji AN.Follow-up or discharge? A new patient outcome analysis. BSR Annual Meeting 2008, Abstract 417

Malcolm McKendrick M. Doctoring data. How to sort out medical advice from medical nonsense. Columbus Publishing, 2014

Mandelbrot B, and Richard Hudson R. The (Mis)Behaviour of Markets. Profile Books, 2004

McCarthy M. Show us the evidence for telehealth, BMJ 2012;344:e469

McCartney M The scam of integrative medicine. BMJ 2011;343:d4446

Mulley G. Stop the medicalisation of old age": BMJ 2012; 344:e803

Multmeier J, Gaissmaier W, Wegwarth O, Collective statistical illiteracy in health. In B. L. Anderson BL, Schukin J (Eds.), Numerical Reasoning in Judgments and Decision Making About Health (pp. 39–58). Cambridge, UK: Cambridge University Press. If you can read German see also

Nezerue CM et al, "Black swan in the kidney": Renal involvement in the antiphospholipid antibody syndrome. Kidney International (2002) 62, 733–744; doi:10.1046/j.1523-1755.2002.00500.x)

Pallis CA, Bamji AN. McIlroy was here. Or was he? BMJ 1979, i, 973-5.

Petty F, Kramer GL, Larrison AL, Neurochemistry of stress: Regional brain levels of biogenic amines and metabolites with ten different stressors, Biogenic amines 1996, 12: 377-394

Pollock A, Price D, Liebe M. Private Finance Initiatives during NHS austerity. BMJ 2011; 342: d324

Quintner JL, The Australian RSI debate: stereotyping and medicine. Disabil Rehabil 1995; 17: 256-62)

Rhodes S. The Times, 16th September 2010

Rosch P (ed) Fat and Cholesterol Don't Cause Heart Attacks, Columbus Publishing, 2016

Sacks O. The Man who Mistook his Wife for a Hat, Summit Books, 1985

Sacks O. Musicophilia. London, Picador, 2007

Shaohua ZI et al, Fatal renal failure due to the Chinese herb "GuanMu Tong" (Aristolochia manshuriensis): autopsy findings and review of literature. Forensic Sci Int. 2010 Jun 15;199(1-3):e5-7. doi: 10.1016/j.forsciint.2010.02.003

Smith R. The BMJ and the 77 specialties of medicine. BMJ 1997; 315: 1680

Southwark News, May 5th 2016. https://www.southwarknews.co.uk/history/9255-2/ (accessed 3rd September 2018)

Spiller RC. Role of infection in irritable bowel syndrome. J Gastroenterol 2007; 42: 41-47

Stoate H, Jones B. Challenging the Citadel: Breaking the hospitals' grip on the NHS. Fabian Ideas 620, 2006

272

Syed M. Real Ideas: The Power of Diverse Thinking, John Murray, 2019
Taggart HM, Alderdice JM. Fatal cholestatic jaundice in elderly patients taking benoxaprofen. Br Med J 1982; 284: 1372.
Taleb NN, The Black Swan. The Impact of the Highly Improbable. Allen Lane, 2007
Taleb NN. The Black Swan. The Impact of the Highly Improbable. Allen Lane, 2007
Tudor Hart J. Our feet set on a new path entirely. To the transformation of primary care and partnership with patients. BMJ 1998; 317:1.
Wafer A., A&E Targets damage MRSA safeguards. November 13th 2004
Willis-Owen CA, Subramanian P, Kumari P, Houlihan-Burne D. Effects of 'bare below the elbows' policy on hand contamination of 92 hospital doctors in a district general hospital. Journal of Hospital Infection; 75: 116-119.
Winfield J, A Bamji A, Medical fitness to drive: some practical problems. J Traffic Med 1980; 8: 54-56

© Banx

About the author

Dr Andrew Bamji was a Consultant Rheumatologist at Queen Mary's Hospital, Sidcup, Kent and Director of the Elmstead Rehabilitation Unit there. Appointed in 1983, initially also to the Brook General Hospital, Woolwich, he undertook various management roles and had a particular interest in efficient clinic management and the early treatment of rheumatoid arthritis. From 2006-8 he was President of the British Society for Rheumatology, having undertaken various committee roles for the Society, and during that period was also a member of Council of the Royal College of Physicians. He has published and presented widely on rheumatology topics, co-authoring "An Atlas of Clinical Rheumatology" (Gower Medical Publishing, 1983) and, as Robin Goodfellow, writing a much-lauded column for the BSR journal "Rheumatology" for five years. He retired from the NHS in 2011 and from private practice in 2014 but has continued to contribute to the NHS debate through the British Medical Journal and letters to "The Times".

He is also an expert on medicine and surgery of the First World War, having developed an interest as the hospital's archivist, when he discovered and recovered the wartime case files of 2500 facial injury patients treated at Sidcup. His book "Faces from the Front" (Helion Press) was released in September 2017 and won first prize in the "Basis of Medicine" category of the BMA Book Awards 2018. He has appeared on television with, among others, Michael Palin, Jeremy Paxman and Michael Portillo, and lectured nationally and internationally; he has twice been awarded the Gillies Gold Medal by the British Association of Plastic, Reconstructive and Aesthetic Surgeons, of which he is an honorary member.

Andrew writes an occasional blog "The Wry Observer", which can be found at https://bamjiinrye.wordpress.com.

Printed in Great Britain
by Amazon

82820460R00163